D1083238

Explorations
in
Elementary Mathematics

TEACHERS' MATHEMATICS
REFERENCE SERIES

Bruce E. Meserve, Series Editor

Hight	A CONCEPT OF LIMITS
Parker	THE STRUCTURE OF NUMBER SYSTEMS
Pettofrezzo	VECTORS AND THEIR APPLICATIONS
Smith	EXPLORATIONS IN ELEMENTARY MATHEMATICS

PRENTICE-HALL INTERNATIONAL, INC., London
PRENTICE-HALL OF AUSTRALIA, PTY. LTD., Sydney
PRENTICE-HALL OF CANADA, LTD., Toronto
PRENTICE-HALL OF INDIA (PRIVATE) LTD., New Delhi
PRENTICE-HALL OF JAPAN, INC., Tokyo

Seaton E. Smith, Jr.

College of Education
Ohio University
formerly, Mathematics Specialist
West Virginia Department of Education

EXPLORATIONS
IN
ELEMENTARY MATHEMATICS

PRENTICE-HALL, INC., ENGLEWOOD CLIFFS, NEW JERSEY

©1966 by Prentice-Hall, Inc.
Englewood Cliffs, New Jersey

All rights reserved. No part of this book
may be reproduced in any form, by mimeograph
or any other means, without permission
in writing from the publisher.

Library of Congress Catalog Card Number:
66-10927

Current printing (last digit):

10   9   8   7   6   5   4   3   2

Printed in the United States of America
C-29605

to Lucille, Jimmy, and Bobby

Series Foreword

EACH BOOK of this series is concerned with an important topic or area of the mathematical training of teachers. The exposition follows the highly successful pattern of the Meserve-Sobel books. There are many illustrative examples to facilitate the use of the books for individual study and in-service programs. There are numerous exercises to provide an opportunity for readers to develop their understanding. The answers for the odd-numbered exercises are in the back of each book; the answers for the even-numbered exercises are available in a separate booklet. Thus each book is designed to serve as a text either in an in-service program or in a college course for prospective teachers or others interested in extending their knowledge of these mathematical concepts. Some of the books are particularly useful as supplementary texts in college and advanced high-school courses.

The topics for these books have been selected becuase of their significance in the rapid evolution of our contemporary mathematics curricula. Each author has tested his materials in preliminary form with hundreds and (in at least one case) thousands of college students and/or school teachers. Briefly, this series consists of books on significant topics presenting tested materials in a manner that has been proved to be highly effective.

The brevity of the books is purposeful. Each book may be used as a supplementary reference text in a more extensive or advanced course. Each book provides the basis for an extensive unit of work in an in-service, college, or school course. Considerable flexibility in meeting the needs of the students is available by using two or more of these books in an extensive course or series of courses.

Frequent additions of books to this series are contemplated.

Bruce E. Meserve, Series Editor

Preface

NATIONAL CONCERN for more effective learning of elementary school mathematics has stimulated many "new" programs in recent years. These programs have in common an increased emphasis on the structural aspects of mathematics and an attempt to teach the why of arithmetical computation. The desire is to lead students to understand mathematical principles rather than merely to present rules for memorization. As a result of the "revolution in school mathematics," many school districts, colleges, universities, and state departments of education are providing in-service courses to prepare elementary school teachers for the teaching of "new" programs. As Mathematics Specialist for the State of West Virginia Department of Education, I conducted and coordinated in-service programs for more than 5,000 elementary school teachers. This book is based upon my work with these teachers.

The purpose of this book is to prepare teachers to teach the modern elementary school mathematics programs. Although mathematically precise language is used throughout the book, a major emphasis has been placed on the need to communicate with the reader who has almost no mathematical background.

The book is designed primarily as an introductory course in modern mathematics for the in-service and pre-service training of elementary school teachers. It may also be studied by parents who are interested in gaining a knowledge of the kind of mathematics that their children are studying in the schools of today. The subject matter is also suitable for the general education of the undergraduate college student with very limited secondary school training in mathematics.

I wish to express my appreciation to all of the numerous individuals who contributed toward the development of this book. In particular, I wish to thank Dr. Patricia Spross, Specialist in Mathematics, U. S. Office of Education, for her comments and suggestions on the final version of the manuscript. I am sincerely indebted to Dr. Bruce E. Meserve of the University of Vermont for his patience and guidance in the molding of the manuscript into textbook form. Thanks are also due to Mrs. Lucille M. Smith for typing the manuscript.

Seaton E. Smith, Jr.

Contents

Explorations
in
Elementary Mathematics

chapter 1

Basic Mathematical Concepts

The use of the term "modern mathematics" in discussions of improvements in mathematics curricula seems to generate considerable misunderstanding. Although it is true that more mathematics has been created in the past half-century than in all previous times, the term "modern mathematics" more appropriately refers to an approach to the study of mathematics than to new mathematics as such. This approach emphasizes the importance of concepts, patterns, and mathematical structure, as well as the development of mathematical skills. The new applications and uses of today's mathematics demand that pupils learn the "why" as well as the "how" at each step in the learning process.

1-1 The Language of Sets

Many areas of mathematics that are called "modern" or "new" have come into prominence recently. The terms are somewhat misleading because they imply that these mathematics were developed or created in the last few years. Actually, the study of most of the new areas of mathematics began many years ago. For example, the theory of sets was introduced by George Cantor, a German mathematician, during the latter part of the nineteenth century. An Englishman by the name of George Boole was one of the first to find a use for the theory of sets in his algebra of sets, sometimes referred to as "Boolean Algebra."

There are two distinct aspects of sets. The first is *set theory*. Set theory is generally taught as a college course in mathematics and is beyond the level

1

of consideration here. The second aspect is *set language*. Set language is being used extensively in programs in modern mathematics at both elementary and secondary school levels. The notions of set and set language can be used to great advantage in clarifying and unifying many other mathematical concepts. An understanding of the concepts and language of sets is an important step in the orderly and meaningful development of mathematical ideas.

1-2 Concept of Sets

Mathematicians consider the term "set" to be undefined because it seems impossible to define the concept of a set in terms of simpler concepts. It is necessary in mathematics to begin with certain undefined terms, and the idea of a set is so intuitive and basic that it is a convenient starting place.

The idea of set is therefore described by synonyms rather than by a precise definition. The term **set** will be used to mean any well-defined collection, group, or class of objects or ideas. The phrase "well-defined" means that the set is described precisely enough for one to tell whether or not any given object belongs to it. We shall be primarily concerned with well-defined sets.

Some examples of sets are the letters in our alphabet, a baseball team, a set of dishes, a coin collection, and a group of children in a school play. In the case of a baseball team, for example, the set is well defined because the team is considered as a single entity and may be distinguished from any other team or group.

The objects contained in a set are called the **elements** of the set (they are also called **members** of the set). In a set of dishes, each dish is an element (member) of the set of dishes. In the case of a coin collection, each coin is a member of the set of coins.

The notation used in denoting sets is very simple. A capital letter generally is used to name the given set, and the names of all the elements may be *represented* in some fashion within braces. Thus, $B = \{1, 2, 3\}$ means that the letter B is used to represent the same set that $\{1, 2, 3\}$ represents. It is read "B is the set whose elements are the numbers 1, 2, and 3." The statement $A = \{\text{Smith, Brown}\}$ is read "A is the set whose elements are Smith and Brown." Notice that commas are used to separate the elements of a set when they are listed between braces. The symbolism $1 \in B$ is used to mean "the element 1 is a member of the set B" or, simply, "1 is in B."

It is also important to note that the order of listing the names of the members of a set is immaterial: the sets $\{1, 2, 3\}$, $\{2, 3, 1\}$, and $\{3, 1, 2\}$ are all the same. Thus, we can state that $\{1, 2, 3\} = \{2, 3, 1\} = \{3, 1, 2\}$. The "$=$" between two symbols for sets means that each symbol stands for the same set.

Exercises

1. When all of the elements of a set are represented within braces, this is known as listing the set. List the members of each of these sets.
   (a) Set A denoting the set of even whole numbers less than 15.
   (b) Set B representing the set of odd whole numbers less than 15.
   (c) Set C denoting the names of months of the year that begin with the letter M.
   (d) Set D representing the names of the days of the week.

2. Describe each of these sets in words.
   (a) Set $E = \{0, 2, 4, 6, 8\}$.
   (b) Set $F = \{5, 10, 15, 20\}$.
   (c) Set $G = \{\text{Tuesday, Thursday}\}$.
   (d) Set $H = \{\text{February, April, June, September, November}\}$.

3. Indicate which of these sets are well defined and which are not. List the elements of each set if possible.
   (a) The set of months of the year that have 31 days.
   (b) The set of interesting movies produced this year.
   (c) The set of great presidents of the United States.
   (d) The set of good basketball players in the State of Virginia.

4. Use set symbols to represent
   (a) The set of whole numbers, ending in 0, between 10 and 100.
   (b) The set of the first two presidents of the United States.
   (c) The set of odd whole numbers greater than zero and less than 10.
   (d) The set of whole numbers less than 100 that are divisible by 13.

1-3 Empty Set

The set that contains no members is another important concept. Consider the set whose elements are all the one-year-old first-grade children in the United States. Clearly, there are no members in this set. The set that has no elements is called the **empty set,** also referred to as the **null set.** The empty set is represented by the symbol { }. Another illustration of the empty set is the set of all United States presidents who were ten years of age when president. Frequently the symbol $\emptyset$ is used to represent the empty set.

Exercises

1. Use the language of sets to represent the set of all odd numbers that are even.

2. Which of the following sets are empty sets?
   (a) The set of whole numbers greater than 7 and less than 8.

(b) The set of odd numbers evenly divisible by 2.

(c) The set of two-digit numerals ending in 7.

(d) The set of squares of even numbers that are odd.

3. Give two examples of sets that have no elements.

4. Consider the set $A = \{0\}$. Is A the empty set? Explain.

1-4 One-to-One Correspondence

From earliest time man probably has been aware of simple numbers in counting. As man's possessions increased, it was necessary to devise a way to keep track of them. Among early methods of keeping count were scratching notches in sticks, tying knots in ropes, and putting pebbles in piles to represent the number of objects being counted. For instance, in the morning the shepherd would build a pile of stones by setting one stone for each sheep as it went out to pasture; at night, when the sheep came back, he would remove one stone from the pile for each sheep that returned. In this very simple way he knew whether or not the number of sheep that went out in the morning was the same as the number that came back at night. This pairing of two things, the sheep and the stone, is an example of one-to-one correspondence.

One-for-one matching of objects was a forerunner of counting. As soon as man began to match things in a definite order, he was counting. Then at the same time he had to invent words and symbols for his counting system in order to communicate his ideas.

The modern-day child, as he learns to count and communicate the concept of number, develops his mathematical insights in much the same way that his primitive ancestors did. The early number experiences of the child lead him through the ideas of "more" and "less" until he discovers that these ideas will not satisfy his needs because they are not precise enough. The child is then ready to deal with a further result of sets in one-to-one correspondence, the idea of number.

Two sets, C and D, are said to be in **one-to-one correspondence** when we have a matching, or pairing, of the elements of C with the elements of D, such that each element of C is matched to one and only one element of D and each element of D is matched to one and only one element of C. For example, consider the sets

$$C = \{c, d, e, f\},$$
$$D = \{1, 2, 3, 4\}.$$

The following illustrations show that the sets C and D may be placed in one-to-one correspondence. Notice that this may be done in more than one way as shown in Figure 1-1.

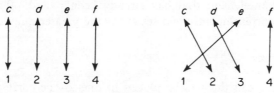

Figure 1-1

Another illustration of a one-to-one correspondence would be the set of names on a class roll and the set of students who are members of the class. Clearly, in a class there should be one name for each child and one child for each name.

It is important to note at this time that matchings of two sets are not always one-to-one correspondences. For example, consider the sets

$$T = \{t, r, s\},$$
$$E = \{e, f, g\}.$$

These sets may be placed in a one-to-one correspondence, but they may also be matched in a manner that does not represent one-to-one correspondence. Observe in Figure 1-2 that e is matched with both t and r, while f is also matched with r, and g is matched with s. In the second illustration, t is matched with both e and f, while r is matched with g, and s is not matched.

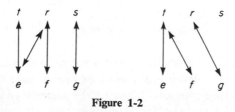

Figure 1-2

Another example of a correspondence that is not one-to-one is shown in Figure 1-3. Since Bill is not matched with anything (or he could be

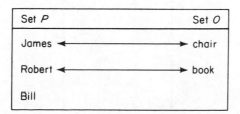

Figure 1-3

matched with an element that has already been paired off), this is not a one-to-one correspondence and set P has the greater number of elements.

Exercises

1. In each part, can the sets be placed in one-to-one correspondence?
  (a) {a, d, p, t} and {5, 7, 8, 3}.
  (b) {@, #, $} and {1, 2, 5, 9}.
  (c) {box, can, bowl, cabinet} and {John, Tom, Mike, Bill}.

2. Indicate in each of the following whether the two sets may be placed in one-to-one correspondence. If they do not match, state which contains the greater number of elements.
  (a) The fingers on your right hand and the fingers on your left hand.
  (b) The stars in the American flag and the states in the United States of America.
  (c) The days in the month of May and the days in the month of November.

3. Consider the two sets $A = \{@, \#, \$, d\}$ and $B = \{*, ¢, \&, x, g\}$.
  (a) If we match each element of A with one and only one element of B, how many elements of B have not been matched?
  (b) Draw a diagram that represents one such matching of the elements of A and B.
  (c) Can we make a one-to-one correspondence between the elements of A and B?

1-5 Counting

After a very long time of making one-to-one correspondences between sets of objects man finally developed a more advanced kind of one-to-one correspondence by using symbols. Most of the ancient civilizations invented their own symbolic systems for counting, and after many centuries of development the number symbols and names that we use today were produced. Our number symbols 1, 2, 3, 4, . . . are of Hindu-Arabic origin.

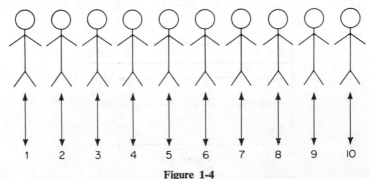

1   2   3   4   5   6   7   8   9   10

Figure 1-4

(*Note:* The three dots after "4" indicate that the numbers go on and on in the same manner.) A one-to-one correspondence between a set of stick men and the set of Hindu-Arabic symbols that are used to count the stick men might be illustrated as in Figure 1-4.

In counting, the number names beginning with 1 are matched in their order with the members of the set, and we know that the set contains as many elements as the last number named. The relationship between counting and one-to-one correspondence is very close, for essentially they are both matching processes. For example, to count the members of the set $\{\square, \triangle, \hexagon, \circ\}$ we would pair the elements with numbers (Figure 1-5).

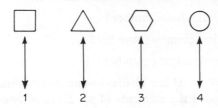

Figure 1-5

The last number we use in this matching process is the one that tells us how many elements the set contains. Hence, we know that there are four elements in this set.

1-6 The Counting Numbers (Natural Numbers)

Let us agree that the first counting number is 1. We then assume that each counting number is followed by another counting number that is 1 more than its predecessor. In this way, the set of **counting numbers** may be generated beginning with 1 and continually counting one more. Hence, the sequence of counting numbers continues without end, as illustrated by the three dots in the example

$$C = \{1, 2, 3, 4, \ldots\}.$$

The set C of counting numbers is also called the set N of **natural numbers:**

$$N = \{1, 2, 3, 4, \ldots\}.$$

Some textbooks refer to the numbers 0, 1, 2, 3, . . . as the natural numbers. In this text, the set of natural numbers will be denoted by the set N, and it will be understood to mean the set $N = \{1, 2, 3, \ldots\}$.

1-7 Whole Numbers

The set of **whole numbers** is the set of counting numbers and zero. We may represent the set of whole numbers as

$$W = \{0, 1, 2, 3, 4, \ldots\}.$$

We notice that the three dots are again used to mean that there are more numbers than we can name. In other words, 4 is the last number named in set W, but it is certainly not the last whole number.

Exercises

1. What is the largest whole number?
2. Is it possible to make a one-to-one correspondence between the set of counting numbers and the set of whole numbers?
3. What is the smallest whole number?
4. What is the smallest counting number?
5. What is the largest counting number?
6. If the elements of set D are in one-to-one correspondence with the elements of set E and if the elements of set E are in one-to-one correspondence with the elements of set R, what may we conclude about the elements of sets D and R?

1-8 Cardinal Numbers

Now let us use one-to-one correspondence to develop the meaning of number. The notions of set and of matching of sets are basic and are a part of every child's experience.

Suppose we consider a set of two space capsules, a set of two books, a set of two airplanes, and a set of two apples. What is common to all of these sets? Obviously, these sets all have the same number of elements, namely two. We shall *imagine* that the same name tag or label is associated with each of the sets (Figure 1-6).

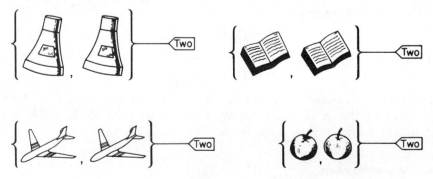

Figure 1-6

We shall call this mental label a number and shall attach this same number concept to any set that can be placed in one-to-one correspondence with any one of the given sets. The property common to all the given sets and to any other set that may be placed in one-to-one correspondence with the given set is "twoness." We naturally need a symbol to represent this property of twoness, and so we agree to use the symbol 2, which was passed down to us by our ancestors. It is important to realize, however, that our number system is man-made and the symbol 2 was invented to represent this number property of twoness, and that we could invent another symbol for the purpose of representing the number two if we so desired. In fact, the Romans attached the symbol II to sets having the twoness property.

The number of elements in a set is often referred to as the **cardinal number** of the set. Cardinal numbers are used to answer the question, "How many members are in the set?" In counting "one, two, three, four," the number names are matched in order with the elements of the set being counted, without regard for the arrangement of the elements, until each element has been placed in one-to-one correspondence with a counting number. For example, consider the set $A = \{\triangle, \bigcirc, \bigcirc, \square\}$ and the set of counting numbers. Notice as illustrated in Figure 1-7 that the elements of set A may be arranged in more than one way for counting.

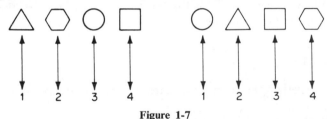

Figure 1-7

The number matched with the last element of the set is the cardinal number of the set. Hence, the cardinal number of set A is 4; that is, as shown in Section 1-5, there are 4 elements in the set. We write $n(A) = 4$, "the number of elements in set A is 4."

1-9 Ordinal Numbers

In counting to determine the position of an item in a group, or the order of the items, a number is used in an ordinal sense. Thus, a person may be seated in the fifth row of a theatre. Page numbers in a book are another illustration of numbers used in an ordinal sense. The common names for the ordinals are "first," "second," "third," "fourth," and so on.

In counting to determine the cardinal number of a set, we matched the

counting numbers in order with the elements of the set being counted without regard for the arrangement of the elements in the set. If we impose an
order on the elements of the set being counted, each element of the set has
an **ordinal number.**

Ordinal numbers are used to answer such questions as, "Which element
in the set is first?" We use numbers in an ordinal sense when the elements
of a set have been arranged in order, and the numbers are used to identify
in their order the elements of the set.

Consider this one-to-one correspondence between the elements of the
sets R and S in Figure 1-8:

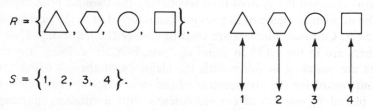

Figure 1-8

When we say that R has 4 elements, the number 4 is used as a cardinal
number. When we say that $\square$ is the fourth element in the set, the number
4 is used as an ordinal number.

Exercises

1. Indicate whether the number in each of these sentences is cardinal or
   ordinal.
   (a) The stool has only three legs.
   (b) He is a member of Lodge 345.
   (c) Twenty-seven children are in Room 21.
   (d) "Name three words that are spelled with four letters."

2. What is the cardinal number of each of the following sets?
   (a) $\{@, \#\}$.   (b) $\{x, y, z, g, h\}$.   (c) $\{\ \}$.   (d) $\{0\}$.

3. Identify the number used in each of the following as either a cardinal
   or ordinal number.
   (a) Charles V.   (b) 200-word essay.
   (c) 40-hour week.   (d) First Prize.

4. Use set symbols to represent
   (a) Two sets that have the same cardinal number, three.
   (b) Two sets in which the cardinal number represented by one set is three
       greater than the cardinal number represented by the other.

1-10 Distinction between Number and Numeral

To a mathematician a **number** is an idea. It is an abstract concept that is used in thinking about the elements in a set. One cannot see, write, or draw a *number*.

Each of these sets contains different elements:

$$\{c, d, e\}, \qquad \{@, \%, \cent\}, \qquad \{\triangle, \square, \bigcirc\}, \qquad \{\text{Bill, Tom, Harry}\}.$$

A common property of these sets is the property of threeness. This is the property that is meant when we speak of the number three. The property of number is abstract. All numbers are abstract ideas, and the symbols we write are the names for these abstract ideas. The symbols are called **numerals.**

It is important to understand that we operate with numbers but we write numerals for the purpose of communicating our results. The symbols 2, V, $4 - 3$, $1 \div 3$, and 2×3 are all numerals.

A **NUMBER** is an **IDEA.**

A **NUMERAL** is a **SYMBOL.**

Exercises

1. Which is larger, the number 6 or the number 7?

2. Which is larger, the numeral 3 or the numeral 4?

3. Which of the following numerals are names for the same number?
   (a) 2. (b) $11 - 8$. (c) 2×0.
   (d) $7 - 5$. (e) $1 + 3$. (f) $6 \div 3$.

1-11 Finite and Infinite Sets

A set may contain any number of elements. In some cases, the number of members may be so large that it would be very tiresome to list them all; for example, the set of all natural numbers less than 500. It is therefore convenient to use three dots to indicate that some of the members are left out of a listing, as $\{1, 2, 3, \ldots, 498, 499\}$ for the set of natural numbers less than 500. The three dots denote that the natural numbers in sequential order from 3 to 498 are included in the set. This notation is obviously quite a time- and space-saver.

Sometimes there is no last number in a set and therefore no end to the list of elements of the set, as, for example, in the set of natural numbers and the set of whole numbers. We say that these sets have an infinite number of elements. They cannot be counted so that the counting comes to an end. Hence, we say that the set of natural numbers is an *infinite set*, and we represent it by {1, 2, 3, . . .}. The three dots are used in this case to mean that the numbers continue in the same manner indefinitely; that is, we can always count one more. In general, any set with elements that can be placed in one-to-one correspondence with the set of all natural numbers is an **infinite set**. The given set may also include elements that have not been placed in one-to-one correspondence with the natural numbers.

When a set is not infinite, we can count the elements in it (using whole numbers), and it is then said to be a **finite set**. Any finite set is either the empty set or has some cardinal number that we may call n for some natural number n. Some examples of finite sets are the set of children in a particular class, the set of players on a football team, the set of people living in West Virginia, and the set of all natural numbers less than 500.

Mathematics deals with both finite and infinite sets.

Exercises

Indicate whether the following sets are finite or infinite.

1. The set of counting numbers.

2. The set of letters in our alphabet.

3. The set of people living in California.

4. The set of two-digit numerals ending in 5.

5. The set of odd numbers evenly divisible by 4.

6. The set of whole numbers.

7. The set of odd whole numbers.

8. The set of counting numbers less than 99.

9. The set of players on a basketball team.

1-12 Equal and Equivalent Sets

Two sets are said to be **equal** (they may also be referred to as **identical**) if every element of each set is an element of the other. Consider these sets:

$$A = \{\text{Elliott, Anne, James}\},$$

$$B = \{\text{Anne, Elliott, James}\}.$$

Then A is equal to B because "A" and "B" are different names for the same set. Recall that the order of the elements listed in a set is immaterial; thus, when the statement "$A = B$" is written, it means that there is one set that has been given two names. In reference to sets, the term "equal" is restricted to the meaning "same as," that is, "identical."

It is not always easy to determine the equality of sets. For example, consider the sets of numbers $D = \{2, 4, 6\}$ and $E = \{3 \times 2, 64 \div 32, 3 + 1\}$; it is possible to determine that $D = E$, but it may not be immediately obvious.

If two sets have the same cardinal number, their elements can be placed in one-to-one correspondence. Such sets are **equivalent sets**. Any two equivalent sets have the same number of elements, but the elements are not necessarily identical. For example, the sets $X = \{1, 2, 3\}$ and $Y = \{\%, @, \#\}$ are equivalent because each set contains the same number of elements, but, since the elements are not identical, set X is not equal to set Y.

It should be noted that equal sets are always equivalent sets but equivalent sets are not necessarily equal sets. The commonly used symbols for denoting the equivalence of sets are $\leftrightarrow$ and $\sim$. In the previous example, the equivalence of sets X and Y may be denoted as $X \leftrightarrow Y$ and as $X \sim Y$ (read as "the set X is equivalent to the set Y"). It would be *incorrect* to say that $X = Y$.

An easy way to determine whether or not two sets are equivalent is to count the elements of each set. As we found in Section 1-8, the number of elements of a set T is the cardinal number of the set T and is written $n(T)$. The number of elements in the set of even natural numbers less than 10, $T = \{2, 4, 6, 8\}$, is 4, and we write $n(T) = 4$. The set M, where $M = \{$Mary, Gene, Sandra, Allen$\}$, also has 4 members; thus, $(n)M = 4$. Since $n(T) = 4$ and $n(M) = 4$, the elements of each of the sets can be placed in one-to-one correspondence with the elements of the set $\{1, 2, 3, 4\}$ and with each other; hence, the cardinal numbers of the sets are the same, and $T \leftrightarrow M$.

Exercises

1. Compare the sets of each pair and indicate whether they are equal sets, equivalent sets, or neither.
   (a) $\{d, e, f, g\}$ and $\{f, d, g, e\}$.
   (b) $\{2, 4, 6, 10\}$ and the set of even natural numbers less than 12.
   (c) $\{1, 3, 5, 7, \ldots\}$ and $\{2, 4, 6, 8, \ldots\}$.
   (d) $\{a, b, c, d, e\}$ and $\{c, e, a, f, b, d\}$.
   (e) $\{$Paul, Dave, George$\}$ and $\{$Pat, Lou, Mary$\}$.

2. What is the cardinal number of each of the following sets?
   (a) $A = \{\ \}$.   (b) $B = \{*, @, \#\}$.   (c) $C = \{a, b, c, d, e, f\}$.
   (d) $D = \{0, 2, 3, 1, 7, 9, 6, 12\}$.   (e) $E = \{0\}$.

3. The sets $R = \{p, a, b, g\}$, $S = \{b, p, g, a\}$, and $T = \{g, t, a, b\}$ are given.

(a) Does $R = S$?   (b) Does $R = T$?

(c) Does $T = S$?   (d) Are sets R, S, and T equivalent sets?

4. If $A = \{7, 9, 11\}$ and $B = \{7 + 4, 14 - 5, 21 \div 3\}$, does $A = B$?

5. List the elements of the set Y, when it is known that $X = Y$ and $X = \{\text{John, Ruth, Bob}\}$.

6. Consider the sets $A = \{2, 3, 4, 5, 6\}$, $B = \{2, 4, 6, 5, 3\}$, $C = \{7, 6, 5, 4,3\}$, $D = \{5, 7, 4, 3, 6\}$, and $E = \{6, 4, 2, 5, 3\}$. Which of these sets are
(a) Equal to A?   (b) Equal to D?   (c) Equal to E?   (d) Equivalent?

1-13 Relations of Equality and Inequality

In the study of mathematics we are continually involved with relations between numbers. A number may be **equal to, not equal to, less than,** or **greater than** a given number. Traditional elementary school mathematics courses have stressed equalities. The symbol $=$ is read "is equal to." We use this symbol between two numerals to indicate that both numerals represent the same number. For example,

$$9 = 9, \text{ nine is equal to nine;}$$

$$8 + 2 = 10, \text{ eight plus two is equal to ten.}$$

For convenience in representing a relation between two numbers that are not equal, the symbol $\neq$ is used, meaning "is not equal to." For example,

$$6 \neq 7, \text{ six is not equal to seven;}$$

$$8 + 4 \neq 5, \text{ eight plus four is not equal to five.}$$

The relation "is not equal to" often is not restrictive enough in comparing two numbers. Many times it is important to know which of the numbers is the larger. Then the symbol $>$, which is read "is greater than," may be used. For example,

$$5 > 3, \text{ five is greater than three;}$$

$$2 > 1, \text{ two is greater than one.}$$

It is just as important to be able to symbolize the relation "is less than." Symbolically, this relation is represented by $<$. For example,

$$1 < 8, \text{ one is less than eight;}$$

$$0 < 9, \text{ zero is less than nine.}$$

If a and b are whole numbers, $a > b$ means $b < a$ and $a = b + n$ for some natural number n. Consider the whole numbers 6 and 7. Since $7 = 6 + 1$,

$$7 > 6 \quad \text{and} \quad 6 < 7.$$

Observe that in the symbols $>$ and $<$ the pointed, or small, end is next to the numeral representing the smaller number, and the open, or large, end is next to the numeral representing the larger number. The symbols $\geq$ and $\leq$ are used to mean "is greater than or equal to" and "is less than or equal to."

Exercises

1. Write each statement with mathematical symbols.
   (a) Twenty-one is greater than eighteen.
   (b) Sixteen is less than thirty-five.
   (c) a is equal to b.
   (d) The set R has the elements r, s, and t.
   (e) c is not equal to d.

2. Tell whether each statement is true or false.
   (a) $3 > 4$.   (b) $8 > 7$.   (c) $9 + 4 \geq 13$.
   (d) $6 + 0 = 0$.   (e) $3 \times 6 > 21$.   (f) $36 \div 3 \leq 9$.
   (g) $7 + 9 < 12 + 5$.   (h) $2 \times 6 \geq 7 + 5$.   (i) $6 \neq 2 + 4$.

For each exercise write a statement using $<$ or $>$ to illustrate the relationship in question.

3. If $6 < 7$, how is $6 + n$ related to $7 + n$ for any natural number n?

4. If a, b, and n are whole numbers and $a < b$, how is $a + n$ related to $b + n$?

5. If $6 < 7$, how is $6 \times n$ related to $7 \times n$ for any natural number n?

6. If a, b, and n are whole numbers and $a < b$, how is $a \times n$ related to $b \times n$?

7. If $2 < 3$ and $3 < 4$, how is 2 related to 4?

8. If a, b, and c are whole numbers, where $a < b$ and $b < c$, how is a related to c?

9. If $4 < 5$ and $8 < 9$, how is 4×8 related to 5×9?

10. If a, b, c, and d are whole numbers, where $a < b$ and $c < d$, how is $a \times c$ related to $b \times d$?

1-14 Number Sentences

When we discuss number relations and write, for example, that seven is less than eight, $7 < 8$, we are writing a **number sentence**. It is important to note that the statement represented by a number sentence may be either *true* or *false*. The statement "five plus four is equal to nine," $5 + 4 = 9$, is a true statement; the statement "five plus four is not equal to ten," $5 + 4 \neq 10$, is a true statement; the statement "three is greater than four," $3 > 4$, is a false statement.

We may also have such number sentences as $3 + \square = 5$ and $7 + 4 = \triangle$. These are called **open number sentences,** and we cannot determine whether they express true or false statements until each of the symbols $\square$ and $\triangle$ is replaced by a symbol for a particular number. The symbol $\square$ or any other symbol used in place of a numeral is a **placeholder,** also called a **variable**.

An open number sentence such as $4 + 3 = \square$ in terms of the symbol $=$ is usually called an **equation,** whereas sentences such as $4 + 3 \neq \triangle$, $4 + 3 > \bigcirc$, and $4 + 3 < \bigcirc$ in terms of the symbols $\neq$, $>$, and $<$ are called **inequalities**.

Relations of equality and inequality are very important in mathematics; they are being introduced in schools at the primary level and their use is being extended to all grade levels. The number line (Section 1-15) is an excellent device for illustrating these number relations.

Exercises

1. Use the correct symbol ($<$, $>$, or $=$) to complete each of these number sentences.
   - **(a)** $1 \underline{\hspace{2em}} 3$.
   - **(b)** $9 + 7 \underline{\hspace{2em}} 3 \times 5$.
   - **(c)** $5 + 3 \underline{\hspace{2em}} 4 + 3 + 1$.
   - **(d)** $4 + 6 \underline{\hspace{2em}} 36 \div 4$.
   - **(e)** $21 - 8 \underline{\hspace{2em}} 7 \times 2$.
   - **(f)** $29 \times 7 \underline{\hspace{2em}} 34 \times 6$.

2. From the set of whole numbers select the number or numbers that will make each open number sentence a correct statement.
   - **(a)** $\square + 3 = 11$.
   - **(b)** $\triangle + \triangle - 3 = 5$.
   - **(c)** $3 + \bigcirc < 4$.
   - **(d)** $\bigcirc - 3 > 15$.
   - **(e)** $\square + \triangle = 10$ and $\square - \triangle = 2$.

3. Tell which of the following number sentences are open sentences. If possible, tell whether the number sentence is true or false.
   - **(a)** $6 + 3 = 4 + 5$.
   - **(b)** $7 - 5 > 4$.
   - **(c)** $2 + \square < 6$.
   - **(d)** $3 \neq 2 + \square$.
   - **(e)** $3 \times 4 > 3 + 8$.
   - **(f)** $2 + 3 + 4 < 15 - 2$.

4. Write $<$, $>$, or $=$ in the blank so that each of the number sentences is a true statement.
   - **(a)** $3 + 4 \underline{\hspace{2em}} 4 + 3$.
   - **(b)** $9 \underline{\hspace{2em}} 6$.
   - **(c)** $2 + 3 \underline{\hspace{2em}} 7$.
   - **(d)** $2 \times 3 \underline{\hspace{2em}} 3 \times 2$.
   - **(e)** $7 + 8 \underline{\hspace{2em}} 8 + 5$.
   - **(f)** $42 - 19 \underline{\hspace{2em}} 19 + 3$.

1-15 Number Line

The **number line** is a widely used teaching device. It is a representation of numbers by points on a line, which is usually pictured horizontally and is thought of as extending without end both to the right and to the left. This endless extension of the line in both directions is sometimes indicated in drawings by arrowheads on the line as shown by Figure 1-9.

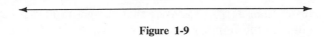

Figure 1-9

To represent (to *graph*) the whole numbers on the number line, an arbitrary point on the line is selected as the graph of the number zero; then a unit of length is chosen and marked off on the line, beginning at the graph of 0 and extending to the right. The right endpoint of this unit segment is the graph of 1 (see Figure 1-10).

Figure 1-10

We use the unit segment from the graph of 0 to the graph of 1 to mark off consecutive points to the right. In this manner, illustrated by Figure 1-11, we locate evenly spaced points on the line as the graphs of the numbers 2, 3, 4, 5, 6, and so on.

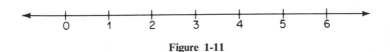

Figure 1-11

The number line is like a ruler, except that conceptually the number line extends without end. Hence, the number line is a straight line and includes points on it that can be placed in one-to-one correspondence with the set of whole numbers. Each number is the **coordinate** of the corresponding point on the number line; each of these points is the **graph** of the corresponding number. Thus, looking at Figure 1-12, we say that the coordinate of the point F is the whole number 5 and that the graph of the whole number 5 is the point F.

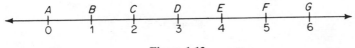

Figure 1-12

As previously mentioned, the number line may be used to illustrate number relations. For example, consider the numbers 3 and 5 graphed on the following number line (Figure 1-13):

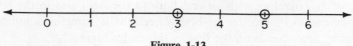

Figure 1-13

Here 5 is greater than 3, $5 > 3$; notice that the graph of 5 is to the right of the graph of 3 on this number line. 3 is less than 5, $3 < 5$; notice that the graph of 3 is to the left of the graph of 5 on the number line.

In our discussion of the number line we have assumed that the graph of 1 is located to the right of the graph of 0. From this assumption it follows in general that a number with a graph on the right of the graph of another number on the line is the greater number. A number with a graph on the left of the graph of another is the lesser number. For example,

$9 > 6$, and the graph of 9 is on the right of the
graph of 6 on the number line;

$4 < 6$, and the graph of 4 is on the left of the
graph of 6 on the number line.

The equality of two numbers may also be shown on the number line. Recall that equality of two numbers indicates that the numerals representing the numbers are actually names for the same number. Hence, two equal numbers are coordinates of the same point on the number line. An example, shown in Figure 1-14, is the relation $\frac{6}{2} = 3$, in which $\frac{6}{2}$ and 3 are symbols for the same number.

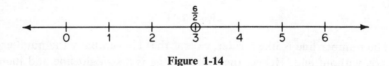

Figure 1-14

In the case of a relation between two numbers that are not equal, the number line may also be used. If two numbers are not coordinates of the same point on the number line, they are not equal. Notice that in the relation $4 \neq 3$ the graphs of 4 and 3 are not the same (Figure 1-15).

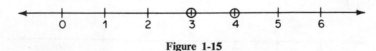

Figure 1-15

Exercises

1. When one number is less than another, what do we know about their graphs on the number line?

2. Use a number line and graph an illustration of
   (a) $4 > 3$.   (b) $2 < 5$.   (c) $2 \neq 3$.

3. Refer to the following number line, in which letters are used to label points, and indicate which point is the graph of each of the numbers.
   (a) 3.   (b) 0.   (c) 6.   (d) 4.   (e) 2.   (f) 1.

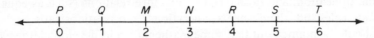

4. Refer to the number line given in Exercise 3 and give the coordinate of
   (a) Point P.   (b) Point Q.   (c) The point midway between M and R.
   (d) The point whose coordinate is twice the coordinate of point N.
   (e) The point whose coordinate is the sum of the coordinates of point Q and point R.

1-16 Precise Mathematical Language

One characteristic of mathematics is the precision of its language. Most of the modern programs in mathematics carefully develop correct usage of mathematical vocabulary. Mathematics is an exact science and requires an exact language. If students are trained in elementary mathematics to communicate ideas clearly and precisely, it is likely thcy will find the training useful in other areas. Certainly, they will have gained a valuable tool for seeing mathematical relationships in greater depth.

Every branch of learning has a vocabulary of its own, and mathematics is no exception. Definitions of terms in mathematics should always be kept in mind as definitions for this field only, regardless of dictionary definitions. For example, many dictionaries make little or no distinction between words such as *number* and *numeral*, and some even define them as synonyms. The word *set* has a dictionary definition, whereas in mathematics we generally consider the term to be undefined except by synonym.

The precise mathematical language that is used in most modern mathematics programs is well within the grasp of elementary school children who have had experience with the concepts involved. The use of mathematically correct language is important, and students should be encouraged to use it.

1-17 A Mathematical System

The idea of a set is a very convenient one in mathematics; however, there is really not a great deal that can be done with just a set of elements. On the other hand, if we have a set and an operation defined on the set, it is interesting to see how the elements of the set behave. The behavior of whole numbers under the arithmetic operations (addition, subtraction, multiplication, and division) will be discussed in Chapters 4 and 5.

For the purposes of study in this text, we shall define a mathematical system as follows:

A **mathematical system** includes a set of elements (such as the set of whole numbers), one or more binary operations (such as addition, subtraction, multiplication, and division), one or more relations (such as equality), and some rules that the elements, operations, and relations satisfy.

It should be pointed out that some mathematicians develop mathematical systems from approaches that are much more rigorous than the one used in this text.

chapter 2

Working with Sets

Set language is an extremely important tool for unifying many fundamental mathematical experiences. We have learned that a set is a well-defined collection of elements and that an empty set is a set containing no elements. The basic notions about sets are being used effectively to develop the understanding that supports the structure of mathematics. In this chapter we shall learn more about set language and the operations on sets.

2-1 Sets and Subsets

Often it is necessary to discuss sets that are part of a given set, that is, sets whose elements are also elements of the given set. Consider the set of students in a particular mathematics class. Assume that B represents the set containing all the members of the class and A represents the set consisting of all the boys in the class. Then each boy in the set A is a member of the set B and A is called a subset of B. In general, a set A is said to be a **subset** of a set B if each element of A is also an element of B. The symbolism $A \subseteq B$ is used to mean "A is subset of B" or, as some people say, "A is included in B." If we let C represent the set of girls in the class who are ten feet tall, then C would be an empty set. However, the set C of girls in the class, regardless of height, is a subset of set B. Therefore, C is a subset of B, $C \subseteq B$, and we have an illustration of the empty set as a subset. We will assume that the empty set is a subset of every set.

It should also be mentioned that a subset may contain all the elements of the set. For example, if you teach in a school for boys, and set D represents all the members of your class and set E represents all the boys in your class, then E is a subset of D. Since set E contains all the elements of set D, $E = D$. From this example, you may conclude that each set is a subset of itself.

It is important to recognize subsets of a given set that are different from the set itself. Thus, if set $K = \{1, 2, 3\}$, there are many subsets of K that are different from K. These subsets are

$$\{1\}, \quad \{2\}, \quad \{3\}, \quad \{1, 2\}, \quad \{1, 3\}, \quad \{2, 3\}, \quad \text{and} \{ \}.$$

Each subset of K that is different from K is called a **proper subset** of K. If $A = \{1, 2\}$, we may write $A \subset K$, which is read "A is a proper subset of K." If $B = \{1, 2, 3\}$, we must use the symbolism $B \subseteq K$, which means "B is a subset of K." Note that the symbol used to represent a proper subset, $\subset$, is different from the symbol used to represent a subset, $\subseteq$. In the previous illustration there is at least one element of K that is not an element of A; therefore we use the symbolism $A \subset K$ to denote that A is a proper subset of K. Since the empty set is a subset of every set, there are seven proper subsets of K.

Perhaps the following problem will clarify some of the points previously discussed. Consider a child who visits the ice-cream store with fifteen cents to spend. As he enters the store a problem is posed as to how he might spend his money. The given set of choices will be called C (Figure 2-1).

$$C = \left\{ 5 ¢ \text{ popsicle, } 5 ¢ \text{ banana bar, } 5 ¢ \text{ cone} \right\}$$

Figure 2-1

What possible purchases can he make with only fifteen cents to spend if he can purchase not more than one of each item? The following choices come to mind:

$$E = \{5¢ \text{ popsicle, } 5¢ \text{ banana bar, } 5¢ \text{ cone}\}$$
$$F = \{5¢ \text{ popsicle, } 5¢ \text{ banana bar}\}$$
$$G = \{5¢ \text{ popsicle, } 5¢ \text{ cone}\}$$
$$H = \{5¢ \text{ banana bar, } 5¢ \text{ cone}\}$$
$$I = \{5¢ \text{ popsicle}\}$$
$$J = \{5¢ \text{ banana bar}\}$$

$$L = \{5¢ \text{ cone}\}$$
$$M = \{\ \}.$$

Notice that each of these eight possible choices is a subset of the original set of choices $C = \{5¢ \text{ popsicle, } 5¢ \text{ banana bar, } 5¢ \text{ cone}\}$. Observe that the given set C is equal to set E; $C = E$. Thus $E \subseteq C$, and E is not a proper subset of C; $E \not\subset C$. Observe also that $F \subset C$, $G \subset C$, $H \subset C$, $I \subset C$, $J \subset C$, $L \subset C$, $M \subset C$.

Exercises

1. Given $B = \{7, 8, 9, 10, 11, 12, 13, 14, 15, 16, 17, 18\}$, find
   (a) The set of the even numbers of B.
   (b) The set of the odd numbers of B.
   (c) Five proper subsets of B that have three elements each.

2. Consider the set $T = \{a, b, c\}$.
   (a) List all the possible subsets of T.
   (b) Consider the subsets that you listed in Exercise 2(a) and indicate which subset is not a proper subset of T.

3. If set A is a proper subset of a finite set C, what can you conclude about the cardinal numbers of the sets A and C? Explain your answer.

4. Given a set with three elements, what is
   (a) The greatest number of subsets that can be formed?
   (b) The greatest number of proper subsets that can be formed?

5. Complete this table.

Set	Subsets	Number of Elements in Original Set	Number of Subsets
$\{d\}$	$\{d\}, \{\ \}$	1	2
$\{d, e\}$	$\{d\}, \{e\}, \{d, e\}, \{\ \}$		
$\{d, e, f\}$			
$\{d, e, f, g\}$			

6. Use the information summarized in Exercise 5 to theorize a formula for the number S of subsets that can be formed from the original set consisting of x elements. Test your theory on a set consisting of five elements; on one consisting of six elements.

2-2 Universal Set

Whenever we discuss a set of elements, we have in mind a particular collection of objects or ideas that have some common characteristic. For example,

we may be considering a set of jet airplanes or a set of pentagons. The
common characteristic of the members of each of these sets is obvious: the
airplanes are powered by jet engines, and the pentagons are geometric
figures with five sides. It should be noted that the elements of each of these
sets can be thought of as elements of a larger set: the jet airplanes are elements also of the set of all airplanes, and the pentagons are elements also
of the set of all geometric figures.

In any situation the set from which all subsets under discussion are
derived is called the **universal set**, also referred to as the **universe**. The universal set is denoted by the capital letter U. Thus, in a discussion about
airplanes the universal set would be the set of all airplanes, and the set of
jet airplanes would be a subset of it.

Exercises

1. Describe a possible universal set for
   (a) The set of six-cylinder automobiles.
   (b) The set of students at George Wythe High School with B grades.
   (c) The set of whole numbers between 6 and 13.

2. Given $U = \{1, 2, 3, 4\}$, indicate whether each of the following is true or
   false.
   (a) $\{2, 3, 4\} \subseteq U$.   **(b)** $\{2, 3, 4, 1\} \subseteq U$.
   (c) $\{\ \} \subseteq U$.   **(d)** $\{3, 2, 4, 1\} \subset U$.

3. Think of each of the following sets as a universal set, and select at least
   one proper subset of each.
   (a) The set of all astronauts.
   (b) The set of three-sided geometric figures.
   (c) The set of natural numbers.

2-3 Union of Sets

In arithmetic, we are familiar with the processes of addition and multiplication. These are called binary operations, and for our present purposes a
binary operation may be defined as one that assigns to *two* given elements
a third element. The word binary implies two.

There are two operations on sets which we will discuss, union and
intersection. Each of these operations is considered to be a binary operation
because it is an operation on two sets which produces one new set. The
new set may coincide with one of the given sets.

Children intuitively discover what is meant by the union of sets when
they combine the elements of two sets of things to form a single set; if the

elements of { } are joined with the element of { }, one obtains the new set { }. A teacher may think of the set of children in her class as the union of the set of girls in the class and the set of boys in the class.

Consider two sets of boys:

$$A = \{\text{Russell, Dave, George}\},$$

$$B = \{\text{Gray, Bob, Paul, Bill}\}.$$

Suppose we wish to form a new set consisting of all the members of set A and all the members of set B. This new set is called the union of set A and set B and is written $A \cup B$. This is read "A union B." Some mathematicians choose to call the symbol "cup" because it is shaped like a cup. In this text, we shall always refer to the symbol $\cup$ as "union." For the previous example, $A \cup B = \{\text{Russell, Dave, George, Gray, Bob, Paul, Bill}\}$.

The **union** of any two sets S and T, written $S \cup T$, is the set consisting of all elements in either S or T or in both S and T. In other words, an element is a member of $S \cup T$ if the element is a member of at least one of the sets S and T. The following examples illustrate the meaning of the union of sets.

Example 1 If $S = \{2, 4, 6, 8\}$ and $T = \{10, 12\}$, then

$$S \cup T = \{2, 4, 6, 8, 10, 12\}.$$

Example 2 If $D = \{\text{James, Sam, Charles}\}$ and $E = \{\text{Don, Joe, Sam}\}$, then

$$D \cup E = \{\text{James, Sam, Charles, Don, Joc}\}.$$

Notice that in Example 2 we do not write the name "Sam" twice. As soon as the name is written once, we know that Sam is a member of the set $D \cup E$. Thus the set {James, Sam, Charles, Don, Joe, Sam} is the same as the set {James, Sam, Charles, Don, Joe}, and it is unnecessary to write "Sam" twice. In Example 3, the 5 and 7 appear only once in $X \cup Y$:

Example 3 If $X = \{5, 6, 7, 8\}$ and $Y = \{1, 5, 7, 9\}$, then

$$X \cup Y = \{1, 5, 6, 7, 8, 9\}.$$

Exercises

1. Given $G = \{2, 4, 6\}$ and $H = \{1, 3, 5\}$, find $G \cup H$ and $n(G \cup H)$.

2. Given $A = \{a, b, c\}$ and $B = \{b, c, d\}$, find $A \cup B$ and $n(A \cup B)$.

3. Given $R = \{\%, @, \#\}$ and $S = \{c, \&, @\}$, find $R \cup S$ and $n(R \cup S)$.

4. Given $D = \{2, 3, 4\}$ and $D \cup E = D$, list each of the sets that can be used for E.

5. If $D \cup E$ is the same set as D, what do we know about sets D and E?

6. Use the elements of the set $\{T, \emptyset, U\}$ and replace each expression by an equivalent set. Remember the meaning of $\emptyset$ and U.

(a) $T \cup U$.   (b) $T \cup T$.   (c) $T \cup \emptyset$.

2-4 Intersection of Sets

It is frequently desirable to obtain the set of elements common to two given sets. Consider the sets D and E used in our discussion of the union of two sets:

$$D = \{\text{James, Sam, Charles}\},$$

$$E = \{\text{Don, Joe, Sam}\}.$$

Let us find the set of boys who belong to both D and E. Clearly, this set is {Sam}.

We have found the set of elements common to sets D and E. This set, $D \cap E$, is the intersection of D and E. The symbol used for intersection is $\cap$. Some mathematicians call this symbol "cap." We shall refer to the symbol $\cap$ as "intersection." For the previous example, $D \cap E$ is read "D intersection E," and $D \cap E = \{\text{Sam}\}$.

The **intersection** of any two sets M and N, written $M \cap N$, is the set consisting of the elements that are in both M and N. The following examples illustrate the meaning of the intersection of sets.

Example 1 If $M = \{1, 3, 5\}$ and $N = \{0, 3, 4, 6\}$, then

$$M \cap N = \{3\}.$$

Example 2 If $G = \{d, e, a, c, b\}$ and $H = \{l, m, a, b, n, d, h\}$, then

$$G \cap H = \{a, b, d\}.$$

Example 3 If $A = \{1, 3, 4, 7\}$ and $B = \{5, 6\}$, then

$$A \cap B = \{\ \}.$$

Notice that in Example 3 the sets A and B have no elements in common, that is, their intersection is the empty set. This could also be represented by $A \cap B = \emptyset$, since $\emptyset = \{\ \}$.

Exercises

1. Given $A = \{a, b, c\}$ and $B = \{b, c, d\}$, find $A \cap B$ and $n(A \cap B)$.

2. Given $R = \{\%, @, \#\}$ and $S = \{\cent, \&, @\}$, find $R \cap S$ and $n(R \cap S)$.

3. Given $G = \{2, 4, 6\}$ and $H = \{1, 3, 5\}$, find $G \cap H$ and $n(G \cap H)$.

4. Given $M = \{2, 3, 4\}$, $N \subseteq M$, and $M \cap N = M$, list each of the sets that can be used for N.

5. If $N \subseteq M$ and $M \cap N$ is the same set as M, what do we know about sets M and N?

6. Given $D = \{a, b, c\}$ and $D \cap E = D \cup E$, list each of the sets that can be used for E.

7. If $D \cap E$ is the same set as $D \cup E$, what do we know about sets D and E?

8. What is the intersection of the set of odd whole numbers less than 10 and the set of whole numbers from 1 to 10 inclusive?

9. Let $A = \{0, 1, 2, 3, \ldots\}$, $B = \{0, 2, 4, 6, \ldots\}$, $C = \{1, 3, 5, 7, \ldots\}$, and $D = \{5, 10, 15, 20, \ldots\}$; find
   - (a) $B \cup C$.
   - (b) $B \cap D$.
   - (c) $A \cap C$.
   - (d) $B \cap C$.
   - (e) $A \cap D$.
   - (f) $C \cap D$.

2-5 Disjoint Sets

Any two sets with no elements in common are called **disjoint sets**. Thus, two sets are disjoint when their intersection is the empty set. Consider the sets $A = \{$Russell, Dave, George$\}$ and $B = \{$Gray, Bob, Paul, Bill$\}$. The intersection of sets A and B is the empty set; hence, we say that A and B are disjoint sets.

Example 1 If $S = \{2, 4, 6, 8\}$ and $T = \{10, 12\}$, then $S \cap T = \{\ \}$. The sets S and T are disjoint sets.

Example 2 If $X = \{5, 6, 7, 8\}$ and $Y = \{1, 5, 7, 9\}$, then $X \cap Y = \{5, 7\}$. The sets X and Y are *not* disjoint sets.

Exercises

Determine whether the sets of each pair are disjoint.

1. $G = \{1, 3, 5, 7\}$ and $H = \{2, 4, 6, 3\}$.
2. $X = \{@, \#, \%\}$ and $Y = \{*, \&, ¢\}$.
3. $R = \{3, 6, 9, 12\}$ and $S = \{1, 5, 11, 13\}$.
4. $A = \{7, 14, 21, 28, \ldots\}$ and $B = \{4, 8, 12, 16, \ldots\}$.

2-6 Complement of a Set

If A is a subset of a universal set U, the set of all elements of U that are not elements of A is called the **complement** of A with respect to U. We use the symbol A' (read "complement of A") to designate the complement of A. It is important to note that $A \subseteq U$, $A' \subseteq U$, $A \cup A' = U$, and $A \cap A' = \emptyset$.

Consider two examples. (a) If the universal set is the set of all airplanes and A is the set of jet airplanes, then A' is the set of all airplanes that are not powered by jet engines. (b) If $U = \{1, 2, 3, \ldots, 10\}$ and $B = \{1, 9, 8, 3\}$, then $B' = \{2, 4, 5, 6, 7, 10\}$.

Exercises

1. Suppose that the universal set is the set of natural numbers less than 5 and that $A = \{2, 4\}$; find A'.

2. If the universal set is the set of all automobiles and C is the set of Chevrolets, describe C'.

3. Suppose $U = \{1, 2, 3, 4, 5, 6, 7, 8, 9\}$, $A = \{1, 2, 3\}$, $B = \{3, 5, 7, 9\}$, and $C = \{6, 7, 8\}$; find each of the following sets.
   (a) $A \cap U$.   (b) $A \cup U$.   (c) B'.   (d) $B' \cap U$.
   (e) $C' \cup U$.   (f) $C' \cap B'$.   (g) $(A \cap C)'$.   (h) $(B \cup C)'$.

2-7 Venn Diagrams

Venn diagrams, named after the English mathematician John Venn, are frequently used to present a visual representation of relations and operations on sets. The points of a rectangular region (that is, the set of all points on and inside the rectangle) may be used to represent the elements of a universal set. In Figure 2-2, the rectangular region represents the set U of all students attending Prince George High School.

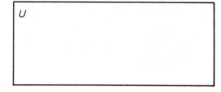

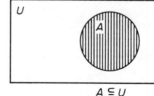

$A \subseteq U$

Figure 2-2   Figure 2-3

A subset of the universal set U may be represented by a circular region within the rectangular region. For example, we may let A represent the set of boys attending Prince George High School. The set A is illustrated by the shaded region in Figure 2-3. Note that the shaded region includes all points on and inside the circle.

A proper subset of the set A may be represented by another circular region within the circular region A. For example, if B is the set of freshman boys attending Prince George High School, then the relationship may be represented as in Figure 2-4.

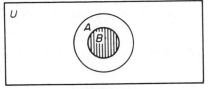

$B \subseteq A$

Figure 2-4

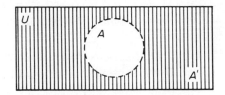

Figure 2-5

If A represents the set of boys attending Prince George High School, then A' denotes the set of girls attending Prince George High School. In Figure 2-5, we have represented A' by shading the points of U that are outside A. A dashed line indicates the boundary of a shaded region when the boundary is not part of the region. Thus, the points on the circle are not included in the shaded region representing A'. Note that $A \cup A' = U$ and $A \cap A' = \emptyset$.

The union of sets D and E is illustrated in Figure 2-6. The elements of the set D are represented by the vertical shading; the elements of the set E, by the horizontal shading. The union of the two sets D and E is represented by the region that is shaded in either or both directions. Note that $D \cup E$ includes all the points of the set D as well as all those of the set E.

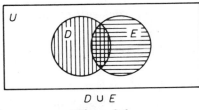

$D \cup E$

Figure 2-6

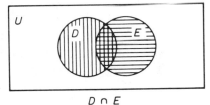

$D \cap E$

Figure 2-7

The intersection of sets D and E is pictured in the Venn diagram in Figure 2-7. The elements of the set D are represented by vertical shading; the elements of the set E, by horizontal shading. The intersection of the two sets D and E is represented by the region that is shaded both vertically and horizontally. Note that $D \cap E$ includes only those points that are in both set D and set E.

Exercises

1. Use Venn diagrams to show union and intersection, locating within circular regions points that represent the elements of the given sets, and solve these problems.

(a) Let $A = \{1, 3, 5, 7\}$ and $B = \{2, 4, 6, 8\}$; find $A \cup B$ and $A \cap B$.

(b) Let $M = \{$Ann, Louise$\}$ and $N = \{$Lucille, Louise$\}$; find $M \cup N$ and $M \cap N$.

2. Use Venn diagrams to give a representation of $(A \cap B) \cup C$ where A, B, and C are subsets of U and $(A \cap B) \cap C \neq \emptyset$.

3. Use Venn diagrams to represent two sets P and Q such that $P \cap Q \neq \emptyset$, and shade properly to illustrate

(a) The union of P and Q.   (b) The intersection of P and Q.

4. Use Venn diagrams to represent two sets D and E such that D is a proper subset of E, and shade properly to illustrate

(a) The union of D and E.   (b) The intersection of D and E.

5. Use Venn diagrams to represent two sets G and H such that $G = H$, and shade properly to illustrate

(a) The union of G and H.   (b) The intersection of G and H.

6. In Exercise 5, what relationship exists between $G \cup H$ and $G \cap H$?

7. Draw Venn diagrams to represent

(a) Two sets R and S such that all elements of R are elements of S and some elements of S are not elements of R.

(b) Three sets A, B, and E such that $A \subset B$ and $B \subset E$.

(c) Three sets X, Y, and Z such that all elements of X are elements of Y, all elements of Z are elements of Y, X and Z have no elements in common, and some elements of Y are not elements of either X or Z.

8. Use Venn diagrams to represents two sets C and D such that $C \cap D \neq \emptyset$, and shade properly to illustrate

(a) $(C \cup D)'$.   (b) $(C \cap D)'$.

9. Use Venn diagrams to represent three sets R, S, and T such that $(R \cap S) \cap T \neq \emptyset$, and shade properly to illustrate

(a) $R \cup (S \cup T)$.   (b) $(R \cup S) \cup T$.

(c) $R \cap (T \cup S)$.   (d) $R \cap (T \cap S)$.

chapter 3

Systems of Numeration

A **numeration system** is an organized procedure for arranging a set of symbols so that they effectively communicate the concept of number. Our numeration system, which is basically of Hindu-Arabic origin, is organized on the basis of two major characteristics:

Place value,
A base of ten.

It should be pointed out that mathematics (and a system of numeration in particular) is man-made. The symbols that man has used to record his numbers have been those he devised. These symbols have been changed and improved upon from time to time throughout recorded history.

3-1 Characteristics of Decimal Notation

The name given our system of numeration is the **decimal system.** This system, which is used in most of the world today, is based on sets of ten. Accordingly, the decimal system is often called the **base ten system.** Probably the base of ten was used because early man used his fingers for counting. When he had counted all ten fingers, he developed a procedure for starting the count over again, perhaps keeping some record of the number of tens.

In our system of counting, we start over when ten is reached and we use a **positional notation** to record the count. Thus, a count of ten is represented as 10, which means one set of ten and no sets of one; a count of eleven is shown as 11, which means one set of ten and one set of one; and so on.

Ten Basic Number Symbols Used in the Decimal System

Set		*Numeral*
{ }	0	is the numeral for a set containing no elements.
{/}	1	is the numeral for a set containing one element.
{//}	2	is the numeral for a set containing two elements.
{///}	3	is the numeral for a set containing three elements.
{////}	4	is the numeral for a set containing four elements.
{/////}	5	is the numeral for a set containing five elements.
{//////}	6	is the numeral for a set containing six elements.
{///////}	7	is the numeral for a set containing seven elements.
{////////}	8	is the numeral for a set containing eight elements.
{/////////}	9	is the numeral for a set containing nine elements.

These ten numerals are called **decimal digits** (also referred to simply as **digits**).

Exercises

1. What are the two major characteristics of the decimal system of numeration?

2. Explain what is meant by the numeral representing a count of
   (**a**) Twelve.   (**b**) Fifteen.   (**c**) Twenty-one.

3-2 Place Value

The principle of **place value,** also called **positional notation**, is used in the decimal system. The value represented by each digit in a given numeral is determined by the position it occupies. For example, consider the numeral 35. The position of the 3 in this numeral indicates that it represents three sets of ten. In 53, on the other hand, the 3 represents three sets of one.

The place values in the decimal system are based on *ten*. In Figure 3-1, beginning at the ones place (also called the "units" place) and to the left, each place has a value ten times as large as the value of the place to its right.

Place – Value Chart For Whole Numbers

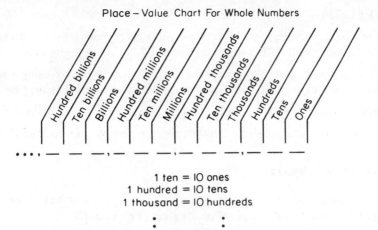

1 ten = 10 ones
1 hundred = 10 tens
1 thousand = 10 hundreds

Figure 3-1

Consider the numeral 2,345 in terms of the place value of each of its digits:

5 is in the ones place; 5 ones = 5 ones.

4 is in the tens place; 4 tens = 40 ones.

3 is in the hundreds place; 3 hundreds = 300 ones.

2 is in the thousands place; 2 thousands = 2,000 ones.

Thus the numeral 2,345 may be analyzed by using the principle of place value. It expresses the number two thousand three hundred forty-five. This may be represented in *expanded form* as

$$(2 \times 1,000) + (3 \times 100) + (4 \times 10) + (5 \times 1); \quad \text{that is,}$$
$$2,000 \quad + \quad 300 \quad + \quad 40 \quad + \quad 5.$$

If the digits of the numeral 2,345 were rearranged, the importance of the place-value principle would become very apparent. For example, consider 5,432:

$$(5 \times 1,000) + (4 \times 100) + (3 \times 10) + (2 \times 1); \quad \text{that is,}$$
$$5,000 \quad + \quad 400 \quad + \quad 30 \quad + \quad 2.$$

Although the same digits are used in the numerals 2,345 and 5,432, the two numerals do *not* name the same number.

Exercises

1. In the decimal system, what value does the digit 2 represent in each of these numerals?

(**a**) 612,734.   (**b**) 3,281.   (**c**) 789,002.   (**d**) 823.

2. What is the smallest whole number you can represent by using each of the decimal digits 4, 3, and 2 exactly once? No other digits may be used.

3. What is the largest whole number you can represent by using each of the decimal digits 4, 3, and 2 exactly once? No other digits may be used.

4. What is the largest whole number represented by two decimal digits?

5. What is the smallest whole number represented by one decimal digit?

3-3 Powers of Numbers

We have seen that in decimal notation each place has a value ten times as large as the value of the place on its right. For example,

$$1 \text{ ten} = 10 \text{ ones},$$

$$1 \text{ hundred} = 10 \text{ tens},$$

$$1 \text{ thousand} = 10 \text{ hundreds},$$

$$1 \text{ ten thousand} = 10 \text{ thousands},$$

$$1 \text{ hundred thousand} = 10 \text{ ten thousands}.$$

However, we are primarily interested in the value of each place in terms of ones. Then,

$$1 \text{ ten} = 10 \text{ ones},$$

$$1 \text{ hundred} = (10 \times 10) \text{ ones},$$

$$1 \text{ thousand} = (10 \times 10 \times 10) \text{ ones},$$

$$1 \text{ ten thousand} = (10 \times 10 \times 10 \times 10) \text{ ones},$$

$$1 \text{ hundred thousand} = (10 \times 10 \times 10 \times 10 \times 10) \text{ ones}.$$

Since the expressions of the form

$$10 \times 10 \times \ldots \times 10$$

become awkward when several 10's are multiplied together, we need a new symbol to indicate the number of 10's that are multiplied together.

Two or more numbers that are multiplied to form a **product** are called **factors** of the product. Thus, 4 and 6 are factors of the product 24, since $4 \times 6 = 24$; 3 and 8 are factors of 24, since $3 \times 8 = 24$; 2 and 12 are also factors of 24, since $2 \times 12 = 24$. Each of the numbers 1, 2, 3, 4, 6, 8, 12, and 24 is a factor of 24 since

$$24 = 1 \times 24 = 2 \times 12 = 3 \times 8 = 4 \times 6.$$

When the same factor is repeated, as in

$$10 \times 10, \quad 10 \times 10 \times 10, \quad \text{and} \quad 10 \times 10 \times 10 \times 10,$$

we use a small numeral above and to the right of the numeral representing the factor, to indicate the number of times the factor is repeated. For example,

$$10 \times 10 = 10^2,$$
$$10 \times 10 \times 10 = 10^3,$$
$$10 \times 10 \times 10 \times 10 = 10^4.$$

The repeated factor is the **base**, the number of times the base is used as a factor is the **exponent**, and the base with its exponent is sometimes called a **power**. In the case of 10^4 (read "ten to the fourth power"), 10 is the base, 4 is the exponent, and 10^4 is the power.

$$10^1 = (10) = 10,$$
$$10^2 = (10 \times 10) = 100,$$
$$10^3 = (10 \times 10 \times 10) = 1,000,$$
$$10^4 = (10 \times 10 \times 10 \times 10) = 10,000,$$
$$10^5 = (10 \times 10 \times 10 \times 10 \times 10) = 100,000.$$

Notice that the numeral for the exponent is usually omitted for the first power of ten; that is, ten is usually written 10 instead of 10^1. Exponents may be used with any number as a base. For example, $6 \times 6 \times 6$ is 6^3, where 6 is the base, 3 is the exponent, and 6^3 is the power.

Exercises

1. Represent each of the following as a power (that is, as a base with an exponent).
   (a) $9 \times 9 \times 9$.   (b) $7 \times 7 \times 7 \times 7$.   (c) 3×3.   (d) 5×25.

2. Which numeral represents the larger number?
   (a) 5^6 or 6^5.   (b) 2^7 or 7^2.

3. What is the relation between the exponent of a power of ten and the number of zeros in the decimal numeral representing the number?

4. Represent the following as repeated factors.
   (a) 10^6.   (b) 2^3.   (c) 4^5.   (d) 5^4.

5. In each of the following, identify the base, the exponent, and the power.
   (a) 3^6.   (b) 7^2.

3-4 Multiplication and Division of Powers

We have studied the exponent as a convention in notation that simplifies the representation of repeated factors. In general, if a and n are natural numbers, then a^n means $a \times a \times a \times \ldots \times a$, where there are n factors in the product. (*Note: $a \times a$ may also be written $a \cdot a$.*)

The use of exponents in the representation of repeated factors also simplifies the calculation of the product of two powers of the same base. For example,

$$4^2 \times 4^3 = (4 \times 4) \times (4 \times 4 \times 4) = (4 \times 4 \times 4 \times 4 \times 4) = 4^5,$$

$$6^3 \times 6^4 = (6 \times 6 \times 6) \times (6 \times 6 \times 6 \times 6)$$
$$= (6 \times 6 \times 6 \times 6 \times 6 \times 6 \times 6) = 6^7,$$

$$a^2 \cdot a^4 = (a \cdot a) \cdot (a \cdot a \cdot a \cdot a) = (a \cdot a \cdot a \cdot a \cdot a \cdot a) = a^6.$$

A careful observation of these three examples should lead us to the inference that

$$4^2 \times 4^3 = 4^{2+3} = 4^5,$$

$$6^3 \times 6^4 = 6^{3+4} = 6^7,$$

$$a^2 \times a^4 = a^{2+4} = a^6.$$

In general, any product of two powers of the same base is a power of that base, and the new exponent is the sum of the exponents of the factors; that is, $b^m \cdot b^n = b^{m+n}$.

We may extend this idea to raising a power to a power. For example,

$$(4^2)^3 = (4 \times 4)^3 = (4 \times 4) \times (4 \times 4) \times (4 \times 4)$$
$$= (4 \times 4 \times 4 \times 4 \times 4 \times 4) = 4^6,$$

$$(6^3)^4 = (6 \times 6 \times 6)^4$$
$$= (6 \times 6 \times 6) \times (6 \times 6 \times 6) \times (6 \times 6 \times 6) \times (6 \times 6 \times 6)$$
$$= (6 \times 6 \times 6 \times 6 \times 6 \times 6 \times 6 \times 6 \times 6 \times 6 \times 6 \times 6) = 6^{12},$$

$$(a^2)^4 = (a \cdot a)^4 = (a \cdot a) \cdot (a \cdot a) \cdot (a \cdot a) \cdot (a \cdot a) = (a \cdot a \cdot a \cdot a \cdot a \cdot a \cdot a \cdot a) = a^8.$$

A careful observation of these three examples should lead us to the inference that

$$(4^2)^3 = 4^{2 \times 3} = 4^6,$$

$$(6^3)^4 = 6^{3 \times 4} = 6^{12},$$

$$(a^2)^4 = a^{2 \times 4} = a^8.$$

In general, any power of a power of a base is a power of that base, and the new exponent is the product of the exponent of the given power and the exponent that indicated the power to which it was raised; that is, $(b^m)^n = b^{m \cdot n}$.

The use of exponents in the representation of repeated factors also simplifies the calculation of the quotient of two powers of the same base.

For example,

$$\frac{4^5}{4^3} = \frac{4 \times 4 \times 4 \times 4 \times 4}{4 \times 4 \times 4} = \frac{4}{4} \times \frac{4}{4} \times \frac{4}{4} \times 4 \times 4$$

$$= 1 \times 1 \times 1 \times 4 \times 4 = 4 \times 4 = 4^2,$$

$$\frac{6^7}{6^4} = \frac{6 \times 6 \times 6 \times 6 \times 6 \times 6 \times 6}{6 \times 6 \times 6 \times 6} = \frac{6}{6} \times \frac{6}{6} \times \frac{6}{6} \times \frac{6}{6} \times 6 \times 6 \times 6$$

$$= 1 \times 1 \times 1 \times 1 \times 6 \times 6 \times 6 = 6 \times 6 \times 6 = 6^3,$$

$$\frac{a^6}{a^2} = \frac{a \cdot a \cdot a \cdot a \cdot a \cdot a}{a \cdot a} = \frac{a}{a} \cdot \frac{a}{a} \cdot a \cdot a \cdot a \cdot a = 1 \cdot 1 \cdot a \cdot a \cdot a \cdot a = a \cdot a \cdot a \cdot a = a^4.$$

A careful observation of these three examples should lead us to the inference that

$$\frac{4^5}{4^3} = 4^{5-3} = 4^2,$$

$$\frac{6^7}{6^4} = 6^{7-4} = 6^3,$$

$$\frac{a^6}{a^2} = a^{6-2} = a^4.$$

In general, any quotient of two powers of the same base is a power of that base, and the new exponent is the difference of the exponents of the given powers; that is, $b^m \div b^n = b^{m-n}$.

Perhaps special attention should be given to the next example, in which a represents any natural number:

$$\frac{a^4}{a^4} = \frac{a \cdot a \cdot a \cdot a}{a \cdot a \cdot a \cdot a} = \frac{a}{a} \cdot \frac{a}{a} \cdot \frac{a}{a} \cdot \frac{a}{a} = 1 \cdot 1 \cdot 1 \cdot 1 = 1.$$

However, using the method of subtracting exponents previously discussed, we have

$$\frac{a^4}{a^4} = a^{4-4} = a^0.$$

Therefore, to insure consistency in the results, we must agree that

$$a^0 = 1,$$

where a represents any natural number.

Another special case of division involving exponents must be considered. If a represents any natural number, then

$$\frac{a^2}{a^4} = \frac{a \cdot a}{a \cdot a \cdot a \cdot a} = \frac{a}{a} \cdot \frac{a}{a} \cdot \frac{1}{a} \cdot \frac{1}{a} = 1 \cdot 1 \cdot \frac{1}{a} \cdot \frac{1}{a} = \frac{1}{a^2}.$$

However, using the method of subtracting exponents, we have

$$\frac{a^2}{a^4} = a^{2-4} = a^{-2},$$

where the -2 is read "negative two" and is called a negative exponent. Therefore, to insure consistency in the results, we must agree that

$$a^{-2} = \frac{1}{a^2} \quad \text{and, in general,} \quad a^{-n} = \frac{1}{a^n}$$

where a and n represent natural numbers.

Observe the pattern of the exponents in the following illustration of powers of ten:

$$10^3 = (10 \times 10 \times 10) = 1,000,$$
$$10^2 = (10 \times 10) = 100,$$
$$10^1 = (10) = 10,$$
$$10^0 = (1) = 1,$$
$$10^{-1} = \left(\frac{1}{10}\right) = \frac{1}{10},$$
$$10^{-2} = \left(\frac{1}{10} \times \frac{1}{10}\right) = \frac{1}{100},$$
$$10^{-3} = \left(\frac{1}{10} \times \frac{1}{10} \times \frac{1}{10}\right) = \frac{1}{1,000},$$
$$10^{-4} = \left(\frac{1}{10} \times \frac{1}{10} \times \frac{1}{10} \times \frac{1}{10}\right) = \frac{1}{10,000},$$
$$10^{-5} = \left(\frac{1}{10} \times \frac{1}{10} \times \frac{1}{10} \times \frac{1}{10} \times \frac{1}{10}\right) = \frac{1}{100,000}.$$

Exercises

1. Use exponents and represent each expression as a single power.
   (a) $2^4 \times 2^3$.   (b) $3^{-4} \times 3^7$.   (c) $6^7 \div 6^2$.
   (d) $4^2 \times 4^7 \div 4$.   (e) $2^0 \times 3^0$.   (f) $(5^2)^6$.

2. Use exponents and represent each expression as a single power where b represents a natural number.
   (a) $b^3 \cdot b^5$.   (b) $b^9 \div b^4$.   (c) $b^2 \cdot b$.
   (d) $b^7 \div b^7$.   (e) $b^2 \div b^5$.   (f) $(b^4)^3$.

3. Use exponents and represent each expression as a single power.
   (a) $(3^7)^2$.   (b) $3^7 \times 3^2$.   (c) $5^0 \times 25^2$.
   (d) $(4^3)^{-2}$.   (e) $8^2 \div 2$.   (f) $21^{13} \div 21^{19}$.

4. In the decimal system, the tens place is how many times as large as the
   (a) Ones place?   (b) Tenths place?
   (c) Hundredths place?   (d) Ten-thousandths place?

5. In the decimal system, the hundredths place is what fraction of the
  (a) Tenths place?   (b) Ones place?
  (c) Tens place?   (d) Hundreds place?

3-5 Base of a System of Numeration

The base of any system of numeration establishes the method of grouping
and the number of digits needed. In the decimal system, we collect in sets
of ten, and we can represent any number by using only the ten digits 0, 1, 2,
3, 4, 5, 6, 7, 8, and 9.

  We may collect in sets other than ten. For example, the Mayan Indians'
system of numeration had a base of 20 and the early Babylonians' system
had a base of 60.

  In the following illustrations a count of the elements in each produces
the same number, but each illustration denotes a different way of grouping
the elements. A subscript with a numeral denotes the base used to obtain
that numeral, that is, the grouping. The general policy is to assume that a
numeral is written in base 10 unless otherwise specified. However, in the
first illustration the subscript "ten" is used for the decimal representation in order that it may easily be compared with the other two illustrations.

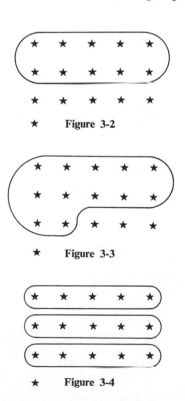

★   **Figure 3-2**

★   **Figure 3-3**

★   **Figure 3-4**

A decimal (base 10) grouping of the 16 elements in Figure 3-2 indicates that the collection contains 1 set of ten elements and 6 more. This could be recorded as 16_{ten} and read as "one six, base ten," or "sixteen, base ten". If the same 16 elements were grouped in dozens (sets of twelve), there would be 1 set of twelve and 4 more. This grouping could be recorded as 14_{twelve} and read as "one four, base twelve" (Figure 3-3).

If the same 16 elements were grouped in sets of five, there would be 3 sets of five and 1 set of one. This could be recorded as 31_{five} and read as "three one, base five" (Figure 3-4).

The three numerals 16_{ten}, 14_{twelve}, and 31_{five} are based upon different ways of collecting and representing the same number of elements; thus these numerals are names for the same number.

We have learned that the position a digit occupies in a numeral determines the value of the digit. In the decimal system of numeration each place (position) is associated with a power of the base, ten. For example, the numeral 4,093 may be represented as

$$(4 \times 1{,}000) + (0 \times 100) + (9 \times 10) + (3 \times 1),$$

which is

$$(4 \times 10^3) + (0 \times 10^2) + (9 \times 10^1) + (3 \times 10^0).$$

The expression

$$(4 \times 10^3) + (0 \times 10^2) + (9 \times 10^1) + (3 \times 10^0)$$

is the **expanded form** of the numeral 4,093. The expanded form of the numeral 12,345.678 is

$$(1 \times 10^4) + (2 \times 10^3) + (3 \times 10^2) + (4 \times 10^1) + (5 \times 10^0)$$
$$+ (6 \times 10^{-1}) + (7 \times 10^{-2}) + (8 \times 10^{-3}).$$

Exercises

1. Represent the following in expanded form.
   (a) 328.   (b) 9,657.   (c) 263,784.   (d) 6.175.

2. What is the meaning attached to the digit 7 in the following numerals?
   (a) 729.   (b) 972.   (c) 297.   (d) 92.07.

3. Copy the given set and group the elements in

   ★ ★ ★ ★ ★ ★   (a) Sets of ten.
                                        (b) Sets of twelve.
   ★ ★ ★ ★ ★ ★   (c) Sets of five.
                                        (d) Sets of seven.
   ★ ★ ★ ★ ★ ★

4. Copy the given set and group the elements in

   ★ ★ ★   (a) Sets of ten.
                        (b) Sets of nine.
   ★ ★ ★   (c) Sets of eight.
                        (d) Sets of six.
   ★ ★ ★

   ★ ★ ★

   ★

5. What is the base of our system of numeration when we collect in
   (a) Sets of ten?   (b) Sets of twelve?
   (c) Sets of five?   (d) Sets of seven?

(e) Sets of nine?   (f) Sets of eight?

(g) Sets of six?   (h) Sets of two?

6. How many digits are needed in order to be able to represent any number when we collect in

(a) Sets of ten?   (b) Sets of twelve?

(c) Sets of five?   (d) Sets of seven?

(e) Sets of nine?   (f) Sets of eight?

(g) Sets of six?   (h) Sets of two?

3-6 Early Egyptian Numerals

Like many other accomplishments of man, the development of our numeration system has gone through many stages to reach the present decimal system. Many earlier civilizations contributed to the development of an understandable, usable system. Characteristics such as the use of symbols, place value, base, and zero should be considered when our system is compared with earlier systems.

The decimal system of notation, which we take for granted, is one of the outstanding achievements of the human mind. In order that we may appreciate our decimal system more fully, we shall compare it with some of the ancient systems of numeration and look for characteristics that make our system superior.

One of the earliest recorded systems of writing numerals is the Egyptian. Their hieroglyphic numerals have been traced back as far as 3,300 B.C. The Egyptians developed a numeration system with which they could express numbers up to millions. Among the Egyptian numerals used were those illustrated in Figure 3-5.

Egyptian Numeral	Name	Our Numeral
I	Stroke	1
∩	Arch or heel bone	10
୨	Coiled rope or scroll	100
⚱	Lotus flower	1,000
◿	Pointing finger	10,000
⌒	Burbot fish or tadpole	100,000
大	Astonished man	1,000,000

Figure 3-5

The Egyptian numerals were carved on wood or stone. There was no symbol for zero, and the system was based on sets of ten with different symbols for ones, tens, hundreds, and so forth. These different symbols were needed because there was no use of place value. The Egyptian system was additive, since the number represented by a particular set of symbols was the sum of the numbers represented by each symbol in the set. Consider these examples:

Egyptian Numeral	*Our Numeral*
IIII	4
∩∩∩ IIIIIII	37
	2,453

Adding and subtracting is relatively easy with Egyptian numerals. For example, the sum of 2,453 and 85 may be represented as follows:

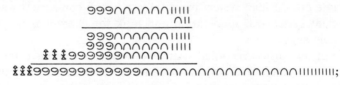

this becomes 𝑥𝑥99999∩∩∩IIIIIIII.

We observe that the ten ∩'s are symbolized by one ꟼ . Hence the sum of 2,453 and 85 is represented by 𝑥𝑥99999∩∩∩IIIIIIII.

Multiplication with Egyptian symbols is much more cumbersome. For example, the product of 12 and 365 may be represented as follows:

$$999∩∩∩∩∩∩ IIIII$$
$$∩ II$$

$$999∩∩∩∩∩∩ IIIII$$
$$999∩∩∩∩∩∩ IIIII$$
$$𝑥𝑥𝑥99999999∩∩∩∩∩$$

$$𝑥𝑥𝑥99999999999999∩∩∩∩∩∩∩∩∩∩∩∩∩∩∩∩∩∩ IIIIIIIIII;$$

this becomes 𝑥𝑥𝑥𝑥999∩∩∩∩∩∩∩.

We observe that the ten I's are symbolized by one ∩, then the eighteen ∩'s are symbolized by one ꟼ and eight ∩'s, and then the thirteen ꟼ's are symbolized by one 𝑥 and three ꟼ's. Hence the product of 12 and 365 is represented by 𝑥𝑥𝑥𝑥999∩∩∩∩∩∩∩.

Exercises

1. Express the following in Egyptian numerals.
    (a) 15.   **(b)** 92.   **(c)** 5,216.   **(d)** 202,002.

2. Use Egyptian numerals to find the sum of
    (a) 15 and 92.   **(b)** 5,216 and 202,002.
    (c) 92 and 5,216.   **(d)** 15 and 5,216.

3. Use decimal numerals to find the sum of
    (a) 15 and 92.   **(b)** 5,216 and 202,002.
    (c) 92 and 5,216.   **(d)** 15 and 5,216.

4. Compare and check the results obtained in
    (a) Exercises 2(a) and 3(a).   **(b)** Exercises 2(b) and 3(b).

(c) Exercises 2(c) and 3(c).   (d) Exercises 2(d) and 3(d).

5. Use Egyptian numerals to find the product of 15 and 92.

6. Use decimal numerals to find the product of 15 and 92.

7. Compare and check the results obtained in Exercises 5 and 6.

8. Express in Egyptian numerals.
   (a) 99.   (b) 999.   (c) 9,999.

3-7 Early Babylonian Numerals

The Babylonians made their numerals by pressing a wedge-shaped instrument (stylus) into wet clay. One wedge shape, ▼, was used to represent 1. The symbol for ten, ◄, was made in two steps by turning the stylus. Among the Babylonian numerals used were those illustrated in Figure 3-6.

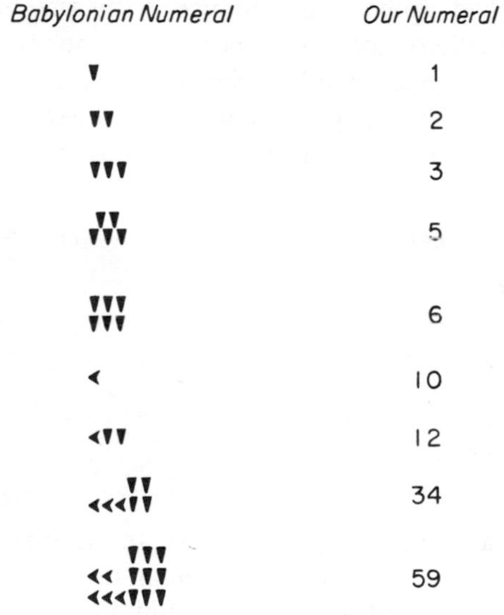

Babylonian Numeral	Our Numeral
▼	1
▼▼	2
▼▼▼	3
▼▼ / ▼▼▼	5
▼▼▼ / ▼▼▼	6
◄	10
◄▼▼	12
◄◄◄▼▼	34
◄◄ ◄◄◄ ▼▼▼▼▼▼	59

Figure 3-6

Notice that these numerals are based upon sets of ten but do not have place value for tens. Oddly enough, the Babylonians used the decimal system for naming only the numbers up to 60. For names of numbers 60 and greater they used the base 60. Actually their system contained a kind of place value. and the symbol ▼ represented 1, 60, 60 × 60, and so on. Since there was no symbol for zero, there was sometimes ambiguity in the value of the symbol as it was written. For example, 62 would be represented by the numeral ▼ ▼▼, which could easily be confused with the numeral ▼▼▼ for 3 The number 3,642 would be represented by the numeral ▼ ◄◄◄▼▼. This numeral should be interpreted as $(1 \times 3{,}600) + (0 \times 60) + (4 \times 10) + (2 \times 1)$.

Exercises

1. Express the following in Babylonian numerals.
    (a) 9.   **(b)** 46.   **(c)** 65.   **(d)** 231.

2. Use Babylonian numerals to find the sum of
    (a) 9 and 46.   **(b)** 65 and 231.   **(c)** 46 and 65.   **(d)** 9 and 65.

3. Use decimal numerals to find the sum of
    (a) 9 and 46.   **(b)** 65 and 231.   **(c)** 46 and 65.   **(d)** 9 and 65.

4. Compare and check the results obtained in
    (a) Exercises 2(a) and 3(a).   **(b)** Exercises 2(b) and 3(b).
    (c) Exercises 2(c) and 3(c).   **(d)** Exercises 2(d) and 3(d).

3-8 Roman Numerals

Most of us have had some acquaintance with the Roman system of numeration, because there are a few traces of it in our culture. For example, we often use Roman numerals to number the chapters in a book, to mark the hours on a clock, to designate dates on cornerstones, and so forth. Among the Roman numerals used were the following:

Roman Numeral	Our Numeral
I	1
V	5
X	10
L	50
C	100
D	500
M	1,000

The early Roman system was essentially an additive system of numeration. The number represented by a particular set of symbols was the sum of the numbers represented by each symbol in the set. Consider these examples:

Roman Numeral	Our Numeral
II	2
III	3
VII	7
XIII	13
XXXVIII	38
CCXXXVI	236

Present-day use of the Roman numerals also involves a subtractive principle. This principle is used only for the numerals for four, nine, forty, ninety, four hundred, nine hundred, and so forth. For example, the numeral IV represents 5 — 1 or 4, the numeral IX represents 10 — 1 or 9, the numeral XL represents 50 — 10 or 40, and so forth.

Adding and subtracting is relatively easy with Roman numerals. For example, the sum of 235 and 63 may be represented as follows:

$$\begin{array}{l} \text{CCXXXV} \\ \underline{\text{LXIII}} \\ \text{CCLXXXXVIII;} \end{array} \quad \text{this becomes CCXCVIII.}$$

We observe that LXXXX is symbolized by XC; hence the sum of 235 and 63 may be represented by CCXCVIII.

Multiplication with Roman numerals is much more cumbersome. For example, the product of 172 and 16 may be represented as follows:

$$\begin{array}{l} \quad\quad\quad\quad\quad \text{CLXXII} \\ \quad\quad\quad\quad\quad \underline{\text{XVI}} \\ \quad\quad\quad \text{C} \quad\, \text{L} \quad \text{XX} \quad \text{II} \\ \quad\quad \text{D} \quad \text{CC LLL} \quad\, \text{VV} \\ \underline{\text{M} \;\; \text{D} \quad \text{CC} \quad\quad \text{XX}} \\ \text{MDDCCCCLLLLXXXXVVII;} \quad\quad \text{this becomes MMDCCLII.} \end{array}$$

We observe that the two V's may be symbolized by one X, the five X's by one L, the five L's by two C's and one L, the seven C's by one D and two C's, and the three D's by one M and one D. Hence the product of 172 and 16 is represented by MMDCCLII.

Exercises

1. Express the following in Roman numerals.
   (a) 12.   (b) 83.   (c) 95.   (d) 1,964.

2. Use Roman numerals to find the sum of
   (a) 12 and 83.   (b) 95 and 1,964.   (c) 83 and 95.   (d) 12 and 95.

3. Use decimal numerals to find the sum of
   (a) 12 and 83.   (b) 95 and 1,964.   (c) 83 and 95.   (d) 12 and 95.

4. Compare and check the results obtained in
   (a) Exercises 2(a) and 3(a).   (b) Exercises 2(b) and 3(b).
   (c) Exercises 2(c) and 3(c).   (d) Exercises 2(d) and 3(d).

5. Use Roman numerals to find the product of 12 and 83.

6. Use decimal numerals to find the product of 12 and 83.

7. Compare and check the results obtained in Exercises 5 and 6.

8. Express in Roman numerals.

   (a) 99.   (b) 999.   (c) 88.   (d) 888.

3-9 Hindu-Arabic Numerals

The Hindu-Arabic system of numeration originated in ancient India and was transmitted to Europe by traders and Arabic invaders. The present forms of the symbols evolved for the most part in Europe, although the historians have not agreed whether the Hindus or the Arabs contributed the symbol for zero—which, it is generally agreed, was developed much later than the other nine symbols. The chart in Figure 3-7 compares the tenth-century form of the Hindu-Arabic numerals with the twentieth-century form.

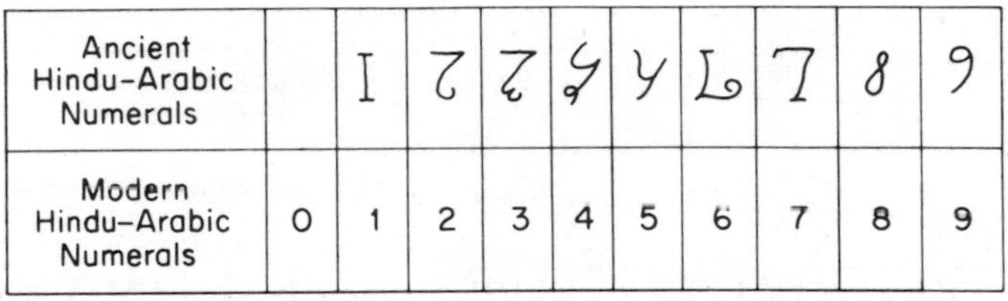

Ancient Hindu–Arabic Numerals		I	Ƨ	Ƹ	४	Ƴ	Ḷ	7	8	9
Modern Hindu–Arabic Numerals	0	1	2	3	4	5	6	7	8	9

Figure 3-7

The Hindu-Arabic system is a place-value system with a base of 10. It employs a special symbol for zero and nine other symbols. Any number may be represented as a sequence of digits and interpreted as the sum of terms composed of each of these digits times the appropriate power of ten. The power of ten is determined by the position the digit occupies in the numeral. There is no use of the repetitive principle; the numeral 11 is interpreted not as "two ones," but as "one set of ten and one set of one." There is no use of the subtractive principle; we do not write "15" to represent "one less than five," as the Romans did when they wrote "IV."

Some of the characteristics of the Hindu-Arabic system of numeration are found in each of the ancient systems that we have discussed. Each of these ancient systems, however, had shortcomings that prevented it from being as acceptable as our decimal system.

chapter 4

Operations:
Addition and Subtraction

Increased emphasis is being placed at the elementary school level on some of the basic patterns and principles of mathematics. Three major purposes in this emphasis are to give the child an understanding of the structure of mathematics, to give him tools for building new ideas and concepts from what he already knows (that is, for making generalizations), and to develop in him an ability to apply generalizations to specific cases. There are many opportunities for the use and application of the basic principles of mathematics from the very beginning of systematic instruction in Grade One. Too often we fail to direct the student's attention to the way these principles operate and to what they permit him to do.

In this chapter some of the principles of the operations of addition and subtraction of whole numbers are identified. Modern courses in elementary school mathematics emphasize these basic principles as unifying concepts that enable us to explain logically why the familiar rules and procedures for adding and subtracting numbers really do work. The greater insight and understanding that the student will gain is also most helpful in providing a firm foundation for work encountered at the secondary school level.

In Chapter 1 we stated that a mathematical system includes a set of elements, one or more binary operations, one or more relations, and some rules that the elements, operations, and relations satisfy. In this chapter the operation of addition on the set of whole numbers is defined, and the basic principles are presented as assumptions. These assumptions are referred to by different writers as postulates, axioms, principles, laws, and properties.

4-1 Addition of Whole Numbers

Addition of two whole numbers may be understood clearly in terms of the union of two sets. Children intuitively discover the meaning of the union of sets when they put the blocks of two sets together to form a single set. For example, the blocks of

$$2 + 3 = 5.$$

The cardinal number (in this case 5) of the union of the two sets is the sum of the cardinal numbers (2 and 3) of the two given sets. This illustrates the statement

Addition of two whole numbers may be defined as finding the cardinal number of a set formed by the union of two disjoint sets. Recall (Section 2-5) that disjoint sets are those with no elements in common.

The importance of the word *disjoint* in the definition of addition is shown in the next example. Let

$$A = \{\text{Tom, Beth, Sam}\},$$

$$B = \{\text{Carl, Tom, Gene, George}\};$$

then

$$A \cup B = \{\text{Tom, Beth, Sam, Carl, Gene, George}\}.$$

The cardinal number of set A is 3, and the cardinal number of set B is 4. However, the cardinal number of $A \cup B$ is 6 rather than $3 + 4$. In order that the cardinal number of $A \cup B$ may be the sum of the cardinal numbers of sets A and B, disjoint sets must be selected. Therefore, *only the union of disjoint sets is used to describe addition of two whole numbers.*

Since set union is an operation on *two* sets, it is called a binary operation. Similarly, the addition of two whole numbers may be described as a binary operation on the cardinal numbers of two disjoint sets. Addition is called a binary operation because it is fundamentally an operation performed on two numbers at a time. In the language of mathematics, $5 + 3$ indicates a binary operation to be performed in a *definite order* on two whole numbers, 5 and 3; that is, $5 + 3$ indicates that the operation is to be completed by adding 3 to 5, which results in the sum 8. The same definite order is indicated in the example below.

$$\begin{array}{r} 5 \\ +3 \\ \hline 8 \end{array}$$

In general, it may be stated that addition is an operation that combines a first number and a second number to produce a unique third number. The first and second numbers are called **addends**, and the result of combining the addends is called the **sum**.

A number line frequently is used as an aid in visualizing the operation of addition. Remember (Section 1-15) how a number line was constructed. A line was drawn and an arbitrary point on the line was selected to represent the graph of 0. Then a unit of length was chosen and marked off on the line, beginning at the graph of 0 and extending to the right. By marking off this unit of length again and again and labeling the endpoints of the segments 1, 2, 3, 4, and so on, the whole-number line may be pictured as in Figure 4-1.

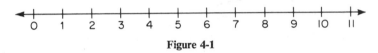

Figure 4-1

The whole number at each of the indicated points represents the number of segments of unit length that are measured off from the graph of 0 to that point. We must realize also that a given whole number may be represented on the number line by any line segment that has the given whole number of unit lengths as the distance between its endpoints. For example, consider the illustrations of the number 2 represented by a line segment of two units' length (Figure 4-2).

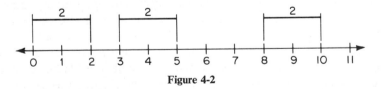

Figure 4-2

The addition of whole numbers may be pictured as an operation moving to the right on the number line. To add 2 and 4 on the number line, start with the graph of 0 and mark off to the right a segment with two units of length; then start at that point and mark off to the right a segment with four units of length. These two line segments have determined a new segment whose left end is at the graph of 0 and whose right end is at the graph of 6; the length of the new line segment is the sum of the lengths of the other two segments. Thus, the picture on the number line in Figure 4-3 represents the sum of 2 and 4.

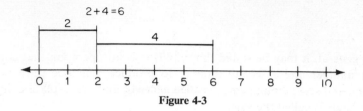

Figure 4-3

Exercises

In each of the Exercises 1 through 4, find the cardinal number of the set formed by the union of the given sets.

1. $A = \{@, \#, \$\}$, $B = \{\rlap{/}c, *, \#, \%\}$.
2. $C = \{c, b, e, f\}$, $D = \{g, d, h, i\}$.
3. $E = \{$baseball, bat, glove$\}$, $F = \{$uniform, base, bat$\}$.
4. $G = \{7, 13, 6, 19\}$, $H = \{11, 5, 17, 23, 4, 9, 12\}$.
5. Referring to Exercises 1 through 4, are these sets disjoint?
   (a) A and B.   (b) C and D.   (c) E and F.   (d) G and H.
6. Represent each sum on a number line.
   (a) $3 + 6$.   (b) $2 + 5$.

4-2 Closure and Uniqueness

Consider each of these sums of whole numbers: $1 + 3$, $4 + 7$, $9 + 13$, $18 + 25$, and $60 + 245$. Would you expect each of these sums to be a whole number? The answer to this question is dependent upon a very important mathematical principle called **closure**. The principle of closure applied to addition of whole numbers means that the sum of two numbers in the set of whole numbers is a number that is also an element of the set of whole numbers. In other words, when one whole number is added to another whole number, the sum is also a whole number. Thus, the set of whole numbers is **closed** with respect to the operation of addition.

In the example $5 + 9 = 14$, note that the addends and the sum are all elements of the set of whole numbers. Is 14 the only possible sum when 5 and 9 are added? The answer to this question is dependent upon an important mathematical principle called **uniqueness**. The principle of uniqueness applied to addition of whole numbers means that there is only one possible sum when two whole numbers are added. Thus, 14 is the *unique* sum of 5 and 9.

A generalized statement of these two principles is: If a and b are whole numbers, then there is one and only one whole number that is called the sum of a and b. This sum is written $a + b$.

Not all sets are closed under addition. It is important to understand that a set is not closed under addition if there exist two elements of the set whose sum is not an element of the set. To illustrate this, one may consider the finite set $S = \{1, 2, 3, 4, 5, 6\}$. This set is not closed under addition because two numbers can be found in the set such that the sum is not in the set; for example, $5 \in S$, $6 \in S$, $5 + 6 = 11$, and 11 is not in set S. In other words, if there is at least one pair of elements in S whose sum is not in S, then S is not closed under the operation of addition.

Exercises

1. State whether or not each set is closed under the operation of addition.
   (a) The set of natural numbers greater than 50.
   (b) The set of counting numbers between 265 and 1,000.
   (c) The set of odd whole numbers less than 50.
   (d) The set of even natural numbers.
   (e) The set of whole numbers whose numerals end in 0.
   (f) The set of odd counting numbers.
   (g) The set of whole numbers.

2. State whether or not each sum is unique.
   (a) $3 + 2$.   (b) $10 + 6$.   (c) $19 + 13$.   (d) $57 + 84$.

4-3 The Commutative Principle of Addition

In the union of two sets, the order in which the elements and sets are given does not affect the union of the two sets. Consider the disjoint sets $A = \{a, b, c\}$ and $D = \{d, e, f, g\}$:

$$A \cup D = \{a, b, c, d, e, f, g\},$$
$$D \cup A = \{d, e, f, g, a, b, c\}.$$

It may be observed in this illustration that $A \cup D$ is the same set as $D \cup A$, since they both contain identical elements; that is, $A \cup D = D \cup A$.

Since the addition of whole numbers may be defined in terms of the union of two disjoint sets, a change in the order of the addends will not affect the sum. Observe that in the above example the cardinal number of set A is 3 and the cardinal number of set D is 4. Note also that 7 is the cardinal number of both $A \cup D$ and $D \cup A$. In other words, $3 + 4 = 7$ and $4 + 3 = 7$. We conclude that $3 + 4 = 4 + 3$.

This example illustrates the **commutative principle of addition**. The commutative principle of the addition of whole numbers may be described by saying that the sum of two whole numbers does not depend on the order of the addition. For each pair of whole numbers a and b,

$$a + b = b + a.$$

The commutative principle of addition should be clear when one thinks in terms of combining sets. However, if addition is developed as counting, it is not quite so obvious that addition has the commutative principle. For example, if we ask a child to add 8 and 5, he will, if he has not memorized the sum, usually begin with one of the numbers and count forward the other number. He may think, "I'll begin with 8 and count forward 5." This is illustrated on the number line in Figure 4-4.

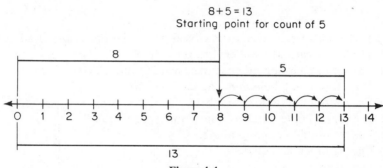

Figure 4-4

It is indeed important to understand that with this approach to addition one would get the same result if he started with 5 and counted forward 8. This is illustrated on the number line in Figure 4-5.

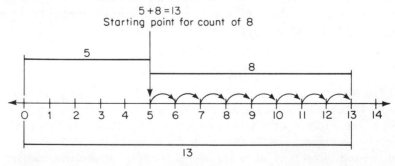

Figure 4-5

Thus, we conclude that $8 + 5 = 5 + 8 = 13$.

Elementary school children frequently use the commutative principle of addition when they reverse the order of the addends to check their work.

Check

	36		25

$$\begin{array}{r} 36 \\ +25 \\ \hline 61 \end{array} \qquad \begin{array}{r} 25 \\ +36 \\ \hline 61 \end{array}$$

We do the same when we add a long column of figures down and check by adding up.

Exercises

1. State whether or not each activity is commutative.
  (a) To give a test, then grade the papers.
  (b) To salt, then pepper, your eggs.
  (c) To pour black paint into white paint.
  (d) To strike a match, then light the fire.

2. Use a number line to show that $4 + 5 = 5 + 4$.

3. Complete each statement to obtain an example of the commutative principle of addition.
  (a) $1 + 2 = $ ____ + ____ .   **(b)** $19 + 6 = $ ____ + ____ .
  (c) $27 + 63 = $ ____ + ____ .   **(d)** $108 + 325 = $ ____ + ____ .

4-4 The Associative Principle of Addition

Recall that addition was defined as a binary operation; that is, an operation upon two numbers. What is meant by $2 + 3 + 4$? It is necessary to establish a procedure for adding more than two numbers. We agree that when more than two numbers are to be added, we must first find the sum of two numbers, then find the sum of this sum and the third number, and then repeat the operation two numbers at a time. In the example $2 + 3 + 4$, there are only two ways (excluding use of the commutative principle) to group (associate) the numbers for addition. Either the 2 and 3 are added first and then the 4 is added to their sum,

$$(2 + 3) + 4 = 5 + 4 = 9,$$

or the 3 and 4 are added first and then their sum is added to 2,

$$2 + (3 + 4) = 2 + 7 = 9.$$

Notice that in this example the way the three numbers are grouped (associated) for addition does not affect the sum.

The two methods of grouping (associating) the three numbers 2, 3, and 4 for addition may be illustrated on the number line. Figure 4-6 represents $(2 + 3) + 4$. Notice that we determine $2 + 3$ first and then add 4

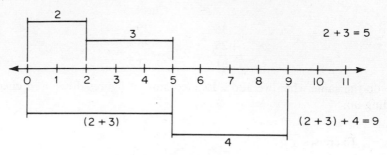

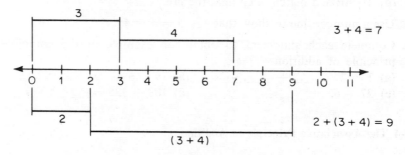

Figure 4-6

to this sum.   Figure 4-7 represents $2 + (3 + 4)$. Notice that we determine $3 + 4$ first and then add this sum to 2.

Figure 4-7

The idea that grouping the three numbers differently, without changing their order, does not change their sum is called the **associative principle of addition** for whole numbers. This principle may be used to make addition easier. For example, in adding 12 and 6 it may be easier to consider $12 + 6 = (10 + 2) + 6 = 10 + (2 + 6) = 10 + 8 = 18$, and in the example $33 + 74 + 26$ it may be easiest to group $33 + (74 + 26) = 33 + 100 = 133$.

The associative principle of addition for whole numbers a, b, and c may be stated as

$$(a + b) + c = a + (b + c).$$

Exercises

1. Show how the associative principle of addition can be used to find each sum in two different ways.
   (a) $15 + 3 + 42$.   (b) $22 + 7 + 18$.
   (c) $109 + 23 + 11$.   (d) $237 + 165 + 35$.

2. Tell which principle, commutative or associative, is illustrated by each equation.
   (a) $15 + 6 = 6 + 15$.
   (b) $(4 + 5) + 6 = 4 + (5 + 6)$.
   (c) $2 + (3 + 4) = (3 + 4) + 2$.
   (d) $d + (e + f) = (d + e) + f$.

3. Use the commutative and associative principles to find each indicated sum.
   (a) $27 + 36 + 13 + 64$.
   (b) $135 + 81 + 15 + 9$.
   (c) $58 + 24 + 32 + 16$.
   (d) $19 + 17 + 11 + 83$.

4. Add without the use of paper and pencil. Did you mentally apply the associative principle?
   (a) $1 + (999 + 27)$.
   (b) $60 + (40 + 39)$.
   (c) $(783 + 89) + 11$.
   (d) $(176 + 80) + 20$.

5. Indicate whether each statement is true or false.
   (a) $18 + 25 > 25 + 18$.
   (b) $(4 + 8) + 7 = (4 + 7) + 8$.
   (c) $505 + 98 = 98 + 505$.
   (d) $(34 + 9) + 10 < 10 + (9 + 34)$.

4-5 Identity Element for Addition

The number zero is the number of elements in the empty set. It is most important that zero be recognized as a specific number that is just as useful as any of the counting numbers, $1, 2, 3, \ldots$. The number zero plays a very special role in the addition of whole numbers. The sum of any whole number and the number zero is always the original whole number. For example,

$$0 + 0 = 0,$$
$$1 + 0 = 1,$$
$$2 + 0 = 2,$$
$$3 + 0 = 3,$$

and, in general, $a + 0 = a$ for each whole number a. This principle is indicated by calling zero the **identity element for addition** of whole numbers; that is, the **additive identity**.

Exercise

1. Complete each statement to make a true number sentence.
   (a) $x + \underline{\quad} = x$.
   (b) $0 + 8 = \underline{\quad}$.
   (c) $\underline{\quad} + 0 = 27$.
   (d) $0 + \underline{\quad} = 0$.

4-6 The Addition Table

Addition facts for decimal digits are sometimes summarized in a table like the following one.

+	0	1	2	3	4	5	6	7	8	9
0	0	1	2	3	4	5	6	7	8	9
1	1	2	3	4	5	6	7	8	9	10
2	2	3	4	5	6	7	8	9	10	11
3	3	4	5	6	7	8	9	10	11	12
4	4	5	6	7	8	9	10	11	12	13
5	5	6	7	8	9	10	11	12	13	14
6	6	7	8	9	10	11	12	13	14	15
7	7	8	9	10	11	12	13	14	15	16
8	8	9	10	11	12	13	14	15	16	17
9	9	10	11	12	13	14	15	16	17	18

Many of the important principles of addition may be observed from the table. A line has been drawn diagonally through the table from the upper left corner to the lower right. The elements drawn through are called *diagonal elements* and form the *main diagonal* of the table. Notice that, except for the diagonal elements, this line divides the table into two equivalent parts. When the table is folded over its main diagonal, the blocks containing 1 fall upon each other, as do the blocks containing 2, and so on. This is due to the commutative principle of addition, which justifies conclusions such as $4 + 3 = 3 + 4$. An understanding of the commutative principle of addition for whole numbers reduces the number of basic facts that must be learned by nearly one-half.

A table of all addition facts would be endless. However, it is interesting to realize that a knowledge of decimal notation makes it sufficient that one learn the facts for the ten decimal digits, a knowledge of the commutative principle of addition makes it sufficient that one learn the facts on and below the main diagonal of the table, and a knowledge of the principle of adding zero provides the basis for the facts in the first column of the table. Accordingly, it is enough to know the sums shown in the following table.

+	0	1	2	3	4	5	6	7	8	9
0										
1		2								
2		3	4							
3		4	5	6						
4		5	6	7	8					
5		6	7	8	9	10				
6		7	8	9	10	11	12			
7		8	9	10	11	12	13	14		
8		9	10	11	12	13	14	15	16	
9		10	11	12	13	14	15	16	17	18

Students in the early grades learn most of these addition facts very easily. The associative principle may be used to explain many of the facts. For example,

$$9 + 9 = 9 + (1 + 8) = (9 + 1) + 8 = 10 + 8 = 18,$$
$$9 + 8 = 9 + (1 + 7) = (9 + 1) + 7 = 10 + 7 = 17,$$
$$9 + 7 = 9 + (1 + 6) = (9 + 1) + 6 = 10 + 6 = 16,$$
$$8 + 8 = 8 + (2 + 6) = (8 + 2) + 6 = 10 + 6 = 16,$$
$$8 + 7 = 8 + (2 + 5) = (8 + 2) + 5 = 10 + 5 = 15,$$
$$8 + 6 = 8 + (2 + 4) = (8 + 2) + 4 = 10 + 4 = 14.$$

The doubles of numbers also are relatively easy for early-grade children to master: $2 + 2 = 4$, $3 + 3 = 6$, $4 + 4 = 8$, and so on. Other sums may be related to the doubles. For example,

$$3 + 4 \text{ is one less than } 4 + 4,$$
$$3 + 4 \text{ is one more than } 3 + 3,$$
$$2 + 3 \text{ is one more than } 2 + 2,$$
$$2 + 3 \text{ is one less than } 3 + 3.$$

This procedure calls attention to a very basic approach to the learning of mathematics at all levels. One does not need to memorize a great many unrelated details. Instead, one should learn a few important basic ideas, and then learn how to use these basic ideas to reason out new facts for himself. All the ideas of mathematics can be derived from a few fundamental ideas and the use of logical reasoning. These fundamental ideas and the ability to reason are the tools that every student should have.

Here is another example of the power of basic ideas in determining the sum of any pair of numbers. Consider $539 + 427$. From the concept of place value,

$$539 = 500 + 30 + 9$$
$$+427 = 400 + 20 + 7.$$

Now, using the previously summarized addition facts along with the concept of place value and the commutative and associative principles, we have

$$500 + 30 + \ 9$$
$$+400 + 20 + \ 7$$
$$900 + 50 + 16.$$

From the concept of place value, $16 = 10 + 6$, and

$$900 + 50 + 16 = 900 + 50 + (10 + 6).$$

Using the associative principle, we have

$$900 + 50 + (10 + 6) = 900 + (50 + 10) + 6.$$

Then, since $50 + 10 = 60$,

$$900 + (50 + 10) + 6 = 900 + 60 + 6.$$

This expanded form may be written in place-value notation as

$$900 + 60 + 6 = 966.$$

Therefore,

$$539 + 427 = 966.$$

By applying the commutative principle of addition, it may also be concluded that

$$427 + 539 = 966.$$

The regrouping for this example is illustrated as follows.

$$539 = 5 \text{ hundreds, } 3 \text{ tens, and } \ 9 \text{ ones}$$
$$+427 = 4 \text{ hundreds, } 2 \text{ tens, and } \ 7 \text{ ones}$$
$$966 = 9 \text{ hundreds, } 5 \text{ tens, and } 16 \text{ ones}$$
$$= (5 \times 100) + (3 \times 10) + (\ 9 \times 1)$$
$$= (4 \times 100) + (2 \times 10) + (\ 7 \times 1)$$
$$= (9 \times 100) + (5 \times 10) + (16 \times 1)$$

The 16 ones are grouped into one set of 1 ten and one set of 6 ones, and then the 1 ten is grouped with the 5 tens. This produces a sum of 9 hundreds, 6 tens, and 6 ones.

Exercises

1. In the addition table for decimal digits, describe briefly the pattern found
   as one proceeds from element to element in
   (a) The horizontal rows from left to right.
   (b) The vertical columns from top to bottom.
   (c) The diagonal blocks from upper left to lower right.
   (d) The diagonal blocks from lower left to upper right.
   (e) The horizontal rows from right to left.

2. Use the concept of place value and the associative principle to find the
   sum of 157 and 365.

$$
\begin{array}{l}
157 = 100 + 50 + 7 \\
+365 = 300 + 60 + 5 \\
\hline
? \ = \ ? + ? + ?
\end{array}
$$

   (a) At each step, illustrate the indicated concept by filling in the ex-
       panded notation.

Place value	$400 + 110 + (? + 2)$
Associative principle	$400 + (110 + ?) + ?$
Addition	$400 + ? + ?$
Place value	$400 + (100 + ?) + ?$
Associative principle	$(400 + ?) + ? + ?$
Addition	$? + ? + ?$
Place-value notation	$?$

   (b) Use a similiar procedure to explain the following.

$$
\begin{array}{r}
249 \\
+657 \\
\hline
\end{array}
$$

3. How does the addition table for whole numbers illustrate the commutative principle?

4-7 Understanding the Addition Algorism

Man has always looked for ways and methods of making his work easier.
The procedures for adding numbers are the result of our efforts to simplify
the operation of addition. Generally, as one becomes more and more familiar
with addition facts, he finds it convenient to arrange the addends in column
form and to use mentally the addition principles of whole numbers and the
concept of place value to determine the sum. A method of arranging numerals so as to reduce the number of steps necessary to determine the correct
result is called an **algorism**. It is most important to realize that the short-cut
method, the algorism, produces the correct answer through numerical mani-

pulations based on the reasoned use of number principles and concepts. Consider these examples.

Example 1	$\overset{1\,1}{239}$	**Example 2**	$\overset{1\,2}{328}$
	$+462$		227
	$\overline{701}$		$+789$
			$\overline{1,344}$

The examples demonstrate the familiar addition algorism. The use of this algorism is highly recommended; the student *must*, however, understand why the process works before he concentrates on developing speed and accuracy in manipulative skills. Even though the student's calculations may become purely automatic, he should be capable of explaining what he is really doing. In Example 1 the calculator is not actually "carrying a one." He understands that the sum of 9 and 2 is 11, which is $10 + 1$. Then the 10 is added to 30, and the sum 40 is added to 60, and so forth. Thus, it should be clear that all "carrying" is based on an application of place-value notation, commutativity, and associativity.

The next three examples illustrate the "partial sums" method of addition. This method was popular in the sixteenth century and it illustrates the principles involved whenever addition is performed. Notice that the renaming occurs during addition.

Example 3	14	**Example 4**	47	**Example 5**	47
	$+\ 7$		$+21$		26
	$\overline{11}$		$\overline{8}$		$+59$
	10		60		$\overline{22}$
	$\overline{21}$		$\overline{68}$		110
					$\overline{132}$

Exercises

1. Use an addition algorism to find each sum.

(a)	456	(b)	680	(c)	108	(d)	333
	$+324$		$+227$		$+\ 94$		$+777$

2. Find each sum, demonstrating the renaming that occurs when you use the partial-sums method of addition.

(a)	27	(b)	278	(c)	2,597	(d)	396
	$+34$		$+165$		$+4,036$		222
							$+137$

4-8 Subtraction of Whole Numbers

It is imperative that children discover and understand the relationship between subtraction and addition. This relationship may be studied in the following statements.

$$\text{If } 7 + 2 = 9, \quad \text{then } 9 - 7 = 2.$$
$$\text{If } 2 + 7 = 9, \quad \text{then } 9 - 2 = 7.$$
$$\text{If } 5 + 3 = 8, \quad \text{then } 8 - 5 = 3.$$
$$\text{If } 3 + 5 = 8, \quad \text{then } 8 - 3 = 5.$$
$$\text{If } \square + \triangle = \bigcirc, \text{ then } \bigcirc - \square = \triangle.$$
$$\text{If } \triangle + \square = \bigcirc, \text{ then } \bigcirc - \triangle = \square.$$

The commutative principle for the addition of whole numbers allows us to state that $7 + 2 = 2 + 7$; therefore, if we have $7 + 2 = 9$, we may change it to $2 + 7 = 9$ and get both $9 - 7 = 2$ and $9 - 2 = 7$ from the original equation, $7 + 2 = 9$. Thus, if $7 + 2 = 9$, then $9 - 7 = 2$ and $9 - 2 = 7$. This may also be expressed with a, b, and c representing whole numbers.

$$\text{If } a + b = c, \text{ then } c - a = b \text{ and } c - b = a.$$

The whole number n for the missing addend that makes $3 + n = 8$ a true statement is called the **difference**, $8 - 3$ (read "eight minus three"), and the operation of finding n is called **subtraction**. The difference $8 - 3$ is another name for the number 5; hence, $8 - 3$ may be replaced by 5:

$$\text{If } 8 - 3 = n, \text{ then } 3 + n = 8 \text{ and } n = 5.$$

Subtraction is a binary operation, since it combines a first number and a second number to produce a unique third number. Frequently, we say that the first number is the **sum**, the second number is an **addend,** and the number to be determined is the **missing addend**. In the example $8 - 3 = n$, 8 is the sum, 3 is an addend, and the variable n stands for the missing addend that will produce 8 when added to 3. If x and y are whole numbers and $y > x$, then the operation of subtracting x from y (that is, $y - x$) is finding some whole number d such that $x + d = y$, and the operation of subtracting d from y, $y - d$, is finding some number x such that $d + x = y$.

The number line may be used to help visualize the operation of subtraction of whole numbers. Consider in Figure 4-8 the example $6 - 4 = (?)$.

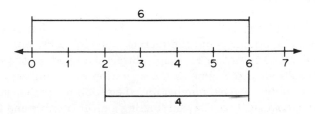

Figure 4-8

Notice that we start at the graph of 0 and find a point 6 units to the right of the graph of 0. This point has a coordinate of 6. Then we start at the graph of 6 and find a point 4 units to its left. This point has a coordinate of 2. Hence, we have a visualization of the statement $6 - 4 = (2)$.

Another way of using the number line to visualize the problem $6 - 4 = (?)$ is to think of the relation between addition and subtraction. Then the difference $6 - 4$ is the whole number n that must be added to 4 to get 6 (Figure 4-9).

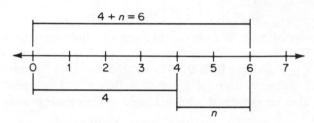

Figure 4-9

From the illustration on the number line it should be clear that n is 2. Since $6 - 4 = n$ means $4 + n = 6$, then $n = 2$.

Exercises

1. Write each number sentence as an equation involving subtraction.
   (a) $7 + 6 = 13$.   (b) $21 + 38 = 59$.
   (c) $4 + 1 = 5$.   (d) $k + h = m$.

2. Write each number sentence as an equation involving addition.
   (a) $27 - 13 = 14$.   (b) $16 - 7 = 9$.
   (c) $145 - 65 = 80$.   (d) $r - s = t$.

3. Draw a number line to illustrate the following.
   (a) $5 - 2 = 3$.   (b) $2 + 3 = 5$.   (c) $7 - 4 = 3$.
   (d) $4 + 3 = 7$.   (e) $9 + 2 = 11$.   (f) $11 - 9 = 2$.

4-9 Inverse Operations

Consider the statements $8 + 3 = 11$ and $11 - 3 = 8$, that is, $(8 + 3) - 3 = 8$. Notice that adding 3 and subtracting 3 "undo" each other. That is, we start with 8, add 3 to obtain 11, then subtract 3 and get 8. The net effect of the two operations is the same as the operation of adding zero. Therefore, we state that adding a given number and then subtracting that same number are **inverse operations**. Likewise, subtracting a given number and then adding the same number back again are inverse operations. For many years we have checked subtraction problems by addition, that is, by an application of this principle of inverse operations, as in the example below.

Check

9   6

−3   +3

‾‾‾‾   ‾‾‾‾

6   9

In general, we say that addition is the inverse operation of subtraction and subtraction is the inverse operation of addition.

Understanding that addition and subtraction are inverse operations allows us to determine unknown subtraction facts from our knowledge of addition facts, by finding missing addends. In other words, a subtraction problem may always be thought of as an addition problem with the sum and one addend known:

$$10 - 2 = 8 \text{ because } 8 + 2 = 10,$$
$$13 - 7 = 6 \text{ because } 6 + 7 = 13,$$
$$35 - 19 = 16 \text{ because } 16 + 19 = 35,$$
$$41 - 23 = 18 \text{ because } 18 + 23 = 41.$$

Exercises

1. What is the inverse of each of the following?
   (a) Closing a door.   (b) Depositing $6.00 in the bank.
   (c) Putting on your shoes.   (d) Placing a pie in the oven.

2. Indicate whether each statement is true or false.
   (a) If $7 + 3 = 10$, then $10 - 3 = 7$ and $(7 + 3) - 3 = 7$.
   (b) If $6 + 8 = 14$, then $14 - 6 = 8$ and $(6 + 8) - 6 = 6$.
   (c) If $12 - 5 = 7$, then $7 + 5 = 12$ and $(12 - 5) + 5 = 12$.
   (d) If $26 + 9 = 35$, then $35 - 9 = 26$ and $(26 + 9) - 9 = 35$.

3. If you add 6 to a whole number n, what must you do to the sum to obtain n?

4. If you subtract 7 from a whole number n, what must you do to the difference to obtain n?

4-10 Principles of Subtraction of Whole Numbers

Although addition and subtraction are closely related operations, a distinction between them becomes evident when subtraction is considered with respect to some of the basic principles that hold for addition. In general, if a basic principle of mathematics is applied to a given operation on the elements of a set of numbers and it leads us to a false conclusion in at least one case, then the principle does not hold for the given operation on the elements of the specified set of numbers.

Commutative principle Since $9 - 4 \neq 4 - 9$, subtraction of whole numbers is not commutative.

Associative principle We may observe that in the following example the associative principle does not hold for subtraction of whole numbers:

$$7 - (6 - 5) \neq (7 - 6) - 5, \text{ because } 7 - 1 \neq 1 - 5.$$

Identity element One principle that does hold for the subtraction of whole numbers is the special property of operating with zero. We have already agreed, for any whole number a, that $a + 0 = a$, and it is also true that $a - 0 = a$. Thus, 0 is an identity element for the subtraction of whole numbers.

Principle of closure Recall that one whole number added to another whole number always produces a whole number as the sum. This principle does not hold for subtraction. Certainly $3 - 5$ is not a whole number. The difference $3 - 5$, if it exists, must be a number that satisfies the equation $5 + \square = 3$. There is no number $\square$ in the set of whole numbers such that $5 + \square = 3$, since any whole number added to 5 produces a whole number greater than or equal to 5, and 3 is less than 5. Therefore, we conclude that differences of whole numbers do not always exist in the set of whole numbers. This is illustrated in the diagram (Figure 4-10). The set of whole numbers is represented as being inside a circle, and the set of other numbers, represented by differences of whole numbers, as being outside the circle.

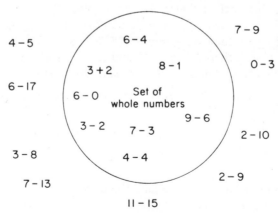

Figure 4-10

Exercises

1. Give an example to show that each of the following principles does not hold for subtraction of whole numbers.
   (a) Commutative.   (b) Associative.   (c) Closure.

2. Indicate whether each statement is true or false.

(a) $11 - (6 - 3) = (11 - 6) - 3.$ (b) $12 - 9 \neq 9 - 12.$

(c) $3 - (2 - 1) > (3 - 2) - 1.$ (d) $8 - 7 = 7 - 8.$

(e) $5 + 0 = 5 - 0.$ (f) $(11 - 0) - 3 = 11 - (0 - 3).$

4-11 Understanding the Subtraction Algorism

A thorough understanding of the addition algorisms and the definition of subtraction makes clear the meaning of the subtraction algorism. For example, to find the difference $43 - 17$, we first use the place-value concept and write

$$43 = \quad 40 + 3$$
$$-17 = -(10 + 7).$$

Since 7 is greater than 3, $40 + 3$ must be renamed. Using the addition facts, 40 can be renamed $30 + 10$, and so $40 + 3 = (30 + 10) + 3$. By the associative principle, $(30 + 10) + 3 = 30 + (10 + 3)$; then, by place value, $30 + (10 + 3) = 30 + 13$. Hence,

$$43 = \quad 40 + 3 = \quad 30 + 13$$
$$-17 = -(10 + 7) = -(10 + \quad 7).$$

Now we must determine what number added to 7 produces the sum 13, and likewise what number added to 10 produces a sum of 30; $7 + \square = 13$ and $10 + \triangle = 30$. Since $7 + 6 = 13$ and $10 + 20 = 30$,

$$43 = \quad 30 + 13$$
$$-17 = -(10 + \quad 7)$$
$$\overline{\quad\quad\quad 20 + \quad 6 = 26.}$$

Most people do not think through all of the steps listed in the previous example. The familiar subtraction algorism (short-cut method) is used, and the problem appears as follows.

$$\overset{3\ 1}{\cancel{4}3}$$
$$-17$$
$$\overline{\quad 26}$$

In using the algorism in this example one must realize that he does not "borrow" a 1; he really "borrows" a 10. This means that he renames 43 as $30 + 13$ and then subtracts 7 from 13 and 10 from 30.

Actually, the word "borrow" is not precise, because it implies paying back. It is suggested that the process be taught as "renaming" or "regrouping" instead of "borrowing."

Another example of renaming may improve the student's understanding of the concepts that are actually applied in subtraction. From the concept of place value we have

$$534 = 500 + 30 + 4$$
$$-245 = -(200 + 40 + 5).$$

Since 5 is greater than 4, it is necessary to rename $500 + 30 + 4$. With our knowledge of the addition facts, 30 can be renamed $20 + 10$ and $500 + 30 + 4$ can be renamed $500 + (20 + 10) + 4$. By the associative principle, $500 + (20 + 10) + 4 = 500 + 20 + (10 + 4)$. Since $10 + 4 = 14$, $500 + 20 + (10 + 4) = 500 + 20 + 14$. We now have the problem

$$500 + 20 + 14$$
$$-(200 + 40 + 5)$$

and must consider the question of subtracting 40 from 20.

Since 40 is larger than 20, we must rename $500 + 20$. With the use of the addition facts, 500 is renamed $400 + 100$, and $500 + 20$ is renamed $(400 + 100) + 20$. By the associative principle, $(400 + 100) + 20 = 400 + (100 + 20)$ and then, by place value, $400 + (100 + 20) = 400 + 120$. Hence,

$$534 = 500 + 30 + 4 = 500 + 20 + 14 = 400 + 120 + 14$$
$$-245 = -(200 + 40 + 5) = -(200 + 40 + 5) = -(200 + 40 + 5)$$
$$200 + 80 + 9$$
$$= 289.$$

An interesting method of subtraction taught in many countries of the world is known as the "Austrian," or "additive," method. Since to subtract 245 from 534 is to determine the missing addend n such that

$$245 + n = 534,$$

students are taught to find the addend by adding to 245 rather than by subtracting from 534. The illustration below shows how this is done.

First, we determine what must be added to 245 to produce a 4 in the ones column.	245 $\underline{+?}$ $?4$	245 $\underline{+9}$ 254
Having added 9, we now have 254 and are working to obtain a 3 in the tens column.	254 $\underline{+?}$ $?34$	254 $\underline{+80}$ 334
We now have 334 and are looking for an addend to produce a 5 in the hundreds column.	334 $\underline{+?}$ 534	334 $\underline{+200}$ 534

By adding 9, 80, and 200 to 245, we obtain 534.

$$
\begin{array}{r}
200 \\
80 \\
+\ \ 9 \\
\hline
289
\end{array}
$$

Thus, we have

$$534 - 245 = 289.$$

Exercises

1. Work each of these examples and show enough steps to illustrate the process used to calculate your answer.

(a)	67	(b)	50	(c)	236	(d)	444
	−19		−13		−158		−355

2. Use the "Austrian" method of subtraction to find the missing addend.

(a)	368	(b)	286	(c)	172	(d)	537
	+ ?		+ ?		+ ?		+ ?
	495		421		301		729

3. Is it possible to use an addition table summarizing addition facts for whole numbers to find the solution to a subtraction problem involving whole numbers? If so, are there limitations?

4-12 The Set of Integers

Subtraction of whole numbers may be defined in terms of an equation of the form $a + \square = c$, where a, $\square$, and c are whole numbers. The statement $\square = c - a$ means that $\square$ is the difference obtained when a is subtracted from c. We have seen that this difference $\square$ does not always exist in the set of whole numbers. For example, if $c = 5$ and $a = 7$, then the equation $7 + \square = 5$ does not have a solution in the set of whole numbers; $5 - 7$ has no meaning when only the set of whole numbers is under consideration. It is necessary to construct an extension of our whole number system in order that each equation of the form $a + \square = c$ will have a unique solution. In other words, we must develop a set of numbers that includes the set of whole numbers as a subset and is closed under the operation of subtraction.

To do this, we construct the set of **integers** consisting of the counting numbers, their negatives, and the number zero. The set of integers is represented by

$$\{\ldots, {}^-4, {}^-3, {}^-2, {}^-1, 0, 1, 2, 3, 4, \ldots\}.$$

The numbers of the set $\{1, 2, 3, 4, \ldots\}$ are called **positive integers** and the numbers of the set $\{{}^-1, {}^-2, {}^-3, {}^-4, \ldots\}$ are called **negative integers**. The negative integers are read "negative one, negative two, negative three, negative four," and so on. Notice that zero is an integer that is neither positive nor negative. The set of integers may be pictured on the number line (Figure 4-11).

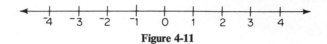

Figure 4-11

In most of the traditional arithmetic programs, the existence of the negative integers has not been recognized. Children in the lower elementary grades have been taught that a larger number cannot be subtracted from a smaller number and that in subtraction problems the larger number always "goes on top." It is important that a child's concept of number not be so restricted, even in the primary grades. When a restriction is necessary, it should be explained in the form "We do not yet have a number to represent . . ." and not as an indication of problems that can never be solved.

In modern programs, children in the primary and intermediate grades develop intuitive notions of negative numbers through the use of a number line and other activities. These notions, suggesting a need for numbers not in the set of whole numbers, should be encouraged in order to provide a basis for the future introduction of negative numbers.

A look at the diagram in Figure 4-12 may clarify the extensions used to develop our number system up to this point. The first set of numbers that we mentioned was the set of counting numbers. By including zero with the set of counting numbers, we extended our system to the set of whole numbers. Finally, by introducing the negative integers we extended our system to the set of integers.

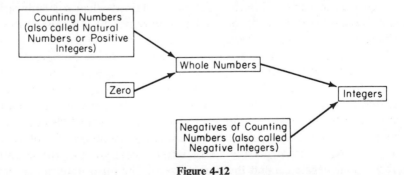

Figure 4-12

We consider the whole numbers greater than zero as positive integers; we consider the opposites (with respect to addition) of the positive integers as the negative integers. As noted, the integer zero is neither positive nor negative. Some authors refer to the integers as signed numbers and use the $+$ symbol with the natural numbers to indicate that they are positive integers. Then, it is easy to lead children to discover that for each positive integer to the right of zero on the number line, there is an opposite number represented to the left of zero, and vice versa. This is illustrated in Figure 4-13, where semicircles denote pairing of opposites on the number line.

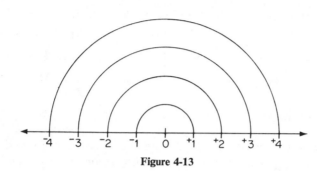

Figure 4-13

We should notice that the $+$ and the $-$ symbols have dual uses. When the $+$ symbol is used to denote the operation of addition, it is read "plus;" however, when this same $+$ symbol is used to denote that the number is a positive integer, it is read "positive." The $-$ symbol, when used to denote subtraction, is read "minus"; however, when this same $-$ symbol is used to indicate that the number is negative, it is read "negative." Some authors suggest that the $+$ symbol used to denote a positive integer and the $-$ symbol used to denote a negative integer should be written in the raised position we have used here (for $^+3$, $^+4$, etc., read "positive three, positive four," etc.).

$5 + 3$	This expression is read "five *plus* three."
$9 - 3$	This expression is read "nine *minus* three."
$^+5, ^+4, ^+3$	The $+$ symbols indicate that these are *positive* integers and would be represented to the right of zero on the number line (read "positive five, positive four, positive three").
$^-6, ^-5, ^-4$	The $-$ symbols indicate that these are *negative* integers and would be represented to the left of zero on the number line (read "negative six, negative five, negative four").
$^+6 + ^-2 = ^+4$	This equation is read "*positive* six *plus negative* two is equal to *positive* four."
$^-5 - ^-7 = ^+2$	This equation is read "*negative* five *minus negative* seven is equal to *positive* two."

Exercises

Read each of the following statements, translating into words.

1. $^+4 + \,^+9 = \,^+13.$
2. $^+7 + \,^-3 = \,^+4.$
3. $^-6 + \,^+8 = \,^+2.$
4. $^-5 + \,^-2 = \,^-7.$
5. $0 + \,^-14 = \,^-14.$
6. $^+6 + 0 = \,^+6.$
7. $^+7 - \,^+5 = \,^+2.$
8. $^+10 - \,^-9 = \,^+19.$
9. $^-3 - \,^+5 = \,^-8.$
10. $^-13 - \,^-10 = \,^-3.$
11. $^-6 - \,^-11 = \,^+5.$
12. $^-20 - \,^-15 = \,^-5.$
13. $^+7 - 0 = \,^+7.$
14. $^+2 - \,^-7 = \,^+9.$
15. $0 - \,^-19 = \,^+19.$
16. $^-4 - \,^+1 = \,^-5.$
17. $^+5 + \,^-4 = \,^+1.$
18. $^+5 - \,^+4 = \,^+1.$
19. $^+16 + \,^+8 = \,^+24.$
20. $^+16 - \,^-8 = \,^+24.$
21. $^-11 - \,^-31 = \,^+20.$

4-13 Additive Inverse

The number line may be used to picture the set of integers and to show that each positive integer may be paired with its opposite, which is called a negative integer. In other words, the positive integers may be placed in one-to-one correspondence with the negative integers. The + symbol is often omitted when we write the numeral for a positive integer; that is, $^+1$ is 1, $^+2$ is 2, $^+3$ is 3, $^+4$ is 4, $^+5$ is 5, and so on.

    Additive inverse is a term used to convey the notion of an opposite with respect to addition. The opposite of 6 is $^-6$ and the opposite of $^-6$ is 6. Since $6 + \,^-6 = 0$ and $^-6 + 6 = 0$, where 0 is the identity element for addition, $^-6$ is called the additive inverse of 6, and 6 is called the additive inverse of $^-6$. The sum of an integer and its additive inverse is always zero. The *additive inverse* of a number is often called **the negative** of the number. Thus, $^-3$ is the negative of 3, and 3 is the negative of $^-3$. In general, the negative of a positive number is a negative number; the negative of a negative number is a positive number; the negative of zero is zero.

    A number line is an excellent model for illustrating operations with signed numbers. Arrows may be used to represent directed line segments for positive and negative numbers. Notice that in the number-line illustrations the arrow points to the *right* if it represents a *positive* number and to the *left* if it represents a *negative* number (Figure 4-14).

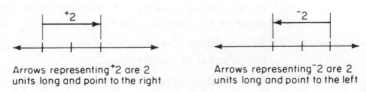

Arrows representing $^+2$ are 2   Arrows representing $^-2$ are 2
units long and point to the right   units long and point to the left

Figure 4-14

To picture the sum of two signed numbers on the number line, we draw the first arrow with its tail (initial point) at the graph of 0 and the second arrow with its tail at the head (terminal point) of the first arrow. The coordinate of the point representing the head of the second arrow is the sum of the two signed numbers.

The equation $4 + {}^-4 = 0$ may be pictured on the number line by using arrows (directed line segments) for 4 and $^-4$ (Figure 4-15). Notice that 4 is represented by a line segment of 4 units' length directed to the right from the graph of 0, and $^-4$ is represented by a line segment of 4 units' length directed to the left from the graph of 4. The coordinate of the other endpoint

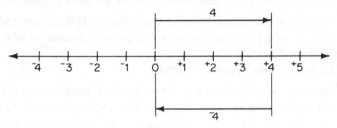

Figure 4-15

of the directed line segment representing $^-4$ is 0. Thus, $^-4$ is the number that yields 0 when added to 4; that is, $^-4$ is the additive inverse, or negative, of 4. We may similarly show that 4 is the additive inverse, or negative, of $^-4$; that is, $^-4 + 4 = 0$ (Figure 4-16).

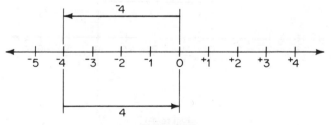

Figure 4-16

Every integer has an additive inverse, since each positive integer has a negative integer as its additive inverse, each negative integer has a positive integer as its additive inverse, and zero is its own additive inverse. In general, for every n where n is an integer, there exists a negative of n such that

$$n + {}^-n = 0.$$

Exercises

1. State the additive inverse of each number.
   (a) ⁻3.   (b) 5.   (c) 17.   (d) ⁻26.   (e) 0.

2. Complete each statement to make a true number sentence.
   (a) $7 + {}^-7 = $ ____.   (b) $^-4 + $ ____ $= 0$.
   (c) ____ $+ 1 = 0$.   (d) $n - 0 = $ ____.

4-14 Addition of Integers

Intuitive notions of the addition of integers may be developed through the use of a number line. There are three types of addition problems:

(1) The sum of two positive integers or of a positive integer and zero.
(2) The sum of a negative integer and a positive integer or of a negative integer and zero.
(3) The sum of two negative integers.

The representation of the sum of two positive integers or of a positive integer and zero is the same as that for the sum of two whole numbers (Section 4-1). In this section we will concentrate on the other two types of sums of integers.

We first use a number line to determine the sum $4 + {}^-3$. The 4 is represented by a line segment of 4 units' length directed to the right from the graph of 0, and ⁻3 is represented by a line segment of 3 units' length directed to the left from the graph of 4. The coordinate of the other endpoint of the directed line segment representing ⁻3 is 1. Thus, $4 + {}^-3 = 1$ (Figure 4-17).

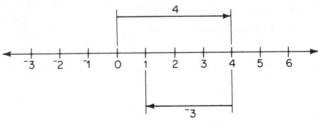

Figure 4-17

The sum $2 + {}^-3$ may be represented as on the number line in Figure 4-18. Thus, $2 + {}^-3 = {}^-1$.

Consider the sum $^-2 + {}^-3$. In this case the line segments are both directed to the left. Observe that $^-2 + {}^-3 = {}^-5$ (Figure 4-19).

After considering several examples of the three types of sums of integers, given in the first two exercises below, the student should be able to discover some generalizations (rules) for the addition of integers.

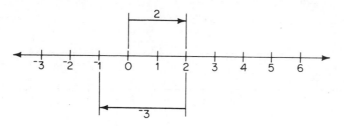

Figure 4-18

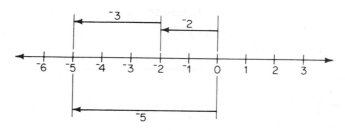

Figure 4-19

Exercises

1. Use a number line to determine each sum.
   (a) 5 + ⁻4.   (b) ⁻1 + ⁻3.   (c) ⁻6 + ⁺5.   (d) ⁻2 + 2.
2. Find each sum.
   (a) ⁻7 + 4.   (b) ⁻9 + ⁻6.   (c) 6 + 5 + ⁻9.
   (d) 17 + (⁻3 + 6).   (e) 13 + ⁻4.   (f) (5 + ⁻2) + ⁻6.
3. Try to state some general rules for the three types of addition problems involving integers.

4-15 Subtraction of Integers

The importance of clearly understanding the relationship between addition and subtraction becomes very evident when we need to subtract integers. In Section 4-8 we studied the relationship between addition and subtraction of whole numbers. This relationship may also be expressed by using a, b, and c as positive integers.

$$\text{If } a + b = c, \text{ then } c - a = b \text{ and } c - b = a.$$

The relationship will apply to all integers; for example,

$$\text{if } 9 + {}^-3 = 6, \text{ then } 6 - 9 = {}^-3 \text{ and } 6 - {}^-3 = 9.$$

These equations may be shown on number lines (Figures 4-20 and 4-21).

$$9 + {}^-3 = 6$$

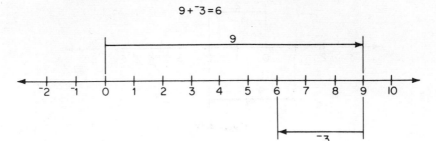

Figure 4-20

$$6 - 9 = {}^-3$$

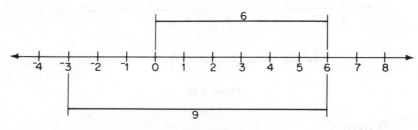

Figure 4-21

The additive point of view may be used when we represent $6 - {}^-3$ on the number line. In other words, we think of the number which added to ${}^-3$ produces 6; that is, ${}^-3 + \square = 6$. The number line in Figure 4-22 makes it clear that 9 is the number that must be added to ${}^-3$ to yield 6.

$${}^-3 + \square = 6$$

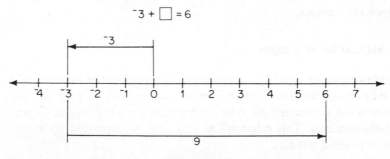

Figure 4-22

Using the number line, we may compare subtraction with the "interpretation of subtraction" given in the following table. Is it correct to state that "subtracting an integer is equivalent to adding its additive inverse"?

Subtraction	Interpretation of Subtraction
$^+5 = {}^+9 - {}^+4$	$^+5 = {}^+9 + {}^-4$
$^+5 = {}^+4 - {}^-1$	$^+5 = {}^+4 + {}^+1$
$^-5 = {}^-1 - {}^+4$	$^-5 = {}^-1 + {}^-4$
$^-5 = {}^-9 - {}^-4$	$^-5 = {}^-9 + {}^+4$

A study of the examples given in the table will lead us to the general statement

$$a - b = a + {}^-b$$

where a and b are integers.

Recall (Section 4-13) that signed numbers may be represented by arrows (directed line segments) when the number line is used to picture the addition of two integers. For example, $3 + 4$ is represented in Figure 4-23.

$$3 + 4 = 7$$

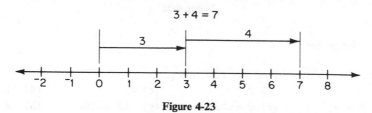

Figure 4-23

The number line also may be used to picture the subtraction of signed numbers. The minus sign, designating the operation of subtraction, is a direction-changing signal when we use arrows to illustrate the subtraction of signed numbers. For example, when 3 and 4 are added, 4 is represented by an arrow of 4 units' length pointing to the right; however, in order to subtract 4 from 3 we add $^-4$ to 3 and represent $^-4$ by an arrow of 4 units' length directed to the left (Figure 4-24).

$$3 - 4 = 3 + {}^-4 = {}^-1$$

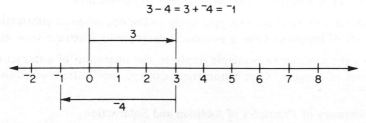

Figure 4-24

Consider the examples $2 + {}^-5$ and $2 - {}^-5$ pictured on the number lines in Figures 4-25 and 4-26 respectively.

$$2 + {}^-5 = {}^-3$$

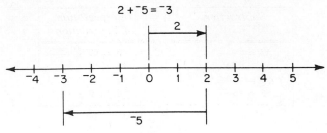

Figure 4-25

$$2 - {}^-5 = 2 + {}^+5 = 7$$

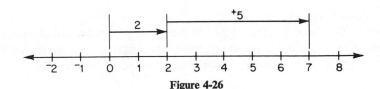

Figure 4-26

Exercises

1. Find the additive inverse of each integer.

(a) $^-6.$ (b) $x.$ (c) $4.$ (d) $^-1.$

(e) $a + b.$ (f) $4 + {}^-3.$ (g) $^-13 + {}^-4.$ (h) $^-a + 2.$

2. Find each difference.

(a) $7 - 9.$ (b) $^-3 - 10.$ (c) $^-8 - {}^-6.$

(d) $14 - {}^-6.$ (e) $(6 + {}^-2) - {}^-11.$ (f) $(^-2 - {}^-5) - {}^-9.$

3. Complete each statement to make a true number sentence.

(a) $0 - 6 = $ ____.   (b) $^-1 - {}^-1 = $ ____.

(c) $2 + $ ____ $ = {}^-3.$ (d) $3 - {}^-2 = $ ____.

4. Use a number line to illustrate the solution to Exercise 3(d).

5. Is the set of integers closed with respect to subtraction?

6. Does the commutative principle apply to the operation of subtraction on the set of integers? Give a numerical example to illustrate your answer.

7. Does the associative principle apply to the operation of subtraction on the set of integers? Give a numerical example to illustrate your answer.

4-16 Summary of Principles of Addition and Subtraction

The table below presents a summary of principles of addition and subtraction for the set of integers. The letters a, b, and c represent arbitrary integers where $a \neq b$ and $b \neq c$.

Principle	Addition	Subtraction
Closure and uniqueness	$a + b$ is a unique integer.	$a - b$ is a unique integer.
Commutativity	$a + b = b + a.$	$a - b \neq b - a.$
Associativity	$a + (b + c) = (a + b) + c.$	$a - (b - c) \neq (a - b) - c.$
Identity element	$a + 0 = a.$	$a - 0 = a.$

The following table summarizes the application of the principles of closure, commutativity, and associativity to the addition and subtraction of whole numbers and integers.

Principle and Operation	Set of Whole Numbers	Set of Integers
Closed under addition	Yes	Yes
Closed under subtraction	No	Yes
Addition is commutative	Yes	Yes
Subtraction is commutative	No	No
Addition is associative	Yes	Yes
Subtraction is associative	No	No

chapter 5

Operations:
Multiplication and Division

In this chapter some of the principles of the operations of multiplication and division of whole numbers are identified. The definition of the operation of multiplication on the set of whole numbers and the basic principles of multiplication are assumed. In order that the operation of division by any number other than zero may always be possible, the set of rational numbers is constructed from the set of integers.

5-1 Multiplication of Whole Numbers

Multiplication is a *binary* operation since it combines two numbers to produce a unique third number. Recall (Section 3-3) that the two numbers that are multiplied are called *factors* and the resulting number is called the *product* of the factors. In the example $3 \times 5 = 15$ the numbers 3 and 5 are factors of 15, and 15 is the product of 3 and 5. Multiplication within the set of whole numbers may be related to repeated addition. In other words, 3×5 may be considered as $5 + 5 + 5$, and 6×2 is equal to $2 + 2 + 2 + 2 + 2 + 2$.

The repeated-addition interpretation is a good intuitive way to introduce multiplication; however, there are several limitations to this approach. Consider the following:

(1) When one of the factors is 0, it is meaningless to think of 0×4 as "add four, zero times" since addition is a binary operation.
(2) When one of the factors is 1, it is also meaningless to think of 1×4

79

as "add four, one time" since the binary operation of addition suggests two addends.

(3) When the factors are very large numbers (for example, 125×50),
the use of the addition process to obtain the product is very time-
consuming.

Therefore, it is desirable to deal with multiplication as a number operation in its own right, as soon as we become familiar with it as an abstract
process.

The multiplication of whole numbers may also be described in terms of
sets. Consider a set of three coats and a set of four hats. No two coats or
two hats are of the same color. How many different combinations of coats
and hats can be made? It is obvious that each coat can be paired with each
of the four hats and that a total of twelve different color combinations can
be formed (Figure 5-1).

If we denote the set of coats by $\{1, 2, 3\}$ and the set of hats by $\{a, b, c, d\}$,
a convenient notation for the set of all possible coat-hat combinations is
illustrated by listing the set of pairs: $\{(1, a), (1, b), (1, c), (1, d), (2, a), (2, b),
(2, c), (2, d), (3, a), (3, b), (3, c), (3, d)\}$.

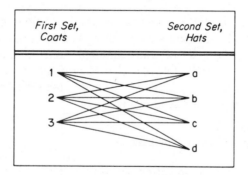

Figure 5-1

Note that a set of twelve combinations (pairs of elements) has been
constructed from a set of three objects and a set of four objects. Each of
these pairs is called an **ordered pair**, because we have assigned a significance
to the order. In the ordered pair $(1, a)$, coat 1 is the **first element**, and hat

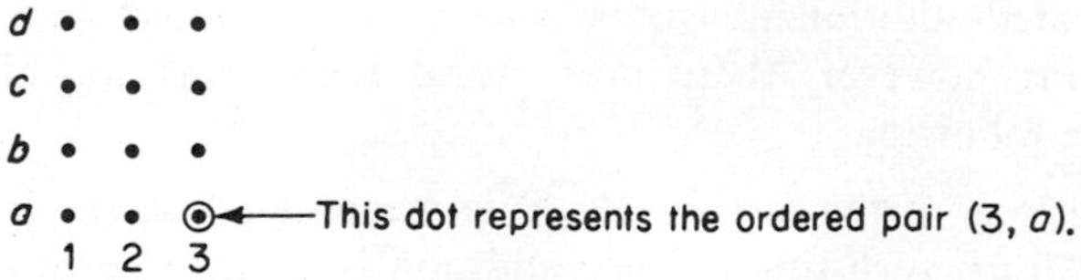

$$
\begin{array}{llll}
d & \bullet & \bullet & \bullet \\
c & \bullet & \bullet & \bullet \\
b & \bullet & \bullet & \bullet \\
a & \bullet & \bullet & \circledcirc \longleftarrow \text{This dot represents the ordered pair } (3, a). \\
  & 1 & 2 & 3
\end{array}
$$

Figure 5-2

a is the **second element**. We may use a rectangular dot array, Figure 5-2, to visualize this set of ordered pairs.

Arrays can be used to relate multiplication to addition. The Figure 5-2 array illustrates that we can determine the number 4 × 3 by deciding how many elements are in a new set formed by joining together four sets with three elements in each set. In order that we may be consistent, we shall agree that a 4 × 3 array has four (horizontal) rows and three (vertical) columns. In other words, the first number indicates the number of rows, and the second gives the number of columns.

It should be noted at this point that there are many different notations for multiplication. For example, each of the following denotes the product "3 times 2":

(a) 3 × 2.　　(b) 3 groups of 2.　　(c) $\begin{array}{r} 2 \\ \times 3 \\ \hline \end{array}$　　(d) 3·2.

(e) 3 twos.　　(f) 2 multiplied by 3.　　(g) (3)(2).　　(h) Multiply 2 by 3.

Multiplication of whole numbers may also be represented on a number line. For example, 3 × 2 = 6 may be represented as 2 + 2 + 2 = 6 (Figure 5-3).

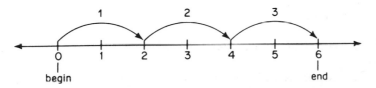

Figure 5-3

Notice that the representation of multiplication on the number line involves jumps of equal size. Begin at the graph of 0 and count off three jumps of 2 (that is, 3 twos) to determine that the coordinate of the terminal point is 6; 3 × 2 = 6.

Exercises

1. Draw a rectangular dot array to represent each product.
　(**a**) 2 × 5.　　　(**b**) 5 × 2.　　　(**c**) 4 × 0.　　　(**d**) 1 × 7.

2. Jack has five different-appearing sport shirts and two different-appearing pairs of pants. Assume that each shirt may be worn with each pair of pants. How many different outfits (combinations) can Jack make?

3. Represent each product on a number line.
　(**a**) 4 × 2.　　　(**b**) 2 × 4.　　　(**c**) 3 × 4.　　　(**d**) 5 × 1.

5-2 Closure and Uniqueness

The principle of **closure** applied to the multiplication of whole numbers means that the product of any two whole numbers is also a whole number. The principle of **uniqueness** indicates that there is only one possible product when two given whole numbers are multiplied. In the example $7 \times 3 = 21$ both the factors and the product are elements of the set of whole numbers. It should also be noted that there is one and only one possible product when 3 is multiplied by 7. Hence, 21 is the *unique* product 7×3.

The principles of closure and uniqueness for the multiplication of whole numbers may be stated as

$$a \times b = c$$

where a and b may be any whole numbers, and the whole number c is the unique product of a and b.

The principle of closure under multiplication does not hold for all sets. In the case of a finite set $X = \{1, 3, 5, 7, 9\}$ a product of two elements of the set may not be a member of the set. For example, $3 \in X$, $9 \in X$, and $3 \times 9 = 27$, but 27 is not an element of the set X. Hence, set X is not closed with respect to the operation of multiplication.

Exercises

1. State whether or not each set is closed under the operation of multiplication.
   (a) The set of even whole numbers.
   (b) The set of odd whole numbers.
   (c) The set of natural numbers greater than 50.
   (d) The set of counting numbers between 15 and 285.
   (e) The set of whole numbers whose numerals end in 0.
   (f) The set of odd natural numbers less than 888.
   (g) The set of counting numbers whose numerals end in 5.

2. State whether or not each product is unique.
   (a) 9×8.   (b) 3×6.   (c) 25×36.   (d) 234×197.

5-3 The Commutative Principle of Multiplication

The order of multiplication of two numbers (factors) in the set of whole numbers does not affect the product. For example, $3 \times 4 = 4 \times 3$, since $3 \times 4 = 12$ and $4 \times 3 = 12$. This illustrates the **commutative principle of multiplication** for whole numbers:

If a and b are any two whole numbers, then $a \times b = b \times a$.

Arrays may be used in leading children to the discovery of the commutative principle of multiplication. A 3 × 4 array has the same number of elements as a 4 × 3 array, but the arrays look different (Figure 5-4).

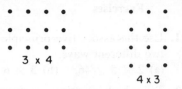

3 x 4

4 x 3

Figure 5-4

The number line also may be used to illustrate the commutative principle of multiplication of whole numbers. Figure 5-5 shows that the effect of three jumps of 4 units' length is the same as four jumps of 3 units' length.

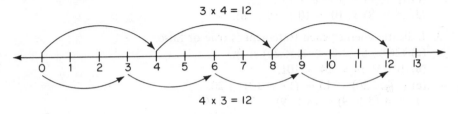

3 x 4 = 12

4 x 3 = 12

Figure 5-5

Exercises

1. Complete each statement to obtain an example of the commutative principle of multiplication.
   (a) 5 × 3 = ____ × ____.   (b) 7 × 9 = ____ × ____.
   (c) 143 × 10 = ____ × ____.   (d) 999 × 4 = ____ × ____.

2. Use a number line to show that 6 × 2 = 2 × 6.

5-4 The Associative Principle of Multiplication

Multiplication, like addition, is a binary operation. When more than two factors are to be multiplied, the factors are grouped for binary operations. For example, 3 × 4 × 5 may be grouped for multiplication as (3 × 4) × 5 or as 3 × (4 × 5). The expression (3 × 4) × 5 indicates 12 × 5, and the expression 3 × (4 × 5) indicates 3 × 20. Both 12 × 5 and 3 × 20 equal 60. Notice that the associative principle does not provide for a change in the order of the factors. It provides only for a change in the grouping.

The **associative principle of multiplication** may be stated as

$$(a \times b) \times c = a \times (b \times c),$$

where a, b, and c represent any whole numbers.

The associative and commutative principles of multiplication provide us with a flexibility in rearranging and grouping the factors in a problem involving only multiplication.

Exercises

1. Use the associative principle of multiplication and find each product in two different ways.
   (a) $2 \times 5 \times 46$.   (b) $3 \times 6 \times 9$.   (c) $50 \times 20 \times 7$.   (d) $4 \times 8 \times 25$.

2. Tell which principle, commutative or associative, is illustrated by each equation.
   (a) $(7 \times 8) \times (9 \times 6) = (9 \times 6) \times (7 \times 8)$.
   (b) $2 \times (3 \times 4) = (2 \times 3) \times 4$.
   (c) $(e \times f) \times g = e \times (f \times g)$.
   (d) $(5 \times 8) \times 10 = 10 \times (5 \times 8)$.

3. Indicate whether each statement is true or false.
   (a) $(26 \times 8) \times 3 < (8 \times 26) \times 3$.
   (b) $101 \times 14 \neq 14 \times 101$.
   (c) $(17 \times 20) \times 13 = (17 \times 13) \times 20$.
   (d) $7 \times (8 \times 9) = (8 \times 9) \times 7$.

4. State the principle that justifies each step illustrated in this example.
$$e \times (f \times g) = (e \times f) \times g$$
$$= (f \times e) \times g$$
$$= f \times (e \times g)$$

5-5 Identity Element for Multiplication

The product of any whole number and the number 1 is the original whole number. For example, $2 \times 1 = 2$, $3 \times 1 = 3$, $4 \times 1 = 4$, $5 \times 1 = 5$, and so on. Each of these statements may be illustrated by an array. A 2×1 array consists of two rows of one element each, and consequently the entire array contains only two elements. A similar situation exists for 3×1, 4×1, and 5×1 arrays (Figure 5-6).

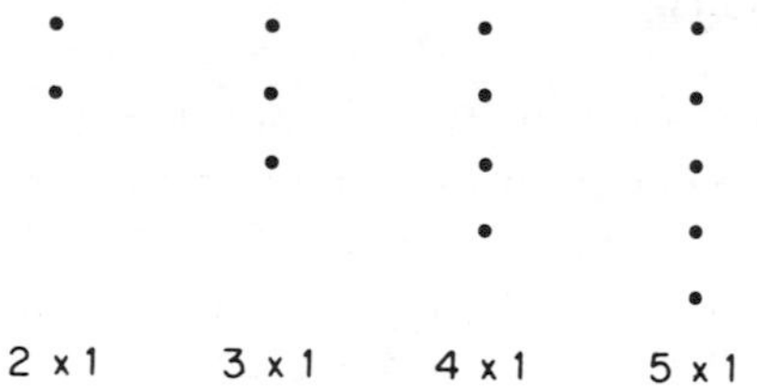

Since $a \times 1 = a$ for any whole number a, the number 1 is called the **identity element for multiplication,** that is, the **multiplicative identity**. Note that the role of 1 in multiplication is similar to that of 0 in addition.

2 x 1   3 x 1   4 x 1   5 x 1

Figure 5-6

Exercise

1. Complete each statement to make a true number sentence.
   (a) $16 \times \underline{\hspace{1cm}} = 16$.   (b) $1 \times d = \underline{\hspace{1cm}}$.
   (c) $\underline{\hspace{1cm}} \times 1 = 8$.   (d) $\underline{\hspace{1cm}} \times 1 = 1$.

5-6 Principle of Multiplication by Zero

The number zero has a special characteristic when used as a factor. It may be difficult to understand multiplication by zero if we think in terms of repeated addition; however, if we return to our discussion of multiplication in terms of sets, the concept should be clearer. Consider 5×0 as the number of pairs that can be formed by selecting a first object from a set of five things and a second object from a set of zero things. We can then see that $5 \times 0 = 0$. If there are 5 coats and 0 hats, there are exactly 0 coat-hat combinations that can be formed.

The product of any whole number and zero is always zero. For example,

$$0 \times 0 = 0,$$
$$1 \times 0 = 0,$$
$$2 \times 0 = 0,$$
$$3 \times 0 = 0,$$
$$4 \times 0 = 0,$$

and, in general, $a \times 0 = 0$ for each whole number a.

Exercises

1. Complete each statement to make a true number sentence.
   (a) $8 \times$ ____ $= 0$.   (b) $0 \times$ ____ $= 0$.
   (c) $7 \times 8 \times 0 =$ ____ .   (d) $(2 \times 3) \times$ ____ $= (7 \times 0) \times 9$.

2. Illustrate a 0×7 array.

5-7 Distributive Principle of Multiplication over Addition

The operations of addition and multiplication have been discussed, and some of the principles of these operations have been considered. The distributive principle, however, involves both addition and multiplication.

Consider the example 3×7 and recall from previous discussions that there are many numerals that represent 7. In other words, 3×7 may also be represented as $3 \times (5 + 2)$. The question that is immediately posed is, "Does $3 \times (5 + 2)$ equal 3×7 or $(3 \times 5) + (3 \times 2)$?" Since 3×7 equals 21 and $(3 \times 5) + (3 \times 2)$ equals $15 + 6 = 21$, we have $3 \times (5 + 2) = 3 \times 7 = (3 \times 5) + (3 \times 2)$. This may be illustrated by arrays (Figure 5-7).

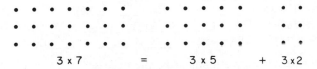

Figure 5-7

The **distributive principle of multiplication over addition** is a very basic and important one. It may be stated in general terms as

$$a \times (b + c) = (a \times b) + (a \times c),$$

where a, b, and c are any whole numbers.

It is important to note that, since multiplication is commutative, we may distribute multiplication over addition from both the left and the right. In other words, we have a left distributive principle,

$$a \times (b + c) = (a \times b) + (a \times c),$$

and also a right distributive principle,

$$(b + c) \times a = (b \times a) + (c \times a).$$

We speak of "the distributive principle" in referring to whichever one of these is applicable.

The distributive principle is the basis of many of our short-cut methods of computation. When we work the following multiplication problem, we apply the distributive principle. In the problem

$$\begin{array}{r} 31 \\ \times\ 2 \\ \hline \end{array}$$

we multiply 1 by 2 and multiply 30 by 2. We then add these products and write the answer 62. Actually $31 = 30 + 1$, and we multiply this sum by 2. Thus we have

$$2 \times (30 + 1) = (2 \times 30) + (2 \times 1) = 60 + 2 = 62.$$

Application of the distributive principle is further illustrated in these examples:

$$(8 \times 27) + (8 \times 73) = 8 \times (27 + 73) = 8 \times 100 = 800,$$
$$(16 \times 12) + (34 \times 12) = (16 + 34) \times 12 = 50 \times 12 = 600,$$
$$30 \times 17 = 30 \times (10 + 7) = (30 \times 10) + (30 \times 7) = 300 + 210 = 510.$$

Exercises

1. Use the distributive principle and insert numerals to make each number sentence true.
   (a) $7 \times (8 + 29) = (7 \times \underline{\quad}) + (\underline{\quad} \times 29)$.
   (b) $(5 \times 3) + (5 \times \underline{\quad}) = \underline{\quad} \times (\underline{\quad} + 26)$.
   (c) $128 \times (64 + 216) = (\underline{\quad} \times \underline{\quad}) + (\underline{\quad} \times \underline{\quad})$.
   (d) $(785 \times 38) + (785 \times 59) = \underline{\quad} \times (\underline{\quad} + \underline{\quad})$.

2. Indicate whether each statement is true or false.
   (a) $2 \times (3 + 4) = (2 \times 3) + (3 \times 4)$.

    (b) $(7 + 8) \times 5 = (7 \times 5) + (8 \times 5)$.

    (c) $(26 \times 8) + (17 \times 8) = (26 \times 17) + 8$.

    (d) $(5 \times 11) + (16 \times 5) = (16 + 11) \times 5$.

3. Apply the distributive principle to compute each of the following.

    (a) $(78 \times 43) + (78 \times 57)$.   **(b)** $(39 \times 5) + (39 \times 5)$.

4. We have illustrated that multiplication is distributive over addition. Is addition distributive over multiplication? That is, if a, b, and c represent any three whole numbers, is it always true that $a + (b \times c) = (a + b) \times (a + c)$?

5. State the principle that justifies each step illustrated in the following example.

$$(30 \times 13) + (37 \times 30) = (30 \times 13) + (30 \times 37)$$
$$= 30 \times (13 + 37)$$
$$= 30 \times 50$$
$$= 1,500$$

6. Is multiplication distributive over subtraction? That is, if a, b, and c represent any three whole numbers, is it always true that $a \times (b - c) = (a \times b) - (a \times c)$? Is it always true that $(b - c) \times a = (b \times a) - (c \times a)$?

5-8 The Multiplication Table

As in addition, a table may be used to summarize multiplication facts. The following table is a summary of the products of the decimal digits.

×	0	1	2	3	4	5	6	7	8	9
0	0	0	0	0	0	0	0	0	0	0
1	0	1	2	3	4	5	6	7	8	9
2	0	2	4	6	8	10	12	14	16	18
3	0	3	6	9	12	15	18	21	24	27
4	0	4	8	12	16	20	24	28	32	36
5	0	5	10	15	20	25	30	35	40	45
6	0	6	12	18	24	30	36	42	48	54
7	0	7	14	21	28	35	42	49	56	63
8	0	8	16	24	32	40	48	56	64	72
9	0	9	18	27	36	45	54	63	72	81

This table may be used to emphasize many of the important principles that apply to the multiplication of whole numbers. The special characteristics of multiplying by 0 and by 1 are shown in the first two rows and the first two columns. A line has been drawn diagonally through the table from the upper left-hand corner to the lower right. The elements drawn through are called *diagonal elements* and form the *main diagonal* of the table. Notice that except for the diagonal elements this line divides the table into two equivalent parts. When the table is folded over its main diagonal, the blocks containing 0 fall upon each other, as do the blocks containing 2, and so on. This is due to the commutative principle of multiplication, which justifies such conclusions as $2 \times 3 = 3 \times 2$.

Further examination of the table will reveal other patterns that are most interesting. For example, study the diagonal elements from upper left to lower right, $\{1, 4, 9, 16, \ldots, 81\}$. These diagonal elements are consecutive squares; that is, each diagonal element is obtained by squaring a number (using the number as a factor two times). What are the differences between the consecutive squares? Look for other patterns and try to explain why they develop.

Special attention should be given to the fact that an understanding of the commutative principle and the special characteristics of 0 and 1 make it unnecessary to learn the entire multiplication table. It is sufficient to know the products shown in the next table.

×	0	1	2	3	4	5	6	7	8	9
0										
1										
2			4							
3			6	9						
4			8	12	16					
5			10	15	20	25				
6			12	18	24	30	36			
7			14	21	28	35	42	49		
8			16	24	32	40	48	56	64	
9			18	27	36	45	54	63	72	81

Actually, some of the simple products in this table could be considered as repeated addition, and this would reduce the number of needed multiplication facts even further. An understanding of the distributive principle and the basic addition facts could also reduce the number of needed multiplication facts. For example, if we wish to multiply 6 by 9, we could think in terms of 6 as $3 + 3$ and then use the distributive principle to determine

$$9 \times 6 = 9 \times (3 + 3) = (9 \times 3) + (9 \times 3) = 27 + 27 = 54.$$

Another example may improve the understanding of concepts that are actually applied in the multiplication process. For example, consider 6×18. From the concept of place value, $18 = 10 + 8$. Hence,

$$6 \times 18 = 6 \times (10 + 8).$$

Applying the distributive principle, we have

$$6 \times (10 + 8) = (6 \times 10) + (6 \times 8).$$

Using the multiplication facts, we have

$$(6 \times 10) + (6 \times 8) = 60 + 48,$$

and, from the concept of place value,

$$60 + 48 = 60 + (40 + 8).$$

Then, using the associative principle, we have

$$60 + (40 + 8) = (60 + 40) + 8,$$

and, by renaming $(60 + 40)$,

$$(60 + 40) + 8 = 100 + 8 = 108.$$

Therefore,

$$6 \times 18 = 108.$$

If we use the expanded notation in vertical form, we obtain

$$
\begin{array}{r}
18 = 10 + 8 \\
\times\ 6 = \times\ 6 \\
\hline
60 + 48 = 60 + (40 + 8) = (60 + 40) + 8 = 108.
\end{array}
$$

Exercises

For Exercises 1 through 4, consider a multiplication table for the whole numbers from 0 to 1,000.

1. What principle of multiplication is illustrated by the top row of facts and the left-hand column of facts?

2. What principle of multiplication is illustrated by the facts in the second row and those in the second column from the left?

3. What are the first four entries in the row named 700? In the column named 700?

4. Is each number represented in the row named 700 matched by an equal number represented in the column named 700?

5. It was pointed out that in the multiplication table for the decimal digits the diagonal elements from upper left to lower right form the set of consecutive squares,

$$\{1, 4, 9, 16, 25, 36, 49, 64, 81\}.$$

What pattern seems to be developing in this set of numbers? Predict the next five numbers that would be represented on the main diagonal of the multiplication table for the whole numbers from 0 to 25.

6. Indicate whether each statement is true or false.
  (a) The product of two even numbers is always an even number.
  (b) The product of two odd numbers is never an odd number.
  (c) The product of an even and an odd number is always an odd number.

7. How does the multiplication table for whole numbers illustrate the commutative principle?

5-9 Understanding the Multiplication Algorism

There are several conventional algorisms that aid in solving multiplication problems. Each of these algorisms can be explained in terms of the principles of multiplication and addition. It is extremely important that children understand *why* these algorisms give the correct result when used properly.

The following examples demonstrate a familiar multiplication algorism.

$$
\begin{array}{cc}
\textbf{Example 1} & \overset{2}{14} \\
& \times\ 7 \\
\hline
& 98 \\
\end{array}
\qquad
\begin{array}{cc}
\textbf{Example 2} & \overset{1}{24} \\
& \times\ 13 \\
\hline
& 72 \\
& 24 \\
\hline
& 312 \\
\end{array}
$$

Using the algorism in Example 1, we think "7 times 4 is 28"; put an 8 in the ones column and a 2 above the 1 in 14 to remind us of the 2 tens in 20. The product of 7 and 10 is 70, and 70 plus 20 equals 90. The sum of 90 and 8 is 98. The principles that allow us to use this "short-cut" method for multiplying 14 by 7 are the same as for 6 × 18, as illustrated in Section 5-8.

In Example 2, we are actually multiplying 20 + 4 by 10 + 3, which is an application of the distributive principle:

$$\begin{array}{r} 24 \\ \times\ 13 \\ \hline 72 \\ 24 \\ \hline 312 \end{array}$$

$$\begin{aligned} 13 \times 24 &= 13 \times (20 + 4) \\ &= (13 \times 20) + (13 \times 4) \\ &= [(10 + 3) \times 20] + [(10 + 3) \times 4] \\ &= [(10 \times 20) + (3 \times 20)] + [(10 \times 4) + (3 \times 4)] \\ &= 200 + 60 + 40 + 12 \\ &= 312. \end{aligned}$$

Consider another algorism for Example 2.

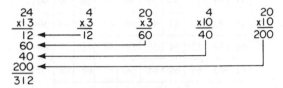

Figure 5-8

Exercises

1. Use a multiplication algorism to find each product.

   (a) $\begin{array}{r} 29 \\ \times\ 6 \\ \hline \end{array}$ (b) $\begin{array}{r} 37 \\ \times 16 \\ \hline \end{array}$

2. Illustrate the use of the distributive principle in determining each product in Exercise 1.

5-10 Prime Numbers

When two numbers are multiplied, each of the two numbers is called a *factor* of the product (see Section 5-1). Any whole number that is a factor of a given whole number is called also a **divisor** of that number. For example, $3 \times 4 = 12$. Here 3 and 4 are called factors (divisors) of 12. We should note that 3 and 4 are not the only factors (divisors) of 12. We could also have $2 \times 6 = 12$ with 2 and 6 as factors, or we could have $1 \times 12 = 12$, where 1 and 12 are factors. For our purposes, the word "factor" is defined as a whole-number factor (that is, divisor) of a number. In the case of 12 we have determined all possible factors: 1, 2, 3, 4, 6, and 12.

In the case of the number 3 there are only two factors, 1 and 3. Similarly, each of the numbers 5, 7, 11, 13, and 17 have only two factors, 1 and the number itself. We define a **prime number** as any whole number greater than 1 that has only itself and 1 as factors. Thus 2, 3, 5, 7, 11, 13, and 17 are the first seven prime numbers.

We can find all the prime numbers less than 100 by listing all the whole numbers from 2 to 99 (inclusive) and then crossing out all multiples of each succeeding prime; see the array.

2	3	~~4~~	5	~~6~~	7	~~8~~	~~9~~	~~10~~
11	~~12~~	13	~~14~~	~~15~~	~~16~~	17	~~18~~	19	~~20~~
~~21~~	~~22~~	23	~~24~~	~~25~~	26	~~27~~	~~28~~	29	~~30~~
31	~~32~~	~~33~~	~~34~~	~~35~~	36	37	~~38~~	~~39~~	40
41	~~42~~	43	44	~~45~~	46	47	~~48~~	~~49~~	~~50~~
~~51~~	~~52~~	53	~~54~~	~~55~~	~~56~~	~~57~~	~~58~~	59	~~60~~
61	~~62~~	~~63~~	~~64~~	~~65~~	~~66~~	67	~~68~~	~~69~~	~~70~~
71	~~72~~	73	~~74~~	~~75~~	~~76~~	~~77~~	~~78~~	79	~~80~~
~~81~~	~~82~~	83	~~84~~	~~85~~	~~86~~	~~87~~	~~88~~	89	~~90~~
~~91~~	~~92~~	~~93~~	~~94~~	~~95~~	~~96~~	97	98	99	

Since 2 is a prime number, cross out all numbers that have 2 as a factor, except 2; that is, 4, 6, 8, 10, 12, ... Since 3 is a prime number, cross out all numbers that have 3 as a factor, except 3; that is, 6, 9, 12, 15, 18, ... Next, cross out all numbers that have 5 as a factor, except 5; that is, 10, 15, 20, 25, 30, ... Do the same with all numbers that have 7 as a factor, except 7; that is, 14, 21, 28, 35, 42, ...

The next prime number is 11 and 11×11 is greater than 99. Thus all the multiples of 11 that are less than 100 have already been crossed out. Similarly, the multiples of all prime numbers greater than 11 have been crossed out already, and we may stop testing.

The twenty-five remaining numbers are the prime numbers less than 100 and may be designated as set P:

$$P = \{2, 3, 5, 7, 11, 13, 17, 19, 23, 29, 31, 37, 41, 43, 47,$$
$$53, 59, 61, 67, 71, 73, 79, 83, 89, 97\}.$$

This process for determining prime numbers is called the *Sieve of Eratosthenes,* after the Greek mathematician who originated the idea.

Each of the numbers that was crossed out of the table may be expressed as a product of prime numbers. These whole numbers are called **composite numbers.** For example, 4 may be expressed as 2×2, 6 may be expressed as 2×3, 8 may be expressed as $2 \times 2 \times 2$, 10 may be expressed as 2×5, and so forth.

The number 1 is a special number and is neither prime nor composite. It is not included in the set of prime numbers partly because its only whole-number factors are 1. The discussion in Section 5-11 will provide another reason for excluding 1 from the set of prime numbers. The number 0 also has special properties and is not included in the set of prime numbers. Thus, the whole numbers may be classified in four subsets: 0, 1, prime numbers, and composite numbers.

How do we determine whether a number is prime? Since a prime number has only itself and 1 as divisors, a systematic approach to this problem would be to test in turn all possible divisors of the number in question: if the number has a divisor other than itself and 1, it is a composite number Actually, we need to try only the prime divisors of the number, because the composite divisors are composed of smaller divisors that will already have been tried. For example, a number that is not divisible by 2 cannot be divisible by 4 or any other multiple of 2.

Is 29 a prime number? We try to divide 29 by 2, then by 3, then by 5, then by 7, then by 11, and so on. Do we continue to test prime divisors until the divisor is greater than 29? In this particular case, we could stop testing with the divisor 7, since $7 \times 7 = 49$ and $49 > 29$. If 29 were divided by a number equal to or greater than 7, the quotient would be a number less than 7. Since we have already tested for divisors less than 7 and determined that none exist, we conclude that 29 is a prime number.

Is 101 a prime number? The answer is yes, because 101 is not divisible by the prime numbers 2, 3, 5, and 7. We need not try other prime divisors, since $11^2 = 121$ and $121 > 101$. Note that 101 divided by 11 produces a quotient of 9 (remainder 2). When the quotient is less than the divisor we may stop testing divisors.

Exercises

1. List the prime numbers between 100 and 200.
2. Indicate whether each of the following is a composite number or a prime number.
   (a) 41.   (b) 313.   (c) 115.   (d) 823.
3. Is zero a prime number?

5-11 Fundamental Theorem of Arithmetic

Every composite number can be expressed as a product of prime numbers that is unique except for the order of the factors. This statement is called the **Fundamental Theorem of Arithmetic** and is also often referred to as the **Unique Factorization Theorem.** Consider the following examples.

Example 1 $18 = 2 \times 9 = 2 \times 3 \times 3,$
$18 = 3 \times 6 = 3 \times 2 \times 3.$

Example 2 $24 = 4 \times 6 = 2 \times 2 \times 2 \times 3,$

$24 = 3 \times 8 = 3 \times 2 \times 4 = 3 \times 2 \times 2 \times 2.$

Notice that the two ways of factoring in each of the examples result in the same product of prime numbers, but the orders of the factors are different. Application of the commutative and associative principles could change the order of the factors so that the two expressions would be identical.

If 1 were called a prime number, the Fundamental Theorem of Arithmetic would have to be rephrased. The number 18, for example, could then be factored as a product of prime numbers in each of these ways:

$$2 \times 3 \times 3 \times 1 = 18,$$

$$2 \times 3 \times 3 \times 1 \times 1 = 18,$$

$$2 \times 3 \times 3 \times 1 \times 1 \times 1 = 18.$$

The expressions would not be identical except for the order of the factors. Therefore, to enable us to keep the Fundamental Theorem of Arithmetic in a simple form (and also for other related reasons) we define the set of prime numbers so as to exclude the number 1.

Exercises

1. Express each composite number as a product of prime numbers.
   (a) 42.   (b) 99.   (c) 148.   (d) 375.

2. Develop an algorism that can be used to determine the prime factors of 1,592.

3. (a) List all factors of 36.
   (b) List the factors of 36 that are composite numbers.
   (c) List the factors of 36 that are prime numbers.

4. Express 36 as a product of
   (a) Two equal factors.   (b) Two composite numbers.
   (c) Two prime numbers.   (d) A prime and a composite number.

5. Represent 18 in all possible ways as a product of counting numbers greater than 1.

6. Express each even number between 2 and 26 as a sum of two prime numbers. Can you do this for all other even numbers?

5-12 Least Common Multiple

Consider the natural numbers 2 and 3. The set of multiples of 2 is

$$\{2, 4, 6, 8, 10, 12, 14, 16, 18, 20, \ldots\},$$

and the set of multiples of 3 is

$$\{3, 6, 9, 12, 15, 18, 21, \ldots\}.$$

Observe that some of the multiples of 2 are also multiples of 3. For example, 6, 12, and 18 are represented in the intersection of the two sets. Hence, we call 6, 12, 18, . . . the *common multiples* of 2 and 3.

If we let M denote the set of common multiples of 2 and 3,

$$M = \{6, 12, 18, 24, 30, 36, \ldots\}.$$

Notice that there is no largest common multiple of 2 and 3 in set M. By continually adding 6 to the preceding common multiple of 2 and 3, we may always find a larger common multiple. There is, however, a smallest element in set M. This element is the number 6. Since 6 is the smallest of the common multiples of 2 and 3, we call 6 the **least common multiple** (L.C.M.) of 2 and 3. Notice that only positive-integral multiples are considered and that the least common multiple is the common multiple that is a factor of each of the common multiples; that is, every common multiple is also a multiple of the least common multiple. Thus, zero multiples and negative-integral multiples are not considered; and in the preceding illustration, the least common multiple 6 is a factor of each of the common multiples in the set $\{6, 12, 18, 24, 30, 36, \ldots\}$.

Example 1 Find the least common multiple of 3 and 4 by using the intersection of sets.

Let A equal the set of multiples of 3,

$$A = \{3, 6, 9, 12, 15, 18, 21, 24, 27, \ldots\},$$

and B equal the set of multiples of 4,

$$B = \{4, 8, 12, 16, 20, 24, 28, 32, \ldots\}.$$

The least number represented in the set resulting from the intersection of A and B is the least common multiple. Since

$$A \cap B = \{12, 24, 36, \ldots\},$$

the least common multiple of 3 and 4 is 12.

Example 2 Find the least common multiple of 3 and 4 by using a number line.

Observe that on the number line 12 is the least common multiple of 3 and 4, since the graph of 12 is the first point on the number line common to the set of multiples of 3 and the set of multiples of 4 (Figure 5-9).

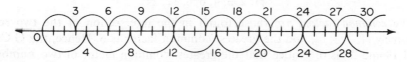

Figure 5-9

Example 3 Find the least common multiple of 6, 8, and 9 by using prime factors.

We may find the least common multiple of 6, 8, and 9 by separating each number into a product of prime factors:

$$6 = 2 \times 3,$$
$$8 = 2 \times 2 \times 2,$$
$$9 = 3 \times 3.$$

The least common multiple is the product of the different prime factors, each factor being used the greatest number of times it occurs as a factor of any one number. Thus the L.C.M. of 6, 8, and 9 is $2 \times 2 \times 2 \times 3 \times 3$; that is, 72.

Exercises

1. Find the prime factorization of
   (a) 4.   (b) 18.   (c) 20.   (d) 32.   (e) 396.

2. Find the least common multiple of
   (a) 4, 18, and 20.   (b) 2, 5, and 11.
   (c) 32 and 396.   (d) 239 and 785.

3. Why is 24 a common multiple of 2 and 3?

4. What is the least common multiple of
   (a) 23 and 23?   (b) 19 and 1?   (c) 6 and 8?   (d) 256 and 87?

5. Use prime factorization and find the least common multiple of the members of each set.
   (a) {9, 12}.   (b) {10, 11, 12}.   (c) {21, 35, 15}.   (d) {57, 98, 121}.

5-13 Greatest Common Factor

The **greatest common factor** (G.C.F.), also called the **greatest common divisor**, of a set of natural numbers is the largest natural number that is a factor of all numbers in the set. For example, the greatest common factor of 18 and 24 is the largest number that is a factor of both 18 and 24. Observe that the set of factors of 18 is

$$\{1, 2, 3, 6, 9, 18\},$$

and the set of factors of 24 is

$$\{1, 2, 3, 4, 6, 8, 12, 24\}.$$

The *common factors* are those found in the intersection of the two sets, namely {1, 2, 3, 6}, and the greatest common factor is 6. Hence, the G.C.F. of 18 and 24 is 6. Notice that the greatest common factor of two numbers has each of the common factors as a factor.

Example 1 Find the greatest common factor of 180 and 390 by using the intersection of sets.

Let D equal the set of factors of 180,

$$D = \{1, 2, 3, 4, 5, 6, 9, 10, 12, 15, 18, 20, 30, 36, 45, 60, 90, 180\},$$

and E equal the set of factors of 390,

$$E = \{1, 2, 3, 5, 6, 10, 13, 15, 26, 30, 39, 65, 78, 130, 195, 390\}.$$

The largest number represented in the set resulting from the intersection of D and E is the greatest common factor. Since

$$D \cap E = \{1, 2, 3, 5, 6, 10, 15, 30\},$$

the greatest common factor of 180 and 390 is 30.

Example 2 Find the greatest common factor of 180 and 390 by prime factorization.

We may find the G.C.F. of 180 and 390 if we separate each number into a product of prime factors and then form a product of the different prime factors, each factor being used the same number of times as the least number of times it occurs as a factor of any one of the given numbers. Thus,

$$180 = 2 \times 90 = 2 \times 2 \times 45 = 2 \times 2 \times 5 \times 9 = 2 \times 2 \times 3 \times 3 \times 5,$$

$$390 = 2 \times 195 = 2 \times 5 \times 39 = 2 \times 3 \times 5 \times 13,$$

and $2 \times 3 \times 5$ is the product of prime factors common to the prime factors of 180 and 390. Since 2, 3, and 5 are the only prime factors common to the prime factors of 180 and 390, the G.C.F. of 180 and 390 is $2 \times 3 \times 5 = 30$.

Exercises

1. Find the G.C.F. of
   (a) 32 and 48.   (b) 64 and 72.   (c) 36, 54, and 72.   (d) 256 and 87.
2. What is the G.C.F. of
   (a) 29 and 13?   (b) 3 and 5?   (c) 41 and 79?   (d) 297 and 121?
3. What is the G.C.F. of two prime numbers?
4. Find the L.C.M. of
   (a) 8 and 12.   (b) 10 and 15.   (c) 12 and 45.   (d) 258 and 570.
5. Find the G.C.F. of each pair of numbers given in Exercise 4.
6. Is it true that the product of the "L.C.M. of 8 and 12" and the "G.C.F. of 8 and 12" is equal to the product of 8 and 12?
7. Does the statement in Exercise 6 hold true for
   (a) 10 and 15?   (b) 12 and 45?
8. What is the greatest common factor of 18 and 18?

9. What is the smallest common factor of 9 and 6?

10. Is it possible for the G.C.F. of a pair of natural numbers to be the same as the L.C.M. of the two numbers?

11. Can the L.C.M. of a pair of natural numbers ever be less than the G.C.F. of the same numbers?

12. Can the L.C.M. of a pair of natural numbers ever be greater than the G.C.F. of the same numbers?

5-14 Division of Whole Numbers

Division is related to multiplication in much the same way that subtraction is related to addition. In many of the modern school mathematics programs division of whole numbers is introduced as a series of repeated subtractions to improve the student's understanding of the usual division algorism. In fact, modern desk calculators operate on this principle of repeated subtraction as the method for division. It is most important that children discover and understand the relationship between division and multiplication. In this chapter, we again find it necessary to extend our number system in order that we may provide solutions for certain division problems, such as $2 \div 3 = \square$.

The close relationship between multiplication and division may be observed in the following statements.

$$\text{If } 3 \times 6 = 18, \text{ then } 18 \div 3 = 6.$$
$$\text{If } 6 \times 3 = 18, \text{ then } 18 \div 6 = 3.$$
$$\text{If } 7 \times 8 = 56, \text{ then } 56 \div 7 = 8.$$
$$\text{If } 8 \times 7 = 56, \text{ then } 56 \div 8 = 7.$$

The commutative principle for the multiplication of whole numbers allows us to state that $3 \times 6 = 6 \times 3$; therefore, if we have $3 \times 6 = 18$, we may change it to $6 \times 3 = 18$ and get both $18 \div 3 = 6$ and $18 \div 6 = 3$ from the original equation $3 \times 6 = 18$. This may also be expressed with a, b, and c as positive integers:

$$\text{If } a \times b = c, \text{ then } c \div a = b \text{ and } c \div b = a.$$

The whole number n for the missing factor that makes $2 \times n = 10$ a true statement is called the **quotient** $10 \div 2$ (read "ten divided by two"), and the operation of finding n is called **division**. The quotient $10 \div 2$ is another name for the number 5 in the set of whole numbers. Hence, $10 \div 2$ may be replaced by 5; that is, $10 \div 2 = 5$.

$$\text{If } 10 \div 2 = n, \text{ then } 2 \times n = 10 \text{ and } n = 5.$$

Division is a binary operation, since it combines a first number and a second number to produce a unique third number. Frequently we say that the first number is the **product**, the second is a **factor**, and the number to be determined is the **missing factor**. In the example $12 \div 3 = \square$, 12 is the product, 3 is a factor of 12, and the variable $\square$ stands for the missing factor that will produce 12 when multiplied by 3.

Although we may relate the division operation to multiplication, it is important to recognize two kinds of division problems. The first is suggested by the question, "How many threes are in twelve?" This may be considered as a request to determine how many subsets of three elements each are contained in a given set of twelve elements. The second type of division problem is that of separating the given set into a certain number of parts, or subsets. For example, we may be asked to divide twelve into fourths or to divide twelve into four equal parts.

Any quotient may be obtained by repeated subtraction. Consider the example $18 \div 6 = \square$. If the question, "How many sixes are in eighteen?" is asked, then the repeated-subtraction process produces the answer. The result of dividing 18 by 6 can be obtained using repeated subtraction, if we subtract 6 from 18 getting 12, then subtract 6 from 12 getting 6, and so on. We continue subtracting 6 until we obtain a difference of zero. The number of times that 6 has been subtracted is the result of 18 divided by 6. Hence, the quotient is 3 (Figure 5-10).

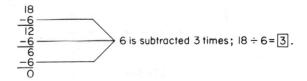

Figure 5-10

The division problem in Figure 5-11 also illustrates the process of repeated subtraction.

$$156 \div 26 = \square$$

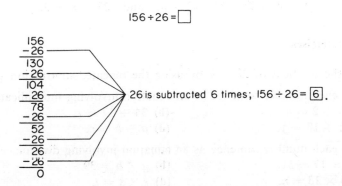

Figure 5-11

If repeated subtraction does not produce a difference of zero, then the missing factor is not a positive integer. Division of whole numbers may be represented on the number line by using a repeated-subtraction approach. Notice that in the case of $12 \div 4 = n$ we begin at the graph of 12 and count off to the left n jumps of 4, or n fours, and the coordinate of the terminal point is 0. Hence, three fours constitute twelve, and there are three fours in twelve; that is, $12 \div 4 = 3$ (Figure 5-12).

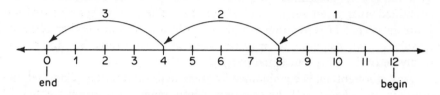

Figure 5-12

Division of whole numbers may also be represented by arrays. Consider the array in Figure 5-13 which contains 27 dots. It has 3 rows. How many columns does it have?

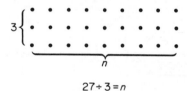

$$27 \div 3 = n$$

Figure 5-13

This again emphasizes the relation between division and multiplication. When we look at the array of 27 dots, we see that there are several different ways in which we could express the problem. For example,

$$3 \times n = 27, \quad 27 \div 3 = n, \quad \text{and} \quad 27 \div n = 3.$$

Exercises

1. Find the quotient of $28 \div 7$ by using the repeated-subtraction process.

2. Write each number sentence as an equation involving multiplication.
   (a) $16 \div 2 = n$.   (b) $34 \div 17 = t$.
   (c) $72 \div 18 = y$.   (d) $a \div b = c$.

3. Write each number sentence as an equation involving division.
   (a) $d \times 17 = 51$.   (b) $g \times b = 39$.
   (c) $26 \times 13 = n$.   (d) $r \times s = t$.

4. Find a whole number as a replacement for the variable such that the statement will be true.

(**a**) $7 \times \square = 56$.   (**b**) $56 \div \square = 7$.   (**c**) $\square \times 6 = 24$.

(**d**) $\square = 24 \div 6$.   (**e**) $791 \div 7 = \square$.   (**f**) $\square \times 7 = 791$.

5-15 Inverse Operations

Consider the statements $3 \times 2 = 6$ and $6 \div 3 = 2$; that is, $(3 \times 2) \div 3 = 2$. Notice that multiplying by 3 and dividing by 3 "undo" each other. That is, we start with 2, multiply by 3 to obtain 6, then divide by 3 and obtain 2. The two operations have the same net effect as the operation of multiplying by 1. Therefore, we state that multiplying by a given number and dividing the product by that same number are **inverse operations**. Similarly, dividing by a given number and multiplying the product by that same number are inverse operations. For many years we have checked division problems by multiplication, that is, by an application of the principle of inverse operations as shown in the example below.

Check

$$\begin{array}{r} 3 \\ 8\overline{)24} \\ 24 \\ \hline 0 \end{array} \qquad \begin{array}{r} 3 \\ \times\ 8 \\ \hline 24 \end{array}$$

In general, we say that multiplication is the inverse operation of division, and division is the inverse operation of multiplication.

Understanding that multiplication and division are inverse operations allows us to determine unknown division facts from our knowledge of multiplication facts, by finding missing factors. In other words, a division problem may always be thought of as a multiplication problem with the product and one factor known:

$$10 \div 2 = 5 \text{ because } 5 \times 2 = 10,$$
$$16 \div 8 = 2 \text{ because } 2 \times 8 = 16,$$
$$28 \div 7 = 4 \text{ because } 4 \times 7 = 28,$$
$$45 \div 15 = 3 \text{ because } 3 \times 15 = 45.$$

Exercises

1. Indicate whether each statement is true or false.

(**a**) If $3 \times 4 = 12$, then $12 \div 3 = 4$ and $(3 \times 4) \div 3 = 4$.

(**b**) If $63 \div 7 = 9$, then $7 \times 9 = 63$ and $(63 \div 7) \times 7 = 63$.

(**c**) If $5 \times 15 = 75$, then $75 \div 5 = 15$ and $(5 \times 15) \div 75 = 5$.

(**d**) If $98 \div 7 = 14$, then $7 \times 14 = 98$ and $(98 \div 7) \times 7 = 98$.

2. If you multiply a natural number n by 8, what must you do to the product to obtain n?

3. If you divide a natural number n by 23, what must you do to the quotient to obtain n?

5-16 Principles of Division of Whole Numbers

Although multiplication and division are closely related operations, certain differences become obvious when we consider division with respect to some of the basic principles that hold for multiplication.

Commutative principle Since $32 \div 4 \neq 4 \div 32$, division of whole numbers is not commutative.

Associative principle We may observe that in the following example the associative principle does not hold for division of whole numbers:

$$18 \div (9 \div 3) \neq (18 \div 9) \div 3 \text{ because } 18 \div 3 \neq 2 \div 3.$$

Identity element We have already agreed that $a \times 1 = a$ for any whole number a. In the equations $4 \div 1 = 4, 5 \div 1 = 5$, and $6 \div 1 = 6$ it appears that any whole number divided by 1 produces that whole number again. Thus we assume that there exists an identity element for the division of whole numbers. This element is 1. For each whole number a, $a \div 1 = a$.

Principle of closure If the set of whole numbers is to be closed with respect to division, there must exist a whole number for the quotient of every two whole numbers. Clearly, there is no whole number equal to $1 \div 2, 2 \div 3$, or $5 \div 6$. Therefore, we conclude that quotients of whole numbers do not always exist within the set of whole numbers and that the set of whole numbers is not closed with respect to division.

Distributive principle of division over addition Since the operation of division is not commutative, we have to consider two cases of distributing division over addition. In the first case we try to distribute from the left:

$$18 \div (6 + 2) \neq (18 \div 6) + (18 \div 2) \text{ since } 18 \div 8 \neq 3 + 9.$$

Hence, we see that the operation of division is not distributive from the left over the operation of addition. In the second case we try to distribute from the right:

$$(12 + 3) \div 3 = (12 \div 3) + (3 \div 3) \text{ because } 15 \div 3 = 4 + 1.$$

In more advanced texts it is proved that division is distributive from the right over the operation of addition.

Exercises

1. Write a number sentence to illustrate that each of these principles does not hold for division of whole numbers.

    (a) Commutative.   **(b)** Associative.   **(c)** Closure.

2. Indicate whether each statement is true or false.

    (a) $8 \div 2 \neq 2 \div 8$.

    (b) $24 \div (8 + 4) = (24 \div 8) + (24 \div 4)$.

    (c) $54 \div (18 \div 3) > (54 \div 18) \div 3$.

    (d) $(45 + 18) \div 9 = (45 \div 9) + (18 \div 9)$.

    (e) $14 \div 1 = 1 \div 14$.

    (f) $2 \div (1 + 1) = (1 + 1) \div 2$.

    (g) $(6 \div 1) \div 1 = 6 \div (1 \div 1)$.

    (h) $17 \times (1 + 1) = (17 \div 1) + (17 \div 1)$.

5-17 Division by Zero

The mathematician considers division by zero to be meaningless in our number system. The statement $5 \div 0 = n$ is equivalent to the statement $0 \times n = 5$. Since for every whole number n we have $0 \times n = 0$, we cannot have $0 \times n = 5$ for any whole number n. Therefore, to insure consistency in our number system, division by zero is excluded.

Notice that $0 \div 0 = n$ is equivalent to $0 \times n = 0$, which is true for every whole number n. For example,

$$0 \div 0 = 1 \text{ because } 0 \times 1 = 0,$$

$$0 \div 0 = 2 \text{ because } 0 \times 2 = 0,$$

$$0 \div 0 = 3 \text{ because } 0 \times 3 = 0.$$

To insure that quotients will represent unique numbers, we consider $0 \div 0$ as meaningless and thus as not defined. Since division by zero has been excluded, the denominator of a fractional number may never be zero or equivalent to zero. The following is a summary of the operations with zero, where n represents any whole number.

$$n + 0 = n$$

$$n - 0 = n$$

$$0 \times n = 0$$

$$0 \div n = 0 \quad \text{(provided } n \neq 0)$$

$$n \div 0 \quad \quad \text{not defined}$$

$0 \div 0$ not defined

0^0 not defined (recall from Chapter 3 that $A^0 = 1$
                   by definition, except when $A = 0$)

Exercise

1. Indicate whether each statement is true or false for every natural number n.

(a) $0 \div n = 0$.   (b) $\dfrac{n \times 0}{n} + n = n$.   (c) $\dfrac{n \times 0}{0} = n$.

5-18 Understanding the Division Algorism

We mentioned previously that division of whole numbers is frequently introduced as a process of repeated subtraction. The purpose of this approach is to improve the student's understanding of the usual division algorisms. The student should be able, in fact, to discover short-cut methods of working division problems for himself, if he understands the repeated-subtraction process.

In the case of $36 \div 9$, the repeated-subtraction process looks like the following.

$$
\begin{array}{rc}
36 & \\
-\ 9 & 1 \\
\hline
27 & \\
-\ 9 & 1 \\
\hline
18 & \\
-\ 9 & 1 \\
\hline
9 & \\
-\ 9 & 1 \\
\hline
0 & 4 \\
\end{array}
$$

We see that 9 is subtracted 4 times from 36 before we get a remainder of 0. Hence, we conclude that $36 \div 9 = 4$. A student with a fair knowledge of the multiplication facts might discover a shorter method for working this same problem. Perhaps he would use the procedure below.

$$
\begin{array}{rc}
9)\ \ 36 & \\
-18 & 2 \\
\hline
18 & \\
-18 & 2 \\
\hline
0 & 4 \\
\end{array}
$$

Since this student knew that $9 \times 2 = 18$, he saw no need to make separate subtractions of 9 each time; hence, he reduced the number of subtractions.

With an example such as $176 \div 16$ this same student might apply his new process again in an effort to shorten the division procedure. Perhaps he would set the problem up as follows.

```
16) 176                        16) 176
    −80  │ 5                       −160 │ 10
    ─────                          ─────
     96                             16
    −64  │ 4        or            − 16  │ 1
    ─────                         ─────
     32                             0   │11
    −32  │ 2
    ─────
      0  │11
```

As the student's understanding improves, he will be able to refine this method of division until it resembles the commonly used algorism. This is illustrated in the next examples.

```
Example 1    238) 5712                Example 2    238) 5712
                 −2380 │ 10                              −4760 │ 20
                 ──────                                  ──────
                  3332                                    952
                 −2380 │ 10                             − 952 │ 4
                 ──────                                  ─────
                  952                                      0   │24
                 − 714 │ 3
                 ─────
                  238
                 − 238 │ 1
                 ─────
                   0   │24
```

```
                  24                                     24
Example 3    238) 5712                Example 4    238) 5712
                 −4760                                 − 476
                 ─────                                 ─────
                  952                                    952
                 − 952                                 −952
                 ─────                                 ─────
                   0                                     0
```

Example 1 illustrates the "guessing" method of working the problem using the repeated-subtraction approach. In Example 2 the student obviously knows his multiplication quite well, and the repeated-subtraction method very closely resembles the usual division algorism, which is illustrated in Examples 3 and 4.

Example 3 points out that our division algorism takes care of place value in the quotient. The 2 in the quotient actually represents 2 tens, because of its position; hence, the product of 2×238 is actually 20×238; that is, 4,760. Example 4 illustrates the streamlined version of our division algorism, which is justified by our understanding of such processes as shown in Examples 1, 2, and 3.

The usual division algorism, illustrated in Example 4, is highly recommended; however, the student should understand "why" it works, and the use of correct terminology should be emphasized. The "goes into" description of division should be discouraged, because it does not convey a precise mathematical idea.

Exercises

1. Find each quotient by using the repeated-subtraction process.

   (a) $15 \div 3$.   (b) $76 \div 19$.   (c) $1,728 \div 216$.

2. For $c \div d$, the division algorism gives us the largest whole number q such that $q \times d \leq c$. If $q \times d = c$, then q is the missing factor and there is no remainder. If $q \times d < c$, then q is the quotient and there is a remainder r such that $0 \leq r < d$ (read "zero is less than or equal to r and r is less than d"). Hence, $c = (q \times d) + r$, where r is greater than or equal to 0. Write the number sentence corresponding to $c = (q \times d) + r$ for each of the following.

   (a) $392 \div 8$.   (b) $923 \div 27$.   (c) $826 \div 42$.   (d) $51 \div 79$.

5-19 Multiplication and Division of Integers

There are three types of product that involve the multiplication of integers:

   (1) The product of two positive integers or of a positive integer and zero.
   (2) The product of a negative integer and a positive integer or of a negative integer and zero.
   (3) The product of two negative integers.

Since we have already worked with the first case, when we dealt with multiplication of whole numbers (Section 5-1), the following discussion will concentrate on the other two possibilities for the multiplication of integers. Some of the blocks in the following table have been filled in as a result of our understanding of the multiplication of whole numbers.

×	-3	-2	-1	0	1	2	3
-3							
-2							
-1							
0				0	0	0	0
1				0	1	2	3
2				0	2	4	6
3				0	3	6	9

In order to complete the table, we will look for patterns that exist and assume that these patterns are reliable. We observe in the right-hand column that each number is three less than the number represented below it. Applying this notion to the empty blocks in this column, we have

3
⁻9
⁻6
⁻3
0
3
6
9

In a like manner, the corresponding row would become

3	⁻9	⁻6	⁻3	0	3	6	9

If we extend this pattern to the remainder of the empty blocks, the table may be completed as follows.

×	⁻3	⁻2	⁻1	0	1	2	3
⁻3	9	6	3	0	⁻3	⁻6	⁻9
⁻2	6	4	2	0	⁻2	⁻4	⁻6
⁻1	3	2	1	0	⁻1	⁻2	⁻3
0	0	0	0	0	0	0	0
1	⁻3	⁻2	⁻1	0	1	2	3
2	⁻6	⁻4	⁻2	0	2	4	6
3	⁻9	⁻6	⁻3	0	3	6	9

By studying the completed table carefully we should be able to discover a pattern in the multiplication of the following:

(1) A positive integer and a positive integer.
(2) A positive integer and a negative integer.
(3) A negative integer and a negative integer.

Division of integers may be considered as the operation that is the inverse of multiplication. If we consider division problems as multiplication problems, then the rules that we stated for the multiplication of integers would apply to division of integers. For example, $9 \div {}^-3 = \square$ may be thought of as another way of writing $^-3 \times \square = 9$. From the previously developed multiplication table for integers we see that the variable $\square$ equals $^-3$, because $^-3 \times {}^-3 = 9$.

Exercises

1. Based on the patterns that develop in the multiplication table for integers, state a rule for each of the three types of multiplication problem involving integers.

2. Find each product.
   (a) $3 \times {}^-7$.
   (b) $^-8 \times {}^-5$.
   (c) $^-2 \times 27$.
   (d) $^-4 \times {}^-5 \times {}^-7$.
   (e) $^-9 \times 6 \times {}^-10$.
   (f) $19 \times 12 \times {}^-6$.

3. Find each quotient.
   (a) $18 \div {}^-3$.
   (b) $^-52 \div {}^-13$.
   (c) $^-28 \div 7$.
   (d) $^-3 \div 0$.
   (e) $0 \div {}^-16$.
   (f) $972 \div 18$.

4. Find an integer as a replacement for the variable, such that the statement will be true.
   (a) $12 \times {}^-12 - \square$.
   (b) $\square \div {}^-8 - 1$.
   (c) $^-19 \times \square = {}^-437$.
   (d) $^-7 \times \square = 0$.
   (e) $\square \div {}^-24 = 0$.
   (f) $^-11 \times \square = 121$.

5-20 Summary of Principles of Multiplication and Division

The table below presents a summary of principles of multiplication and division for integers. The letters a, b, and c represent arbitrary integers, where $a \neq b$, $b \neq c$, $a \neq 0$, $b \neq 0$, and $c \neq 0$.

Principle	*Multiplication*	*Division*
Closure and uniqueness	$a \times b$ is a unique integer.	$a \div b$ is not always a unique integer. Note: $a \div b$ is a unique number, but it is not necessarily an integer.
Commutativity	$a \times b = b \times a$.	$a \div b \neq b \div a$.
Associativity	$(a \times b) \times c = a \times (b \times c)$.	$(a \div b) \div c \neq a \div (b \div c)$.
Identity element	$a \times 1 = a$.	$a \div 1 = a$.
Distributivity	$a \times (b + c)$ $= (a \times b) + (a \times c)$.	From the left: $a \div (b + c)$ $\neq (a \div b) + (a \div c)$. From the right: $(b + c) \div a$ $= (b \div a) + (c \div a)$.

The following table summarizes the application of the principles of closure, commutativity, and associativity to the multiplication and division of whole numbers and integers.

Principle and Operation	Set of Whole Numbers	Set of Integers
Closed under multiplication	Yes	Yes
Closed under division	No	No
Multiplication is commutative	Yes	Yes
Division is commutative	No	No
Multiplication is associative	Yes	Yes
Division is associative	No	No

Rational Number System

Quotients $c \div b$, where c and b are whole numbers and $b \neq 0$, have been defined as $c \div b = a$, where $a \times b = c$. We have mentioned that the quotient a does not always exist in the set of whole numbers. For example, if $c = 4$ and $b = 5$, then there is no whole number a such that $a \times 5 = 4$. Therefore, we must construct an extension of our number system, if each equation of the form $a \times b = c$ is to have a unique solution when $b \neq 0$. In other words, we must try to develop a set of numbers that is closed under the operation of division by any number other than zero.

6-1 Rational Numbers

The set of **rational numbers** consists of all numbers that may be expressed in the form $\frac{a}{b}$, where the *numerator a* and the *denominator b* are integers and $b \neq 0$. This set of numbers is constructed in order that the operation of division (except division by zero) may always be possible. Note that $\frac{a}{b}$ means $a \div b$.

We should observe that the set of natural numbers, the set of whole numbers, and the set of integers may be considered as subsets of the set of rational numbers. For example, the natural number 6 may be expressed in the form $\frac{6}{1}$ and thus is a rational number, and, for any natural number n, $n = \frac{n}{1}$. The integer $^-7$ may be expressed as $\frac{^-7}{1}$ and thus is a rational num-

111

ber, and, for any integer k, $k = \dfrac{k}{1}$. We should also note that $\dfrac{k}{k} = 1$ for any integer $k \neq 0$.

The set of rational numbers consists of two major subsets:

(1) The set of *nonnegative rational numbers*, such as

$$\frac{0}{2}, \frac{4}{9}, \frac{1}{2}, \frac{3}{5}, \frac{7}{7}, \frac{9}{1}, \frac{11}{4}.$$

(2) The set of *negative rational numbers*, such as

$$\frac{^-4}{3}, \frac{^-7}{8}, \frac{^-8}{1}, \frac{^-1}{10}, \frac{5}{^-9}, \frac{^-15}{3}, \frac{11}{^-12}.$$

The set of **nonnegative integers** consists of zero and the positive integers.

6-2 Fractional Numbers and Fractional Numerals

The set of rational numbers also includes many numbers that are not natural numbers, whole numbers, or integers. Some examples of these are

$$\frac{1}{2}, \frac{2}{3}, \frac{3}{4}, \frac{9}{7}, \frac{^-5}{6}, \frac{7}{^-8}, \frac{^-9}{^-5}.$$

We have probably been calling them fractional numbers rather than rational numbers. This is acceptable, since a **fractional number** is a number that may be expressed in the form $\dfrac{c}{d}$, where c and d represent any numbers (except $d \neq 0$). Thus, all rational numbers may be called fractional numbers.

It should be emphasized, however, that *not all* fractional numbers are rational numbers. The definition of a rational number specifies that the numerator and denominator are integers, and some fractional numbers do not satisfy this definition. For example,

$$\frac{\pi}{4}, \frac{\sqrt{3}}{2}, \text{ and } \frac{\sqrt{5}}{12}$$

are fractional numbers that are not rational numbers. Numbers that are not rational will be discussed in Chapter 8.

A fractional number is a number that is represented by a "fractional numeral" (also referred to as a "fraction"). In the past, "fraction" has been used to refer to both the number and the numeral representing the concept. To avoid confusion, we shall use the word *fraction* only when referring to the numeral. We shall use the term *fractional number* to discuss the idea of number.

The term **like fractions** refers to fractions that have identical numerals representing denominators. Likeness is a property of numerals and not a property of numbers. For example, $\dfrac{5}{9}$ and $\dfrac{7}{9}$ are like fractions, while $\dfrac{5}{9}$ and $\dfrac{10}{18}$ are unlike fractions (even though they represent the same number).

Exercises

1. State whether the fractions of each pair are like fractions or unlike fractions.

(a) $\dfrac{3}{4}$ and $\dfrac{3}{5}$.

(b) $\dfrac{2}{9}$ and $\dfrac{6}{9}$.

(c) $\dfrac{1}{2}$ and $\dfrac{3}{2}$.

(d) $\dfrac{4}{8}$ and $\dfrac{7}{14}$.

2. State whether or not each fraction represents a rational number.

(a) $\dfrac{9}{4}$.

(b) $\dfrac{2}{^-5}$.

(c) $\dfrac{\pi}{2}$.

(d) $\dfrac{^-6}{^-6}$.

6-3 Equality and Inequality of Rational Numbers

Consider the possible relations between any two rational numbers $\dfrac{a}{b}$ and $\dfrac{c}{d}$; either $\dfrac{a}{b}$ is equal to $\dfrac{c}{d}$ $\left(\text{that is, } \dfrac{a}{b} = \dfrac{c}{d}\right)$, or $\dfrac{a}{b}$ is not equal to $\dfrac{c}{d}$ $\left(\text{that is, } \dfrac{a}{b} \neq \dfrac{c}{d}\right)$. Study the following examples of relations between two rational numbers.

Example 1 $\dfrac{1}{2} = \dfrac{27}{54}$

$1 \times 54 = 2 \times 27$

$54 = 54$

Example 2 $\dfrac{1}{3} = \dfrac{2}{6}$

$1 \times 6 = 3 \times 2$

$6 = 6$

Example 3 $\dfrac{2}{3} \neq \dfrac{3}{4}$

$2 \times 4 \neq 3 \times 3$

$8 \neq 9$

Example 4 $\dfrac{1}{2} \neq \dfrac{9}{16}$

$1 \times 16 \neq 2 \times 9$

$16 \neq 18$

In Example 1, we observe that $\dfrac{1}{2} = \dfrac{27}{54}$ and $1 \times 54 = 2 \times 27$, whereas, in Example 3, $\dfrac{2}{3} \neq \dfrac{3}{4}$ and $2 \times 4 \neq 3 \times 3$. In general, we say that $\dfrac{a}{b} = \dfrac{c}{d}$ if and only if $a \times d = b \times c$, and it follows that $\dfrac{a}{b} \neq \dfrac{c}{d}$ if and only if $a \times d \neq b \times c$. We should note that the products $a \times d$ and $b \times c$ are products of integers.

If $\dfrac{a}{b} \neq \dfrac{c}{d}$, we may go one step further and state that $\dfrac{a}{b} > \dfrac{c}{d}$ or $\dfrac{a}{b} < \dfrac{c}{d}$. Thus, we say that the set of rational numbers is **ordered**; that is, if we have two rational numbers, one is either less than, greater than, or equal to the other. Consider the following examples.

Example 5 $\dfrac{2}{3} > \dfrac{7}{11}$ **Example 6** $\dfrac{-3}{5} < \dfrac{-4}{9}$

$2 \times 11 > 3 \times 7$ $-3 \times 9 < 5 \times {}^-4$

$22 > 21$ $-27 < {}^-20$

In Example 5, we observe that $\dfrac{2}{3} > \dfrac{7}{11}$ and $2 \times 11 > 3 \times 7$, whereas, in Example 6, $\dfrac{-3}{5} < \dfrac{-4}{9}$ and $-3 \times 9 < 5 \times {}^-4$. In general, when $b > 0$ and $d > 0$, we make the definition

$$\frac{a}{b} > \frac{c}{d}, \qquad \text{if and only if } a \times d > b \times c,$$

and it follows that

$$\frac{a}{b} < \frac{c}{d}, \qquad \text{if and only if } a \times d < b \times c.$$

Exercises

1. Indicate whether each of these statements is true or false.

   (a) $\dfrac{9}{39} = \dfrac{6}{26}$.

   (b) $\dfrac{-31}{79} = \dfrac{-113}{317}$.

   (c) $\dfrac{-12}{25} > \dfrac{-11}{23}$.

   (d) $\dfrac{213}{789} < \dfrac{97}{353}$.

   (e) $\dfrac{17}{41} \neq \dfrac{35}{83}$.

   (f) $\dfrac{67}{-5} > \dfrac{141}{-11}$.

2. Use one of the symbols, $=$ or $\neq$, to indicate the relation between the rational numbers of each pair.

   (a) $\dfrac{7}{8} \bigcirc \dfrac{21}{24}$.

   (b) $\dfrac{8}{15} \bigcirc \dfrac{7}{13}$.

   (c) $\dfrac{29}{-8} \bigcirc \dfrac{177}{-51}$.

   (d) $\dfrac{9}{14} \bigcirc \dfrac{5}{8}$.

3. Use one of the symbols, $=$, $>$, or $<$, to indicate the relation between the rational numbers of each pair.

   (a) $\dfrac{6}{7} \bigcirc \dfrac{5}{8}$.

   (b) $\dfrac{18}{19} \bigcirc \dfrac{23}{24}$.

   (c) $\dfrac{-5}{4} \bigcirc \dfrac{-7}{6}$.

   (d) $\dfrac{2}{3} \bigcirc \dfrac{42}{63}$.

4. Is the set of natural numbers ordered?

5. Is the set of whole numbers ordered?

6. Is the set of integers ordered?

6-4 Numerals—the Names for Numbers

A number may have several different names, that is, numerals. Consider the abstract number concept called "threeness." Each of the following is a name for the number three: 3, III, $1 + 1 + 1$, 3×1, and $7 - 4$. Notice that $\frac{3}{1}$, $\frac{6}{2}$, $\frac{9}{3}$, $\frac{12}{4}$, and $\frac{15}{5}$ are also names for the number three. In Section 6-3 we stated that the rational numbers $\frac{a}{b}$ and $\frac{c}{d}$ are equal if and only if $a \times d = b \times c$. This definition leads us to a very useful relation of equality,

$$\frac{a}{b} = \frac{a \times k}{b \times k} \qquad \text{for any integer } k \neq 0,$$

since $a \times b \times k = b \times a \times k$. Thus, $\frac{a \times k}{b \times k}$ represents the same number as $\frac{a}{b}$, and we may find as many names for a rational number as we like. For example,

$$\frac{2}{3} = \frac{2 \times 2}{3 \times 2} = \frac{4}{6},$$

$$\frac{2}{3} = \frac{2 \times 3}{3 \times 3} = \frac{6}{9},$$

$$\frac{2}{3} = \frac{2 \times {}^-4}{3 \times {}^-4} = \frac{{}^-8}{{}^-12},$$

$$\frac{2}{3} = \frac{2 \times 19}{3 \times 19} = \frac{38}{57}.$$

The equality $\frac{a}{b} = \frac{a \times k}{b \times k}$ may be interpreted as meaning that the numerator a and the denominator b of any rational number may both be multiplied by the same integer k, where $k \neq 0$, without any change in the rational number represented. Thus we may express any rational number as a fraction with a positive integer as denominator. For example,

$$\frac{{}^-8}{{}^-12} = \frac{{}^-8 \times {}^-1}{{}^-12 \times {}^-1} = \frac{8}{12}, \qquad \frac{3}{{}^-4} = \frac{3 \times {}^-1}{{}^-4 \times {}^-1} = \frac{{}^-3}{4},$$

and so on. This allows us to apply the general statements on order relation in Section 6-3.

Two fractions that name the same number are called **equivalent fractions**. Thus, $\frac{2}{3}$, $\frac{4}{6}$, $\frac{6}{9}$, $\frac{{}^-8}{{}^-12}$, and $\frac{38}{57}$ are called equivalent fractions.

The relation $\frac{a \times k}{b \times k} = \frac{a}{b}$ allows us to express rational numbers in lower terms (that is, with smaller numbers for numerator and denominator) by finding common factors k in both the numerator and denominator. For example,

$$\frac{6}{9} = \frac{2 \times 3}{3 \times 3} = \frac{2}{3},$$

$$\frac{48}{64} = \frac{3 \times 16}{4 \times 16} = \frac{3}{4},$$

$$\frac{29}{58} = \frac{1 \times 29}{2 \times 29} = \frac{1}{2},$$

$$\frac{75}{25} = \frac{3 \times 25}{1 \times 25} = \frac{3}{1}.$$

The equality $\frac{a \times k}{b \times k} = \frac{a}{b}$ means that both the numerator $a \times k$ and the denominator $b \times k$ of any rational number may be divided by the same integer k, where $k \neq 0$, without changing the rational number represented. Consider the following examples.

Example 1 $\frac{18}{27} = \frac{18 \div 3}{27 \div 3} = \frac{6}{9}$ **Example 2** $\frac{18}{27} = \frac{18 \div 9}{27 \div 9} = \frac{2}{3}$

Example 3 $\frac{7}{13} = \frac{7 \div 1}{13 \div 1} = \frac{7}{13}$

In Example 1 the rational number $\frac{18}{27}$ has been expressed in *lower terms*. It is important to note that in Example 2, $\frac{18}{27}$ has been expressed in **lowest terms**. A rational number is said to be in lowest terms (also called **simplest form**) when it cannot be reduced further; that is, when the greatest common factor of its numerator and denominator is 1. In Example 3 the rational number $\frac{7}{13}$ is in simplest form, since the only common factor of 7 and 13 is 1; thus, $\frac{7}{13}$ cannot be reduced further.

The greatest common factor has an important application in the renaming of a rational number. If we want to express $\frac{39}{429}$ in simplest form, we must find the largest divisor of the numerator and the denominator. The G.C.F. of 39 and 429 is the divisor we need. The factors of 39 are the set $\{1, 3, 13, 39\}$ and the factors of 429 are the set $\{1, 3, 11, 13, 33, 39, 143, 429\}$. Thus the set of the common factors of 39 and 429 is $\{1, 3, 13, 39\}$, and the G.C.F. of 39 and 429 is 39. Hence, we have

$$\frac{39}{429} = \frac{39 \div 39}{429 \div 39} = \frac{1}{11},$$

where $\frac{1}{11}$ is the simplest form of the rational number $\frac{39}{429}$.

Exercises

1. Give three different names for each rational number.

(a) 7.

(b) $\frac{1}{5}$.

(c) $\frac{^{-}2}{3}$.

(d) $\frac{0}{4}$.

(e) $\frac{^{-}9}{^{-}7}$.

(f) $\frac{125}{75}$.

(g) $\frac{26}{^{-}4}$.

(h) $\frac{183}{792}$.

2. Replace the variable with an integer to make each statement true.

(a) $\frac{6}{7} = \frac{6 \times \square}{7 \times \square} = \frac{^{-}54}{^{-}63}$.

(b) $\frac{2}{3} = \frac{\square}{78}$.

(c) $\frac{\square}{6} = \frac{^{-}20}{24}$.

(d) $\frac{0}{3} = \frac{\square}{39}$.

3. Indicate whether or not each pair of fractions may be called equivalent fractions.

(a) $\frac{6}{9}$ and $\frac{38}{57}$.

(b) $\frac{25}{75}$ and $\frac{9}{29}$.

(c) $\frac{^{-}8}{^{-}12}$ and $\frac{14}{21}$.

(d) $\frac{117}{13}$ and $\frac{863}{96}$.

4. Express each rational number in simplest form.

(a) $\frac{36}{45}$.

(b) $\frac{51}{85}$.

(c) $\frac{^{-}12}{^{-}28}$.

(d) $\frac{97}{101}$.

5. Find the greatest common factor of the numerator and denominator of each rational number.

(a) $\frac{18}{24}$.

(b) $\frac{^{-}29}{66}$.

(c) $\frac{496}{368}$.

(d) $\frac{^{-}224}{^{-}784}$.

6-5 Multiplication of Rational Numbers

A readiness for the multiplication of rational numbers may be developed through activities with visual aids. Consider the rectangular model in Figure 6-1.

We observe that the large rectangular model is divided vertically into fifths and horizontally into eighths. This provides us with 40 small rectangular blocks of exactly the same size and shape within the large rectangle. Therefore, each small rectangular block is $\frac{1}{40}$ of the large rectangular model.

Suppose we have the problem $\frac{1}{5} \times \frac{7}{8} = \square$. This may be read "What is one-fifth of seven-eighths?" To represent this problem on our rectangular model, we could shade the small rectangular blocks contained within the

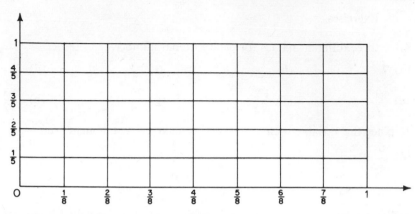

Figure 6-1

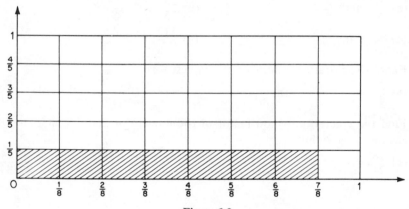

Figure 6-2

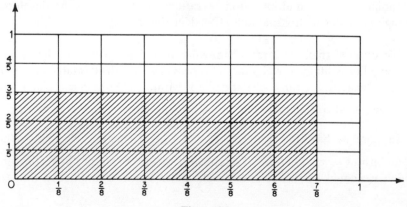

Figure 6-3

region bounded above by the horizontal line representing $\frac{1}{5}$ and bounded on the right by the vertical line representing $\frac{7}{8}$, as illustrated in Figure 6-2.

We now have 7 of the 40 small blocks shaded, as a representation of $\frac{1}{5} \times \frac{7}{8}$. Therefore, we could say that $\frac{1}{5} \times \frac{7}{8} = \frac{7}{40}$.

To represent $\frac{3}{5} \times \frac{7}{8}$ in a similar manner, our rectangular model could be shaded as in Figure 6-3. Thus, we see that $\frac{3}{5} \times \frac{7}{8} = \frac{21}{40}$.

Notice that in each of these examples we could have arrived at the same result if we had determined the product of the numerators and the product of the denominators and then expressed the result as a rational number, with the product of the numerators as its numerator and the product of the denominators as its denominator. For example,

$$\frac{1}{5} \times \frac{7}{8} = \frac{1 \times 7}{5 \times 8} = \frac{7}{40},$$

$$\frac{3}{5} \times \frac{7}{8} = \frac{3 \times 7}{5 \times 8} = \frac{21}{40}.$$

In general, for rational numbers $\frac{a}{b}$ and $\frac{c}{d}$, we define multiplication as

$$\frac{a}{b} \times \frac{c}{d} = \frac{a \times c}{b \times d} = \frac{ac}{bd}.$$

Note that the product of the numerators may be represented as an integer ac, where a and c are integers, and the product of the denominators may be represented as an integer bd, where b and d are integers different from zero. Thus the product of any two rational numbers is a rational number. This definition of multiplication of rational numbers includes multiplication of a rational number and an integer, since $\frac{a}{b} \times \frac{c}{d}$ may represent $\frac{a}{b} \times \frac{c}{1}$ where $\frac{c}{1}$ is any integer.

Exercises

1. Draw a rectangular model and shade it properly to represent the following.

    (a) $\frac{3}{4} \times \frac{2}{7}$.

    (b) $\frac{1}{2} \times \frac{2}{3}$.

2. Find each product.

    (a) $\frac{7}{9} \times \frac{5}{8}$.

    (b) $\frac{1}{5} \times \frac{3}{4}$.

    (c) $\frac{3}{5} \times \frac{5}{3}$.

    (d) $^-3 \times \frac{5}{6}$.

    (e) $\frac{7}{4} \times \frac{6}{11}$.

    (f) $\frac{1}{3} \times 5$.

    (g) $\frac{4}{7} \times \frac{^-3}{8}$.

    (h) $\frac{^-2}{3} \times \frac{^-5}{11}$.

6-6 Principles of Multiplication of Rational Numbers

We noted earlier that increased emphasis has been placed on some of the basic patterns and principles of elementary school mathematics. We also pointed out that these underlying principles would be discussed and then accepted as assumptions.

Principles of closure and uniqueness The principle of *closure* applied to the multiplication of rational numbers means that the product of any two rational numbers is also a rational number. The principle of *uniqueness* indicates that there is only one possible product when two given rational numbers are multiplied. For example, $\frac{1}{2} \times \frac{1}{3} = \frac{1}{6}$ illustrates that the factors and the product are members of the set of rational numbers. We should also note that $\frac{1}{6}$ is the only possible product when $\frac{1}{2}$ and $\frac{1}{3}$ are multiplied. Hence, the number $\frac{1}{6}$ is the *unique* product of $\frac{1}{2}$ and $\frac{1}{3}$. Notice that the number $\frac{1}{6}$ may also be expressed as $\frac{2}{12}$, $\frac{3}{18}$, $\frac{4}{24}$, and so on. In general, for the rational numbers $\frac{a}{b}$ and $\frac{c}{d}$, as explained in Section 6-5,

$$\frac{a}{b} \times \frac{c}{d} = \frac{ac}{bd},$$

where the rational number $\frac{ac}{bd}$ is the unique product of $\frac{a}{b}$ and $\frac{c}{d}$.

Commutative principle The order of the multiplication of two factors from the set of rational numbers does not change the product. In the case of $\frac{1}{2}$ and $\frac{1}{4}$, we note that

$$\frac{1}{2} \times \frac{1}{4} = \frac{1}{8} \quad \text{and} \quad \frac{1}{4} \times \frac{1}{2} = \frac{1}{8}.$$

Thus,

$$\frac{1}{2} \times \frac{1}{4} = \frac{1}{4} \times \frac{1}{2}.$$

The multiplication of rational numbers is *commutative* and, for any two rational numbers $\frac{a}{b}$ and $\frac{c}{d}$,

$$\frac{a}{b} \times \frac{c}{d} = \frac{ac}{bd} = \frac{ca}{db} = \frac{c}{d} \times \frac{a}{b}$$

since the multiplication of integers is commutative.

Associative principle If more than two rational numbers are to be multiplied, the factors are grouped for binary operations. For example, $\frac{1}{2} \times \frac{1}{3} \times \frac{1}{4}$ may be grouped for multiplication as

$$\left(\frac{1}{2} \times \frac{1}{3}\right) \times \frac{1}{4} \quad \text{or} \quad \frac{1}{2} \times \left(\frac{1}{3} \times \frac{1}{4}\right).$$

Since

$$\left(\frac{1}{2} \times \frac{1}{3}\right) \times \frac{1}{4} = \frac{1}{6} \times \frac{1}{4} = \frac{1}{24}$$

and

$$\frac{1}{2} \times \left(\frac{1}{3} \times \frac{1}{4}\right) = \frac{1}{2} \times \frac{1}{12} = \frac{1}{24},$$

we have

$$\left(\frac{1}{2} \times \frac{1}{3}\right) \times \frac{1}{4} = \frac{1}{2} \times \left(\frac{1}{3} \times \frac{1}{4}\right).$$

In general, for the rational numbers $\frac{a}{b}$, $\frac{c}{d}$, and $\frac{e}{f}$,

$$\left(\frac{a}{b} \times \frac{c}{d}\right) \times \frac{e}{f} = \frac{a}{b} \times \left(\frac{c}{d} \times \frac{e}{f}\right),$$

and we say that the multiplication of rational numbers is *associative*.

Identity element The product of any rational number and the number 1 is always the original rational number. For example,

$$\frac{1}{2} \times 1 = \frac{1}{2}, \qquad \frac{2}{3} \times 1 = \frac{2}{3}, \qquad \frac{^-3}{4} \times 1 = \frac{^-3}{4},$$

and so on. Thus,

$$\frac{a}{b} \times 1 = \frac{a}{b} \times \frac{1}{1} = \frac{a \times 1}{b \times 1} = \frac{a}{b}$$

for any rational number $\frac{a}{b}$, and 1 is called the *identity element for multiplication* of rational numbers (also referred to as the *multiplicative identity*).

Multiplication by zero The product of the number zero and any rational number is always zero. Thus, for any rational number $\frac{a}{b}$,

$$\frac{a}{b} \times 0 = \frac{a}{b} \times \frac{0}{1} = \frac{a \times 0}{b \times 1} = \frac{0}{b} = 0.$$

Multiplicative inverse In the set of rational numbers there exist pairs of numbers such that each have a product of 1. For example,

$$2 \times \frac{1}{2} = 1, \qquad \frac{1}{3} \times 3 = 1, \qquad \frac{^-2}{5} \times \frac{5}{^-2} = 1,$$

and so on. The numbers in each pair are called reciprocals of each other (also referred to as *multiplicative inverses*). Since $\frac{5}{8} \times \frac{8}{5} = 1$, $\frac{5}{8}$ is the reciprocal of $\frac{8}{5}$, and $\frac{8}{5}$ is the reciprocal of $\frac{5}{8}$. Therefore, the extension of our number system to the set of rational numbers enables us to state a new principle. For each rational number $\frac{a}{b}$, where $\frac{a}{b} \neq 0$, there exists another rational number $\frac{b}{a}$, called the **reciprocal (multiplicative inverse)** of $\frac{a}{b}$, such that

$$\frac{a}{b} \times \frac{b}{a} = \frac{ab}{ba} = \frac{ab}{ab} = 1.$$

Exercises

1. Find each product.

   (a) $\left(\frac{1}{3} \times \frac{1}{5}\right) \times \frac{3}{8}$.   (b) $\frac{1}{3} \times \left(\frac{1}{5} \times \frac{3}{8}\right)$.

2. What may be concluded from a comparison of the two answers in Exercise 1?

3. What principle of multiplication of rational numbers is suggested in Exercises 1 and 2?

4. (a) Does $\frac{5}{9} \times \frac{7}{8}$ equal a rational number?

   (b) How many different rational numbers can you find for the product of $\frac{5}{9}$ and $\frac{7}{8}$?

   (c) What principles of multiplication of rational numbers are suggested by your answers to parts (a) and (b)?

5. What is the multiplicative identity for the rational number system?

6. Calculate each product.

   (a) $\frac{2}{3} \times \frac{3}{2}$.   (b) $\frac{^-3}{8} \times \frac{5}{9}$.   (c) $\frac{5}{9} \times \frac{^-3}{8}$.

   (d) $\frac{11}{13} \times 0$.   (e) $\frac{9}{11} \times \frac{^-4}{^-4}$.   (f) $1 \times \frac{33}{77}$.

7. Find a rational number as a replacement for the variable, such that the statement will be true.

   (a) $\frac{6}{7} \times \square = 1$.   (b) $\frac{^-13}{14} \times \square = 1$.

   (c) $\frac{2}{9} \times \square = 0$.   (d) $0 \times \square = 1$.

8. When is the reciprocal of a positive number
   (a) Equal to the number?
   (b) Less than the number?
   (c) Greater than the number?

9. What rational number does not have a multiplicative inverse?

10. What is the reciprocal of

(a) $^-5$? (b) 1? (c) $\frac{23}{24}$? (d) $\frac{7}{^-8}$?

6-7 Addition of Rational Numbers

If two rational numbers are to be added, they are usually represented by like fractions whose denominators are the least common denominator. Finding the least common denominator is a problem of finding the least common multiple of the numbers represented by the denominators. Recall (Section 5-12) that the least common multiple of two or more numbers is the smallest number contained in the sets of multiples of the numbers under consideration.

A readiness for the addition of rational numbers may be developed in the primary grades through activities involving visual aids. The number line is also helpful in developing an understanding of the addition of rational numbers. To find the sum of $\frac{1}{7}$ and $\frac{3}{7}$ we find a point on the number line that represents $\frac{1}{7}$. We then move from the graph of $\frac{1}{7}$ to the right to a point that represents $\frac{3}{7}$ more. The sum of $\frac{1}{7}$ and $\frac{3}{7}$ may be determined as $\frac{4}{7}$ from the number line; $\frac{1}{7} + \frac{3}{7} = \frac{4}{7}$ (Figure 6-4).

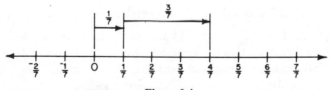

Figure 6-4

To add $\frac{2}{5}$ and $\frac{4}{5}$ on the number line, we operate in a similar manner; $\frac{2}{5} + \frac{4}{5} = \frac{6}{5}$ (Figure 6-5).

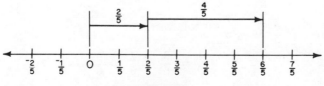

Figure 6-5

The sum of $\frac{3}{6}$ and $\frac{-2}{6}$ is represented on the number line; $\frac{3}{6} + \frac{-2}{6}$ $= \frac{1}{6}$ (Figure 6-6).

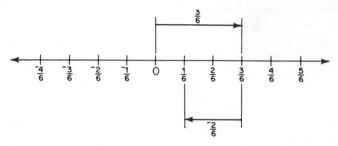

Figure 6-6

A study of these illustrations reveals that the sum of two rational numbers with the same denominator is the rational number represented by the fraction whose numerator is the sum of the numerators and whose denominator is the common denominator. In general, we write

$$\frac{a}{b} + \frac{c}{b} = \frac{a+c}{b}.$$

Observe that the sum of the numerators, $a + c$, is the sum of two integers.

Now let us consider the more difficult case of adding rational numbers represented by unlike fractions. For example, add $\frac{1}{2}$ and $\frac{1}{3}$. We cannot add these rational numbers as we did previously, because they have different denominators. We must find the least common multiple of the denominators and then find equivalent fractions with the least common multiple as the denominator for $\frac{1}{2}$ and $\frac{1}{3}$. The L.C.M. of 2 and 3 is 6. Fractions representing the multiplicative identity may be used to change unlike fractions to like fractions, once the least common multiple has been determined:

$$\frac{1}{2} \times 1 = \frac{1}{2} \times \frac{3}{3} = \frac{3}{6},$$

$$\frac{1}{3} \times 1 = \frac{1}{3} \times \frac{2}{2} = \frac{2}{6}.$$

Since $\frac{1}{2} = \frac{3}{6}$ and $\frac{1}{3} = \frac{2}{6}$, it follows that

$$\frac{1}{2} + \frac{1}{3} = \frac{3}{6} + \frac{2}{6} = \frac{5}{6}.$$

If we let $\frac{a}{b}$ and $\frac{c}{d}$ represent any two rational numbers, we may find

the sum of $\frac{a}{b}$ and $\frac{c}{d}$ as follows.

$\frac{a}{b} = \frac{a}{b} \times 1$	$\frac{c}{d} = \frac{c}{d} \times 1$	Multiplicative indentity
$\frac{a}{b} \times 1 = \frac{a}{b} \times \frac{d}{d}$	$\frac{c}{d} \times 1 = \frac{c}{d} \times \frac{b}{b}$	Substitution of $\frac{d}{d}$ for 1 and $\frac{b}{b}$ for 1, to yield a common multiple for each denominator
$\frac{a}{b} \times \frac{d}{d} = \frac{ad}{bd}$	$\frac{c}{d} \times \frac{b}{b} = \frac{cb}{db}$	Multiplication
	$\frac{cb}{db} = \frac{bc}{bd}$	Commutative principle of multiplication for the integers b, c, and d
$\frac{a}{b} + \frac{c}{d} = \frac{ad}{bd} + \frac{bc}{bd} = \frac{ad + bc}{bd}$		Definition of addition of rational numbers represented by like fractions

In general, for rational numbers $\frac{a}{b}$ and $\frac{c}{d}$, we define addition as

$$\frac{a}{b} + \frac{c}{d} = \frac{ad + bc}{bd}.$$

Note that the numerator may be represented as an integer $ad + bc$, where ad and bc are integers, and the denominator may be represented as an integer bd, where b and d are integers different from zero. Thus, the sum of any two rational numbers is a rational number. This definition of the addition of rational numbers includes the addition of an integer and a rational number, since $\frac{a}{b} + \frac{c}{d}$ may represent $\frac{a}{1} + \frac{c}{d}$, where $\frac{a}{1}$ is an integer. For example,

$$6 + \frac{2}{3} = \frac{6}{1} + \frac{2}{3} = \frac{18 + 2}{3} = \frac{20}{3} = 6\frac{2}{3}.$$

Thus the sum of an integer and a rational number such as $6 + \frac{2}{3}$ is often written $6\frac{2}{3}$, and the numeral is called a **mixed numeral**, since the numeral includes the representation of both an integer and a fractional number. All mixed numerals represent rational numbers.

Exercises

1. Represent each sum on a number line.

(a) $\dfrac{4}{3} + \dfrac{2}{3}$.   (b) $\dfrac{2}{7} + \dfrac{4}{7}$.   (c) $\dfrac{5}{6} + \dfrac{-4}{6}$.

2. Find each sum.

(a) $\dfrac{3}{7} + \dfrac{9}{7}$.   (b) $\dfrac{6}{13} + \dfrac{-5}{13}$.

(c) $\dfrac{1}{8} + \dfrac{4}{8}$.   (d) $\dfrac{3}{17} + \dfrac{5}{17} + \dfrac{6}{17}$.

3. What is the lowest common denominator of

(a) $\dfrac{5}{6}$ and $\dfrac{7}{8}$?   (b) $\dfrac{7}{12}$ and $\dfrac{2}{3}$?   (c) $\dfrac{8}{15}$ and $\dfrac{4}{9}$?

4. Find each sum.

(a) $\dfrac{4}{9}$ (b) $\dfrac{11}{5}$ (c) $\dfrac{-13}{16}$ (d) 7 (e) $\dfrac{7}{10}$ (f) $\dfrac{3}{8}$

$+\dfrac{5}{6}$ $+\dfrac{10}{3}$ $+\dfrac{7}{12}$ $+\dfrac{5}{9}$ $+\dfrac{4}{15}$ $+\dfrac{-2}{3}$

6-8 Principles of Addition of Rational Numbers

The following principles of addition for rational numbers are illustrated and assumed. In more advanced courses, these principles may be proved using our definitions and the principles of addition and multiplication of integers.

Principles of closure and uniqueness The principle of *closure* applied to the addition of rational numbers means that the sum of any two rational numbers in also a rational number. The principle of *uniqueness* indicates that there is only one possible sum when two rational numbers are added. For example, $\dfrac{1}{5} + \dfrac{2}{5} = \dfrac{3}{5}$ illustrates that the addends and the sum are elements of the set of rational numbers. We should also note that $\dfrac{3}{5}$ is the only possible sum when $\dfrac{1}{5}$ and $\dfrac{2}{5}$ are added; that is, the number $\dfrac{3}{5}$ is the unique sum of $\dfrac{1}{5}$ and $\dfrac{2}{5}$. Notice that the number $\dfrac{3}{5}$ may also be expressed as $\dfrac{6}{10}, \dfrac{9}{15}, \dfrac{12}{20}$, and so on. In general, for the rational numbers $\dfrac{a}{b}$ and $\dfrac{c}{d}$, as explained in Section 6-7,

$$\frac{a}{b} + \frac{c}{d} = \frac{ad + bc}{bd},$$

where the rational number $\dfrac{ad + bc}{bd}$ is the unique sum of $\dfrac{a}{b}$ and $\dfrac{c}{d}$.

Commutative principle The order of the addition of two rational numbers does not affect the sum. This may be illustrated by the case of $\frac{2}{7}$ and $\frac{4}{7}$. Since

$$\frac{2}{7} + \frac{4}{7} = \frac{6}{7} \quad \text{and} \quad \frac{4}{7} + \frac{2}{7} = \frac{6}{7},$$

we have

$$\frac{2}{7} + \frac{4}{7} = \frac{4}{7} + \frac{2}{7}.$$

Addition of rational numbers is *commutative* and, for any two rational numbers $\frac{a}{b}$ and $\frac{c}{d}$,

$$\frac{a}{b} + \frac{c}{d} = \frac{c}{d} + \frac{a}{b}.$$

Associative principle Three or more rational numbers may be grouped differently for addition, without changing their order, and the sum will not be affected. For example,

$$\frac{2}{9} + \frac{4}{9} + \frac{5}{9}$$

may be grouped for addition as

$$\left(\frac{2}{9} + \frac{4}{9}\right) + \frac{5}{9} \quad \text{or} \quad \frac{2}{9} + \left(\frac{4}{9} + \frac{5}{9}\right).$$

Since

$$\left(\frac{2}{9} + \frac{4}{9}\right) + \frac{5}{9} = \frac{6}{9} + \frac{5}{9} = \frac{11}{9}$$

and

$$\frac{2}{9} + \left(\frac{4}{9} + \frac{5}{9}\right) = \frac{2}{9} + \frac{9}{9} = \frac{11}{9},$$

we have

$$\left(\frac{2}{9} + \frac{4}{9}\right) + \frac{5}{9} = \frac{2}{9} + \left(\frac{4}{9} + \frac{5}{9}\right).$$

In general, for the rational numbers $\frac{a}{b}$, $\frac{c}{d}$, and $\frac{e}{f}$,

$$\left(\frac{a}{b} + \frac{c}{d}\right) + \frac{e}{f} = \frac{a}{b} + \left(\frac{c}{d} + \frac{e}{f}\right),$$

and we say that the addition of rational numbers is *associative*.

Identity element The sum of any rational number and the number zero is always the original rational number. For example,

$$\frac{1}{2} + 0 = \frac{1}{2}, \quad \frac{3}{4} + 0 = \frac{3}{4}, \quad \frac{-7}{9} + 0 = \frac{-7}{9},$$

and so on. Thus, $\frac{a}{b} + 0 = \frac{a}{b}$ for any rational number $\frac{a}{b}$, and 0 is called the *identity element for addition* of rational numbers (also referred to as the *additive identity*).

Distributive principle of multiplication over addition Multiplication is *distributive* over addition for the set of rational numbers. For example,

$$\frac{1}{3} \times \left(\frac{3}{4} + \frac{2}{4}\right) = \frac{1}{3} \times \left(\frac{5}{4}\right) = \frac{5}{12}$$

and

$$\frac{1}{3} \times \left(\frac{3}{4} + \frac{2}{4}\right) = \left(\frac{1}{3} \times \frac{3}{4}\right) + \left(\frac{1}{3} \times \frac{2}{4}\right) = \frac{3}{12} + \frac{2}{12} = \frac{5}{12}.$$

In general, we may distribute multiplication over addition from both the left and the right when we have the rational numbers $\frac{a}{b}, \frac{c}{d}$, and $\frac{e}{f}$. In other words, we have a left distributive principle,

$$\frac{a}{b} \times \left(\frac{c}{d} + \frac{e}{f}\right) = \left(\frac{a}{b} \times \frac{c}{d}\right) + \left(\frac{a}{b} \times \frac{e}{f}\right),$$

and also a right distributive principle,

$$\left(\frac{c}{d} + \frac{e}{f}\right) \times \frac{a}{b} = \left(\frac{c}{d} \times \frac{a}{b}\right) + \left(\frac{e}{f} \times \frac{a}{b}\right).$$

We speak of "the distributive principle" when referring to either of these cases.

Exercises

1. Find each sum.

   (a) $\frac{6}{7} + \frac{3}{91}$.   (b) $\frac{3}{91} + \frac{6}{7}$.

2. What may be concluded from a comparison of the two answers in Exercise 1?

3. What principle of addition for rational numbers is suggested in Exercises 1 and 2?

4. (a) Does $\frac{5}{6} + \frac{7}{8}$ equal a rational number?

   (b) How many different rational numbers can you find for the sum of $\frac{5}{6}$ and $\frac{7}{8}$?

   (c) What principles of addition for rational numbers are suggested by your answers to parts (a) and (b)?

5. What is the additive identity for the rational number system?

6. Find each sum.

(a) $\left(\dfrac{1}{2} + \dfrac{1}{3}\right) + \dfrac{1}{4}.$ (b) $\dfrac{1}{2} + \left(\dfrac{1}{3} + \dfrac{1}{4}\right).$

7. What may be concluded from a comparison of the two answers in Exercise 6?

8. What principle of addition for rational numbers is suggested in Exercises 6 and 7?

9. Compute the following.

(a) $\dfrac{2}{3} + 1.$ (b) $\dfrac{3}{4} + 0.$ (c) $\dfrac{9}{17} \times \dfrac{7}{8}.$

(d) $\left(\dfrac{5}{17} + \dfrac{4}{17}\right) \times \dfrac{7}{8}.$ (e) $\dfrac{7}{8} \times \left(\dfrac{5}{17} + \dfrac{4}{17}\right).$

6-9 Subtraction of Rational Numbers

The negative of the rational number $\dfrac{3}{4}$ may be expressed in any one of these ways:

$$-\dfrac{3}{4}, \quad \dfrac{^-3}{4}, \quad \dfrac{3}{^-4}.$$

The form $\dfrac{^-3}{4}$ is generally preferred for the sake of consistency and convenience.

Two rational numbers are called *additive inverses* of each other if their sum is zero. In the example

$$\dfrac{3}{4} + \dfrac{^-3}{4} = \dfrac{3 + {}^-3}{4} = \dfrac{0}{4} = 0,$$

$\dfrac{^-3}{4}$ is the additive inverse of $\dfrac{3}{4}$, and $\dfrac{3}{4}$ is the additive inverse of $\dfrac{^-3}{4}$. Recall (Section 4-13) that the additive inverse of a number is also called *the negative of* the number. Thus $\dfrac{^-3}{4}$ is the negative of $\dfrac{3}{4}$, and $\dfrac{3}{4}$ is the negative of $\dfrac{^-3}{4}$.

Every rational number $\dfrac{a}{b}$ has an additive inverse $\dfrac{^-a}{b}$, since the positive rational numbers may be placed in one-to-one correspondence with the negative rational numbers, and since $0 + 0 = 0$. Thus, as in the case of integers, we may define subtraction of rational numbers in terms of an equivalent addition statement. In general, for rational numbers $\dfrac{a}{b}$ and $\dfrac{c}{d}$,

$$\dfrac{a}{b} - \dfrac{c}{d} = \dfrac{a}{b} + \dfrac{^-c}{d},$$

and we recall (Section 6-7) that

$$\frac{a}{b} + \frac{{}^-c}{d} = \frac{ad + b({}^-c)}{bd}.$$

Note that the products ad, $b({}^-c)$, and bd are products of integers.

Perhaps the following examples will clarify the definition of subtraction of rational numbers.

Example 1 Find the difference $\dfrac{7}{9} - \dfrac{3}{6}$.

$$\frac{7}{9} - \frac{3}{6} = \frac{7}{9} + \frac{{}^-3}{6}$$

(Note that $\dfrac{{}^-3}{6}$ is the additive

$$= \frac{(7 \times 6) + (9 \times {}^-3)}{9 \times 6}$$

inverse of $\dfrac{3}{6}$.)

$$= \frac{42 + {}^-27}{54}$$

$$= \frac{15}{54}.$$

If the simplified form of $\dfrac{15}{54}$ is desired, we may divide both the numerator 15 and the denominator 54 by 3; thus,

$$\frac{15}{54} - \frac{15 \div 3}{54 \div 3} = \frac{5}{18}.$$

Example 2 Find the difference $\dfrac{2}{3} - \dfrac{{}^-3}{4}$.

$$\frac{2}{3} - \frac{{}^-3}{4} = \frac{2}{3} + \frac{3}{4}$$

(Note that $\dfrac{3}{4}$ is the additive

$$= \frac{(2 \times 4) + (3 \times 3)}{3 \times 4}$$

inverse of $\dfrac{{}^-3}{4}$.)

$$= \frac{8 + 9}{12}$$

$$= \frac{17}{12}.$$

Example 3 Find the difference $\dfrac{{}^-4}{5} - \dfrac{3}{7}$.

$$\frac{{}^-4}{5} - \frac{3}{7} = \frac{{}^-4}{5} + \frac{{}^-3}{7}$$

(Note that $\dfrac{{}^-3}{7}$ is the additive

$$= \frac{({}^-4 \times 7) + (5 \times {}^-3)}{5 \times 7}$$

inverse of $\dfrac{3}{7}$.)

$$= \frac{{}^-28 + {}^-15}{35}$$

$$= \frac{{}^-43}{35}.$$

Example 4 Find the difference $\frac{^-1}{2} - \frac{^-3}{11}$.

$$\frac{^-1}{2} - \frac{^-3}{11} = \frac{^-1}{2} + \frac{3}{11}$$

(Note that $\frac{3}{11}$ is the additive

$$= \frac{(^-1 \times 11) + (2 \times 3)}{2 \times 11}$$

inverse of $\frac{^-3}{11}$.)

$$= \frac{^-11 + 6}{22}$$

$$= \frac{^-5}{22}.$$

We may also use a number line to represent the subtraction of rational numbers. The difference $\frac{1}{3} - \frac{2}{3}$ is pictured on the number line (Figure 6-7);

$$\frac{1}{3} - \frac{2}{3} = \frac{1}{3} + \frac{^-2}{3} = \frac{1 + ^-2}{3} = \frac{^-1}{3}.$$

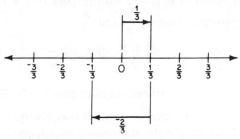

Figure 6-7

In general, the difference between two rational numbers with the same denominator is

$$\frac{a}{b} - \frac{c}{b} = \frac{a}{b} + \frac{^-c}{b} = \frac{a + ^-c}{b}.$$

Exercises

1. Represent each difference on a number line.

   (a) $\frac{6}{7} - \frac{2}{7}.$ (b) $\frac{^-2}{5} - \frac{^-4}{5}.$ (c) $\frac{9}{4} - \frac{5}{4}.$

2. Find each difference.

   (a) $\frac{12}{7} - \frac{9}{7}.$ (b) $\frac{11}{13} - \frac{5}{13}.$ (c) $\frac{7}{9} - \frac{7}{9}.$

   (d) $\frac{4}{5} - \frac{1}{5}.$ (e) $\frac{5}{8} - \frac{^-3}{8}.$ (f) $\frac{^-12}{7} - \frac{9}{7}.$

3. Find each difference.

(a) $\dfrac{2}{3} - \dfrac{3}{8}$.

(b) $\dfrac{13}{4} - 0$.

(c) $\dfrac{^-12}{9} - \dfrac{^-4}{3}$.

(d) $\begin{array}{r} \dfrac{6}{13} \\ -\dfrac{2}{7} \\ \hline \end{array}$

(e) $\begin{array}{r} \dfrac{9}{10} \\ -\dfrac{14}{15} \\ \hline \end{array}$

(f) $\begin{array}{r} \dfrac{1}{12} \\ -\dfrac{3}{32} \\ \hline \end{array}$

6-10 Principles of Subtraction of Rational Numbers

Recall (Section 4-10) that a basic principle of mathematics does not hold for a given operation on the elements of a set of numbers if it leads us to a false conclusion in at least one case.

Principles of closure and uniqueness The difference between any two given rational numbers is always a *unique* rational number. Thus we may say that the set of rational numbers is *closed* with respect to the operation of subtraction. For any rational numbers $\dfrac{a}{b}$ and $\dfrac{c}{d}$,

$$\frac{a}{b} - \frac{c}{d} - \frac{a}{b} + \frac{^-c}{d} = \frac{ad + b(^-c)}{bd} = \frac{ad + {^-bc}}{bd} = \frac{ad - bc}{bd},$$

where $\dfrac{ad - bc}{bd}$ is the unique rational number called the difference $\dfrac{a}{b} - \dfrac{c}{d}$.

Observe that ad and bc are integers and, consequently, the subtraction of rational numbers behaves like the subtraction of integers.

Commutative principle Since the commutative principle does not hold for the subtraction of integers, and since like fractions, when subtracted, behave like their numerators, we may assume that the subtraction of rational numbers is not commutative. For example,

$$\frac{3}{4} - \frac{1}{4} \neq \frac{1}{4} - \frac{3}{4}$$

because

$$\frac{3 - 1}{4} \neq \frac{1 - 3}{4}; \quad \text{that is,} \quad \frac{2}{4} \neq \frac{^-2}{4}.$$

Associative principle Since the associative principle does not hold for the subtraction of integers, we may assume that it does not hold for the subtraction of rational numbers. For example,

$$\left(\frac{7}{8} - \frac{5}{8}\right) - \frac{1}{8} \neq \frac{7}{8} - \left(\frac{5}{8} - \frac{1}{8}\right)$$

because

$$\left(\frac{7 - 5}{8}\right) - \frac{1}{8} \neq \frac{7}{8} - \left(\frac{5 - 1}{8}\right);$$

that is,

$$\frac{2}{8} - \frac{1}{8} \neq \frac{7}{8} - \frac{4}{8} \quad \text{and} \quad \frac{1}{8} \neq \frac{3}{8}.$$

Identity element Zero subtracted from any rational number yields the given rational number as the difference. For example, $\frac{2}{3} - 0 = \frac{2}{3}$ and, in general, $\frac{a}{b} - 0 = \frac{a}{b}$ for each rational number. Thus, 0 is the identity element for the subtraction of rational numbers.

Additive inverse Two rational numbers are called *additive inverses* of each other if their sum is zero. Every rational number $\frac{a}{b}$ has an additive inverse $\frac{-a}{b}$, since the positive rational numbers may be placed in one-to-one correspondence with the negative rational numbers and since $0 + 0 = 0$. In general, for every $\frac{a}{b}$ where $\frac{a}{b}$ is a rational number, there exists a negative of $\frac{a}{b}$, such that

$$\frac{a}{b} + \frac{-a}{b} = 0.$$

Exercises

1. (a) What is n if $n = \frac{13}{14} - \frac{8}{14}$?

   (b) What is n if $n = \frac{8}{14} - \frac{13}{14}$?

   (c) Does $\frac{13}{14} - \frac{8}{14} = \frac{8}{14} - \frac{13}{14}$?

   (d) Does the commutative principle hold for subtraction of rational numbers?

2. (a) What is n if $n = \left(\frac{9}{11} - \frac{5}{11}\right) - \frac{3}{11}$?

   (b) What is n if $n = \frac{9}{11} - \left(\frac{5}{11} - \frac{3}{11}\right)$?

   (c) Does $\left(\frac{9}{11} - \frac{5}{11}\right) - \frac{3}{11} = \frac{9}{11} - \left(\frac{5}{11} - \frac{3}{11}\right)$?

   (d) Does the associative principle hold for subtraction of rational numbers?

3. Find each difference.

   (a) $\frac{7}{8} - 0.$ (b) $\frac{6}{5} - \frac{6}{5}.$ (c) $\frac{3}{7} - \frac{0}{8}.$ (d) $\frac{26}{8} - \frac{13}{4}.$

4. State the additive inverse of each number.

    (a) $\dfrac{^-5}{8}$.   (b) $\dfrac{7}{3}$.   (c) $\dfrac{0}{4}$.   (d) $\dfrac{^-11}{9}$.

5. Indicate whether each statement is true or false.

    (a) $\dfrac{5}{16} - 2$ is a rational number.

    (b) $\left(\dfrac{2}{3} - \dfrac{1}{4}\right) - \dfrac{1}{8} > \dfrac{2}{3} - \left(\dfrac{1}{4} - \dfrac{1}{8}\right)$.

    (c) $\dfrac{5}{13} - \dfrac{13}{5} = \dfrac{13}{5} - \dfrac{5}{13}$.

    (d) $0 - \dfrac{3}{7} = 0$.

6-11 Division of Rational Numbers

We have learned that $3 \div 4$ may be expressed in the form $\dfrac{3}{4}$ and, in general, $a \div b$ may be expressed in the form $\dfrac{a}{b}$, where a and b represent integers and $b \neq 0$. We shall assume that the division of rational numbers is analogous to the division of integers, and that the form $a \div b = \dfrac{a}{b}$ may be used, where a and b represent rational numbers and $b \neq 0$. For example, if $a = \dfrac{2}{3}$ and $b = \dfrac{3}{4}$, we have

$$\frac{2}{3} \div \frac{3}{4} = \frac{\frac{2}{3}}{\frac{3}{4}}.$$

By using the multiplicative identity and applying certain mathematical principles, we can determine the desired quotient as follows.

$$\frac{\frac{2}{3}}{\frac{3}{4}} = \frac{\frac{2}{3}}{\frac{3}{4}} \times 1 \qquad\qquad \text{Multiplicative identity}$$

$$\frac{\frac{2}{3}}{\frac{3}{4}} \times 1 = \frac{\frac{2}{3}}{\frac{3}{4}} \times \frac{\frac{4}{3}}{\frac{4}{3}} \qquad\qquad \text{Substitution of } \dfrac{\frac{4}{3}}{\frac{4}{3}} \text{ for } 1$$

$$\frac{\frac{2}{3}}{\frac{3}{4}} \times \frac{\frac{4}{3}}{\frac{4}{3}} = \frac{\frac{2}{3} \times \frac{4}{3}}{1} \qquad\qquad \text{Product of reciprocals is 1}$$

$$\frac{\frac{2}{3} \times \frac{4}{3}}{1} = \frac{2}{3} \times \frac{4}{3} \qquad \text{Principle of dividing by 1}$$

$$\frac{2}{3} \times \frac{4}{3} = \frac{8}{9} \qquad \text{Multiplication of rational numbers}$$

Thus we have $\dfrac{2}{3} \div \dfrac{3}{4} = \dfrac{2}{3} \times \dfrac{4}{3} = \dfrac{8}{9}.$

To gain further understanding of the division of rational numbers, study the following examples.

Example 1 Find the quotient $8 \div 4$.

$$8 \div 4 = \frac{8}{1} \div \frac{4}{1} \qquad \qquad \text{Any whole number } a \text{ may be expressed in the form of the rational number } \frac{a}{1}$$

$$\frac{8}{1} \div \frac{4}{1} = \frac{\frac{8}{1}}{\frac{4}{1}} \qquad \qquad \text{Division of rational numbers may be represented by a fraction}$$

$$\frac{\frac{8}{1}}{\frac{4}{1}} = \frac{\frac{8}{1}}{\frac{4}{1}} \times 1 \qquad \qquad \text{Multiplicative identity}$$

$$\frac{\frac{8}{1}}{\frac{4}{1}} \times 1 = \frac{\frac{8}{1}}{\frac{4}{1}} \times \frac{\frac{1}{4}}{\frac{1}{4}} \qquad \text{Substitution of } \frac{\frac{1}{4}}{\frac{1}{4}} \text{ for } 1$$

$$\frac{\frac{8}{1}}{\frac{4}{1}} \times \frac{\frac{1}{4}}{\frac{1}{4}} = \frac{\frac{8}{1} \times \frac{1}{4}}{1} \qquad \text{Product of reciprocals is 1}$$

$$\frac{\frac{8}{1} \times \frac{1}{4}}{1} = \frac{8}{1} \times \frac{1}{4} \qquad \qquad \text{Principle of dividing by 1}$$

$$\frac{8}{1} \times \frac{1}{4} = \frac{8}{4} \qquad \qquad \text{Multiplication of rational numbers}$$

Thus $8 \div 4 = \dfrac{8}{1} \times \dfrac{1}{4} = \dfrac{8}{4}.$

Example 2 Find the quotient $9 \div \dfrac{5}{7}$.

$$9 \div \frac{5}{7} = \frac{9}{1} \div \frac{5}{7}$$

Any whole number may be expressed in the form of the rational number $\dfrac{a}{1}$

$$\frac{9}{1} \div \frac{5}{7} = \frac{\dfrac{9}{1}}{\dfrac{5}{7}}$$

Division of rational numbers may be represented by a fraction

$$\frac{\dfrac{9}{1}}{\dfrac{5}{7}} = \frac{\dfrac{9}{1}}{\dfrac{5}{7}} \times 1$$

Multiplicative identity

$$\frac{\dfrac{9}{1}}{\dfrac{5}{7}} \times 1 = \frac{\dfrac{9}{1}}{\dfrac{5}{7}} \times \frac{\dfrac{7}{5}}{\dfrac{7}{5}}$$

Substitution of $\dfrac{\dfrac{7}{5}}{\dfrac{7}{5}}$ for 1

$$\frac{\dfrac{9}{1}}{\dfrac{5}{7}} \times \frac{\dfrac{7}{5}}{\dfrac{7}{5}} = \frac{\dfrac{9}{1} \times \dfrac{7}{5}}{1}$$

Product of reciprocals is 1

$$\frac{\dfrac{9}{1} \times \dfrac{7}{5}}{1} = \frac{9}{1} \times \frac{7}{5}$$

Principle of dividing by 1

$$\frac{9}{1} \times \frac{7}{5} = \frac{63}{5}$$

Multiplication of rational numbers

Thus $9 \div \dfrac{5}{7} = \dfrac{9}{1} \times \dfrac{7}{5} = \dfrac{63}{5}$.

Example 3 Find the quotient $\dfrac{2}{9} \div \dfrac{3}{8}$.

$$\frac{2}{9} \div \frac{3}{8} = \frac{\dfrac{2}{9}}{\dfrac{3}{8}}$$

Division of rational numbers may be represented by a fraction

$$\frac{\dfrac{2}{9}}{\dfrac{3}{8}} = \frac{\dfrac{2}{9}}{\dfrac{3}{8}} \times 1$$

Multiplicative identity

$$\frac{\frac{2}{9}}{\frac{3}{8}} \times 1 = \frac{\frac{2}{9}}{\frac{3}{8}} \times \frac{\frac{8}{3}}{\frac{8}{3}} \qquad \text{Substitution of } \frac{\frac{8}{3}}{\frac{8}{3}} \text{ for } 1$$

$$\frac{\frac{2}{9}}{\frac{3}{8}} \times \frac{\frac{8}{3}}{\frac{8}{3}} = \frac{\frac{2}{9} \times \frac{8}{3}}{1} \qquad \text{Product of reciprocals is } 1$$

$$\frac{\frac{2}{9} \times \frac{8}{3}}{1} = \frac{2}{9} \times \frac{8}{3} \qquad \text{Principle of dividing by } 1$$

$$\frac{2}{9} \times \frac{8}{3} = \frac{16}{27} \qquad \text{Multiplication of rational numbers}$$

Thus $\dfrac{2}{9} \div \dfrac{3}{8} = \dfrac{2}{9} \times \dfrac{8}{3} = \dfrac{16}{27}$.

These examples provide some foundation for the familiar rule "invert the divisor and multiply." We observe that division by a rational number has the same result as multiplication by the reciprocal of the divisor. In general, if we are given two rational numbers $\dfrac{a}{b}$ and $\dfrac{c}{d}$ where $c \neq 0$,

$$\frac{a}{b} \div \frac{c}{d} = \frac{\frac{a}{b}}{\frac{c}{d}} \qquad \text{Division of rational numbers may be represented by a fraction}$$

$$\frac{\frac{a}{b}}{\frac{c}{d}} = \frac{\frac{a}{b}}{\frac{c}{d}} \times 1 \qquad \text{Multiplicative identity}$$

$$\frac{\frac{a}{b}}{\frac{c}{d}} \times 1 = \frac{\frac{a}{b}}{\frac{c}{d}} \times \frac{\frac{d}{c}}{\frac{d}{c}} \qquad \text{Substitution of } \frac{\frac{d}{c}}{\frac{d}{c}} \text{ for } 1$$

$$\frac{\frac{a}{b}}{\frac{c}{d}} \times \frac{\frac{d}{c}}{\frac{d}{c}} = \frac{\frac{a}{b} \times \frac{d}{c}}{1} \qquad \text{Product of reciprocals is } 1$$

$$\frac{\frac{a}{b} \times \frac{d}{c}}{1} = \frac{a}{b} \times \frac{d}{c} \qquad \text{Principle of dividing by } 1$$

$$\frac{a}{b} \times \frac{d}{c} = \frac{ad}{bc} \qquad \text{Multiplication of rational numbers}$$

Thus, for rational numbers $\frac{a}{b}$ and $\frac{c}{d}$, where $c \neq 0$,

$$\frac{a}{b} \div \frac{c}{d} = \frac{a}{b} \times \frac{d}{c} = \frac{ad}{bc}.$$

Exercises

1. Find each quotient.

    (a) $\frac{5}{9} \div \frac{2}{9}.$ (b) $\frac{1}{6} \div \frac{1}{6}.$ (c) $\frac{11}{13} \div \frac{13}{11}.$

    (d) $\frac{e}{f} \div \frac{g}{h}.$ (e) $\dfrac{\frac{4}{7}}{\frac{4}{1}}.$ (f) $\frac{13}{4} \div \frac{5}{8}.$

2. Find a rational number as a replacement for each variable, such that the statement will be true.

    (a) $8 \div \frac{4}{3} = \square.$ (b) $\bigcirc \times \frac{4}{3} = 8.$

    (c) $\frac{23}{24} \div \frac{5}{6} = \triangle.$ (d) $\frac{5}{6} \times \bigcirc = \frac{23}{24}.$

3. In Exercise 2, is it true to state that
    (a) $\square = \bigcirc$?   (b) $\triangle = \bigcirc$?

4. From Exercise 2 and other similar examples, what may we generalize about the relationship between multiplication and division of rational numbers?

6-12 Principles of Division of Rational Numbers

Principles of closure and uniqueness Except for division by zero, the quotient of any two rational numbers is a *unique* rational number. Thus, we say that the set of rational numbers different from zero is *closed* with respect to the operation of division.

Commutative principle As was the case with the division of integers, the division of rational numbers is not commutative. For example,

$$\frac{1}{2} \div \frac{1}{3} \neq \frac{1}{3} \div \frac{1}{2}$$

because

$$\frac{1}{2} \times \frac{3}{1} \neq \frac{1}{3} \times \frac{2}{1}; \quad \text{that is,} \quad \frac{3}{2} \neq \frac{2}{3}.$$

Associative principle The associative principle does not hold for division in the set of rational numbers. For example,

$$\left(\frac{1}{4} \div \frac{3}{8}\right) \div \frac{1}{16} \neq \frac{1}{4} \div \left(\frac{3}{8} \div \frac{1}{16}\right),$$

because

$$\left(\frac{1}{4} \times \frac{8}{3}\right) \div \frac{1}{16} \neq \frac{1}{4} \div \left(\frac{3}{8} \times \frac{16}{1}\right);$$

that is,

$$\frac{8}{12} \div \frac{1}{16} \neq \frac{1}{4} \div \frac{48}{8} \quad \text{and} \quad \frac{32}{3} \neq \frac{1}{24}.$$

Identity element Any rational number divided by the number 1 results in the given rational number as the quotient; that is, in general, $\frac{a}{b} \div 1 = \frac{a}{b}$. Thus, 1 is the identity element for the division of rational numbers.

Distributive principle of division over addition As with the division of integers, there is a distribution of division over the addition of rational numbers from the right, but not the left. Observe these examples:

Distributive from the right:

$$\left(\frac{4}{3} + \frac{2}{3}\right) \div \frac{1}{2} = \left(\frac{4}{3} \div \frac{1}{2}\right) + \left(\frac{2}{3} \div \frac{1}{2}\right),$$

because

$$\frac{6}{3} \div \frac{1}{2} = \frac{8}{3} + \frac{4}{3},$$

and

$$\frac{12}{3} = \frac{12}{3}.$$

Distributive from the left:

$$\frac{1}{2} \div \left(\frac{4}{3} + \frac{2}{3}\right) \neq \left(\frac{1}{2} \div \frac{4}{3}\right) + \left(\frac{1}{2} \div \frac{2}{3}\right),$$

because

$$\frac{1}{2} \div \frac{6}{3} \neq \frac{3}{8} + \frac{3}{4},$$

and

$$\frac{3}{12} \neq \frac{9}{8}.$$

Principle of division by zero As stated in Section 5-17, division by zero is meaningless in our number system. This also applies to the set of rational numbers.

Exercise

1. Indicate whether each statement is true or false.

(a) $\frac{9}{11} \div \frac{3}{2} \neq \frac{3}{2} \div \frac{9}{11}$.

(b) $\frac{7}{8} \div 1 = \frac{7}{8}$.

(c) $0 \div \frac{5}{9} \neq \frac{5}{9}$.

(d) $\frac{2}{13} \div \frac{1}{2}$ is a rational number.

(e) $\left(\frac{5}{8} + \frac{4}{8}\right) \div \frac{3}{2} = \left(\frac{5}{8} \div \frac{3}{2}\right) + \left(\frac{4}{8} \div \frac{3}{2}\right)$.

(f) $\left(\frac{1}{6} \times \frac{0}{3}\right) \div \frac{0}{7} = 0$.

(g) $\frac{11}{16} \div 1 = 1 \div \frac{11}{16}$.

(h) $\frac{1}{4} \div \left(\frac{1}{5} \div \frac{1}{6}\right) > \left(\frac{1}{4} \div \frac{1}{5}\right) \div \frac{1}{6}$.

6-13 Mixed Numerals and Computation

In Section 6-7 we learned that numerals such as $6\frac{2}{3}$, $2\frac{5}{8}$, and $^-5\frac{7}{4}$ are called mixed numerals, and that all such numerals represent rational numbers. We have developed computational procedures for adding, subtracting, multiplying, and dividing rational numbers. Now we may apply these same computational procedures to rational numbers represented by mixed numerals, if we change the mixed numerals to fractions.

The definition for the addition of two rational numbers,

$$\frac{a}{b} + \frac{c}{d} = \frac{ad + bc}{bd},$$

provides us with a procedure for working with mixed numerals such as $2\frac{1}{3}$. The numeral $2\frac{1}{3}$ (read "two and one-third") actually represents the sum $2 + \frac{1}{3}$. Since $\frac{2}{1}$ is another name for the integer 2,

$$2 + \frac{1}{3} = \frac{2}{1} + \frac{1}{3} = \frac{6+1}{3} = \frac{7}{3}.$$

Using a similar procedure, we may represent any mixed numeral as a fraction of the form $\frac{a}{b}$.

A second procedure for computation with rational numbers represented by mixed numerals is to regroup, using the commutative and associative principles, in order to work with the integers and rational fractional numbers separately. Consider these examples illustrating several procedures for computation with rational numbers represented by mixed numerals.

Example 1 Find the sum $1\frac{1}{3} + 2\frac{1}{4}$.

(a) $1\frac{1}{3} + 2\frac{1}{4} = \left(1 + \frac{1}{3}\right) + \left(2 + \frac{1}{4}\right)$

$\qquad\qquad = \left(\frac{1}{1} + \frac{1}{3}\right) + \left(\frac{2}{1} + \frac{1}{4}\right)$

$\qquad\qquad = \frac{3+1}{3} + \frac{8+1}{4}$

$\qquad\qquad = \frac{4}{3} + \frac{9}{4}$

$\qquad\qquad = \frac{16+27}{12}$

$\qquad\qquad = \frac{43}{12}$

$\qquad\qquad = \frac{36+7}{12}$

$\qquad\qquad = \frac{36}{12} + \frac{7}{12}$

$\qquad\qquad = 3 + \frac{7}{12}$

$\qquad\qquad = 3\frac{7}{12}.$

(b) $1\frac{1}{3} + 2\frac{1}{4} = \left(1 + \frac{1}{3}\right) + \left(2 + \frac{1}{4}\right)$

$\qquad\qquad = (1 + 2) + \left(\frac{1}{3} + \frac{1}{4}\right)$

$\qquad\qquad = 3 + \frac{4+3}{12}$

$\qquad\qquad = 3 + \frac{7}{12}$

$\qquad\qquad = 3\frac{7}{12}.$

(c) $1\frac{1}{3} = 1\frac{4}{12}$

$\underline{+\ 2\frac{1}{4} = 2\frac{3}{12}}$

$\qquad\quad 3\frac{7}{12}.$

Example 2 Find the sum $6\frac{5}{7} + 2\frac{1}{2}$.

(a) $6\frac{5}{7} + 2\frac{1}{2} = \left(6 + \frac{5}{7}\right) + \left(2 + \frac{1}{2}\right)$

$$= \left(\frac{6}{1} + \frac{5}{7}\right) + \left(\frac{2}{1} + \frac{1}{2}\right)$$

$$= \frac{42 + 5}{7} + \frac{4 + 1}{2}$$

$$= \frac{47}{7} + \frac{5}{2}$$

$$= \frac{94 + 35}{14}$$

$$= \frac{129}{14}$$

$$= \frac{126 + 3}{14}$$

$$= \frac{126}{14} + \frac{3}{14}$$

$$= 9 + \frac{3}{14}$$

$$= 9\frac{3}{14}.$$

(b) $6\frac{5}{7} + 2\frac{1}{2} = \left(6 + \frac{5}{7}\right) + \left(2 + \frac{1}{2}\right)$

$$= (6 + 2) + \left(\frac{5}{7} + \frac{1}{2}\right)$$

$$= 8 + \frac{10 + 7}{14}$$

$$= 8 + \frac{17}{14}$$

$$= 8 + \frac{14 + 3}{14}$$

$$= 8 + \frac{14}{14} + \frac{3}{14}$$

$$= 8 + 1 + \frac{3}{14}$$

$$= 9 + \frac{3}{14}$$

$$= 9\frac{3}{14}.$$

(c) $6\dfrac{5}{7} = 6\dfrac{10}{14}$

$\underline{+\ 2\dfrac{1}{2} = 2\dfrac{7}{14}}$

$\phantom{+\ 2\dfrac{1}{2} = }8\dfrac{17}{14} = 9\dfrac{3}{14}.$

Example 3 Find the difference $5\dfrac{1}{2} - 3\dfrac{1}{3}$.

(a) $5\dfrac{1}{2} - 3\dfrac{1}{3} = \left(5 + \dfrac{1}{2}\right) - \left(3 + \dfrac{1}{3}\right)$

$\phantom{5\dfrac{1}{2} - 3\dfrac{1}{3}\ } = \left(\dfrac{5}{1} + \dfrac{1}{2}\right) - \left(\dfrac{3}{1} + \dfrac{1}{3}\right)$

$\phantom{5\dfrac{1}{2} - 3\dfrac{1}{3}\ } = \dfrac{10 + 1}{2} - \dfrac{9 + 1}{3}$

$\phantom{5\dfrac{1}{2} - 3\dfrac{1}{3}\ } = \dfrac{11}{2} - \dfrac{10}{3}$

$\phantom{5\dfrac{1}{2} - 3\dfrac{1}{3}\ } = \dfrac{33 - 20}{6}$

$\phantom{5\dfrac{1}{2} - 3\dfrac{1}{3}\ } = \dfrac{13}{6}$

$\phantom{5\dfrac{1}{2} - 3\dfrac{1}{3}\ } = \dfrac{12 + 1}{6}$

$\phantom{5\dfrac{1}{2} - 3\dfrac{1}{3}\ } = \dfrac{12}{6} + \dfrac{1}{6}$

$\phantom{5\dfrac{1}{2} - 3\dfrac{1}{3}\ } = 2 + \dfrac{1}{6}$

$\phantom{5\dfrac{1}{2} - 3\dfrac{1}{3}\ } = 2\dfrac{1}{6}.$

(b) $5\dfrac{1}{2} - 3\dfrac{1}{3} = \left(5 + \dfrac{1}{2}\right) - \left(3 + \dfrac{1}{3}\right)$

$\phantom{5\dfrac{1}{2} - 3\dfrac{1}{3}\ } = (5 - 3) + \left(\dfrac{1}{2} - \dfrac{1}{3}\right)$

$\phantom{5\dfrac{1}{2} - 3\dfrac{1}{3}\ } = 2 + \left(\dfrac{3 - 2}{6}\right)$

$\phantom{5\dfrac{1}{2} - 3\dfrac{1}{3}\ } = 2 + \dfrac{1}{6}$

$\phantom{5\dfrac{1}{2} - 3\dfrac{1}{3}\ } = 2\dfrac{1}{6}.$

(c) $5\dfrac{1}{2} = 5\dfrac{3}{6}$

$\dfrac{-3\dfrac{1}{3} = 3\dfrac{2}{6}}{2\dfrac{1}{6}}.$

Example 4 Find the difference $6\dfrac{1}{3} - 3\dfrac{2}{3}$.

(a) $6\dfrac{1}{3} - 3\dfrac{2}{3} = \left(6 + \dfrac{1}{3}\right) - \left(3 + \dfrac{2}{3}\right)$

$= \left(\dfrac{6}{1} + \dfrac{1}{3}\right) - \left(\dfrac{3}{1} + \dfrac{2}{3}\right)$

$= \dfrac{18 + 1}{3} - \dfrac{9 + 2}{3}$

$= \dfrac{19}{3} - \dfrac{11}{3}$

$= \dfrac{19 - 11}{3}$

$= \dfrac{8}{3}$

$= \dfrac{6 + 2}{3}$

$= \dfrac{6}{3} + \dfrac{2}{3}$

$= 2 + \dfrac{2}{3}$

$= 2\dfrac{2}{3}.$

(b) $6\dfrac{1}{3} = 6 + \dfrac{1}{3} = 5 + 1 + \dfrac{1}{3} = 5 + \dfrac{3}{3} + \dfrac{1}{3} = 5 + \dfrac{4}{3}$

$\dfrac{-3\dfrac{2}{3} = 3 + \dfrac{2}{3} = 3 \qquad + \dfrac{2}{3} = 3 \qquad + \dfrac{2}{3} = 3 + \dfrac{2}{3}}{2 + \dfrac{2}{3} = 2\dfrac{2}{3}.}$

Example 5 Find the product $2\dfrac{1}{5} \times 3\dfrac{1}{4}$.

$2\dfrac{1}{5} \times 3\dfrac{1}{4} = \left(2 + \dfrac{1}{5}\right) \times \left(3 + \dfrac{1}{4}\right)$

$= \left(\dfrac{2}{1} + \dfrac{1}{5}\right) \times \left(\dfrac{3}{1} + \dfrac{1}{4}\right)$

$= \dfrac{10 + 1}{5} \times \dfrac{12 + 1}{4}$

$$= \frac{11}{5} \times \frac{13}{4}$$

$$= \frac{143}{20}$$

$$= \frac{140 + 3}{20}$$

$$= \frac{140}{20} + \frac{3}{20}$$

$$= 7 + \frac{3}{20}$$

$$= 7\frac{3}{20}.$$

Example 6 Find the quotient $3\frac{3}{5} \div 2\frac{1}{3}$.

$$3\frac{3}{5} \div 2\frac{1}{3} = \left(3 + \frac{3}{5}\right) \div \left(2 + \frac{1}{3}\right)$$

$$= \left(\frac{3}{1} + \frac{3}{5}\right) \div \left(\frac{2}{1} + \frac{1}{3}\right)$$

$$= \left(\frac{15 + 3}{5}\right) \div \left(\frac{6 + 1}{3}\right)$$

$$= \frac{18}{5} \div \frac{7}{3}$$

$$= \frac{18}{5} \times \frac{3}{7}$$

$$= \frac{54}{35}$$

$$= \frac{35 + 19}{35}$$

$$= \frac{35}{35} + \frac{19}{35}$$

$$= 1 + \frac{19}{35}$$

$$= 1\frac{19}{35}.$$

Exercises

1. Find each sum.

   (a) $3\frac{2}{3} + 6\frac{1}{4}$.

   (b) $2\frac{5}{8} + 1\frac{3}{5}$.

   (c) $5\frac{1}{6} + 8\frac{6}{7}$.

   (d) $7\frac{1}{2} + 19\frac{5}{6}$.

2. Find each difference.

(a) $5\frac{1}{4} - 2\frac{1}{5}$.

(b) $1\frac{2}{7} - \frac{1}{8}$.

(c) $13 - \frac{14}{15}$.

(d) $28\frac{11}{19} - 19\frac{16}{23}$.

3. Find each product.

(a) $4\frac{2}{3} \times 6\frac{3}{8}$.

(b) $7\frac{5}{6} \times 5\frac{1}{4}$.

(c) $1\frac{4}{7} \times \frac{7}{9}$.

(d) $5\frac{3}{5} \times 9\frac{11}{19}$.

4. Find each quotient.

(a) $4\frac{3}{8} \div 3\frac{5}{9}$.

(b) $1\frac{6}{7} \div 6\frac{1}{3}$.

(c) $8\frac{1}{2} \div 5\frac{3}{5}$.

(d) $12\frac{3}{4} \div 12\frac{2}{3}$.

6-14 Density of the Rational Numbers

We say that the set of rational numbers is **dense**; that is, there is always at least one rational number between any two distinct rational numbers.

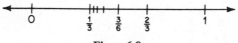

Figure 6-8

The density of the rational numbers may be illustrated with any two rational numbers; for example, $\frac{1}{3}$ and $\frac{2}{3}$. How many rational numbers can we find between these two numbers? Since $\frac{1}{3} = \frac{2}{6}$ and $\frac{2}{3} = \frac{4}{6}$, we can find $\frac{3}{6}$ $\left(\text{that is, } \frac{1}{2}\right)$ between $\frac{1}{3}$ and $\frac{2}{3}$. Notice that we can find the number halfway between $\frac{1}{3}$ and $\frac{2}{3}$ by adding the two numbers and dividing by 2:

$$\frac{1}{3} + \frac{2}{3} = \frac{3}{3} \quad \text{and} \quad \frac{3}{3} \div 2 = \frac{3}{3} \times \frac{1}{2} = \frac{3}{6}.$$

In a similar manner we can find a number between $\frac{1}{3}$ and $\frac{3}{6}$:

$$\frac{1}{3} + \frac{3}{6} = \frac{5}{6} \quad \text{and} \quad \frac{5}{6} \div 2 = \frac{5}{6} \times \frac{1}{2} = \frac{5}{12}.$$

Following the same procedure, we can find a number halfway between $\frac{1}{3}$

and $\frac{5}{12}$. This process can be continued indefinitely. Thus, between any two distinct rational numbers there are infinitely many rational numbers. This means that the number of points representing rational numbers on any segment of the number line is unlimited. We should note that the principle of density does not apply to the set of whole numbers. For example, what are the whole numbers between 1 and 2?

Exercises

1. Is the set of integers dense?

2. If we are given the rational number $\frac{1}{2}$, what is the next largest rational number?

3. How many rational numbers are there between 0 and 1?

4. Using the procedure described in Section 6-14, find five rational numbers between $\frac{2}{5}$ and $\frac{3}{5}$.

5. What is the smallest positive rational number?

6. What is the largest positive rational number?

chapter 7

Ratio, Percent, and Decimals

In dealing with ratio, percent, and decimals we must be careful not to confuse the concepts of number and numeral. It is important to realize that $\frac{1}{4}$, 25%, and 0.25 are different names for the same number. Convenience and social applications make it necessary for us to develop facility in translating from one form of naming a number to another. The ability to change from the percent form to the fractional or decimal form makes it possible for us to use the basic computational algorisms for fractions and decimals. Thus, we do not need to develop special algorisms for use with percent.

7-1 Ratio and Proportion

A comparison of two numbers by division is a **ratio**. The rational number $\frac{3}{4}$ may be considered a ratio, the comparison of 3 to 4. There are several alternate ways of representing the same ratio, such as

$$3:4, \quad 3 \div 4, \quad \text{and} \quad \frac{3}{4}.$$

Each of these may be read "the ratio of three to four" and also "three is to four."

In some instances ratios are equal to each other. For example, the ratios $\frac{3}{4}$ and $\frac{18}{24}$ are equal; that is, $\frac{3}{4} = \frac{18}{24}$. A statement that two ratios are equal is a **proportion**. Thus the statement $\frac{3}{4} = \frac{18}{24}$ is a proportion and may be read "three is to four as eighteen is to twenty-four." A proportion merely indicates two different names for the same ratio.

The equality of two ratios may be determined by applying some of the same principles that we studied in Chapter 6. We learned that two rational numbers are equal if the numerator of the first times the denominator of the second is equal to the denominator of the first times the numerator of the second. For example,

$$\frac{3}{4} = \frac{18}{24}, \text{ since } 3 \times 24 = 4 \times 18.$$

The same relationship holds for any two equal ratios. In general, for the ratios $\frac{a}{b}$ and $\frac{c}{d}$,

$$\frac{a}{b} = \frac{c}{d} \text{ if } a \times d = b \times c,$$

and

$$a \times d = b \times c \text{ if } \frac{a}{b} = \frac{c}{d}.$$

Exercises

1. Express the ratio of the first number to the second number as a fraction.
   (a) 4, 9.   (b) 30, 55.   (c) 32, 56.   (d) 53, 17.

2. Represent each of the ratios in Exercise 1 as a rational number in simplest form.

3. In comparing two measurements, we change both measures to the same unit of measure, to avoid confusion. Expressed in simplest form, what is the ratio of
   (a) 1 foot to 1 yard?   (b) 10 minutes to 1 hour?
   (c) 3 feet to 24 inches?   (d) 10 cents to 5 dollars?

4. Find three equivalent ratios for the following.
   (a) $\frac{1}{2}$.   (b) $\frac{2}{3}$.   (c) $\frac{7}{8}$.   (d) $\frac{18}{45}$.

5. In each statement find a replacement for the variable such that the statement will be true.
   (a) $\frac{5}{6} = \frac{\square}{54}$.   (b) $\frac{11}{13} = \frac{33}{\square}$.   (c) $\frac{\square}{1} = \frac{5}{8}$.   (d) $\frac{1}{3} = \frac{\square}{7}$.

6. In each proportion determine the number that the letter t represents.
   (a) $\frac{5}{15} = \frac{t}{36}$.   (b) $\frac{25}{t} = \frac{10}{5}$.   (c) $\frac{70}{17} = \frac{30}{t}$.   (d) $\frac{3}{8} = \frac{t}{15}$.

7. Indicate whether each statement is true or false.
   (a) $\frac{3}{4} = \frac{2}{3}$.   (b) $\frac{6}{8} = \frac{9}{12}$.   (c) $\frac{11}{14} = \frac{13}{17}$.   (d) $\frac{24}{6} = \frac{28}{7}$.

8. Proportions are extremely useful in solving problems. Write a proportion and find the missing number for each of the following.

(a) If 5 pounds of hamburger will serve 9 persons, how many pounds will be needed to serve 17 persons?

(b) If 3 loaves of bread cost 78¢, what is the cost of 8 loaves?

7-2 Percent

Ratios are frequently expressed with denominators of one hundred. For example,

$$\frac{7}{10} = \frac{70}{100}.$$

The expression $\frac{70}{100}$ may be read as "the ratio of 70 to 100," or as "70 percent." The term percent is derived from the Latin phrase "per centum," which means "by the hundred." Hence, 70 percent means $\frac{70}{100}$.

The symbol % may be substituted for the word "percent." It is important to note that the % symbol, division by 100, and multiplication by $\frac{1}{100}$ are different notations for the same mathematical idea. Any rational number may be represented by a fraction with a denominator of 100 and, if $\frac{1}{100}$ is replaced with a percent symbol, may be written as a percent. For example,

$$\frac{3}{5} = \frac{3}{5} \times \frac{20}{20} = \frac{60}{100} = 60 \times \frac{1}{100} = 60\%,$$

$$\frac{9}{25} = \frac{9}{25} \times \frac{4}{4} = \frac{36}{100} = 36 \times \frac{1}{100} = 36\%,$$

$$\frac{2}{7} = \frac{2}{7} \times \frac{100}{100} = \frac{200}{700} = \frac{200}{7} \times \frac{1}{100} = 28\frac{4}{7} \times \frac{1}{100} = 28\frac{4}{7}\%.$$

We may use the idea of proportion to express any rational number $\frac{a}{b}$ in percent notation by finding the number n such that $\frac{a}{b} = \frac{n}{100}$. Thus, $\frac{a}{b} = \frac{n}{100} = n$ percent. For example, if $\frac{2}{3}$ is to be expressed as a percent, we set up the proportion $\frac{2}{3} = \frac{n}{100}$. Then $2 \times 100 = 3 \times n$ and $\frac{200}{3} = n$, that is, $66\frac{2}{3}$. If in the original proportion we replace n by its equivalent, we have

$$\frac{2}{3} = \frac{66\frac{2}{3}}{100} = 66\frac{2}{3} \times \frac{1}{100} = 66\frac{2}{3}\%.$$

For emphasis, we recall that fractions and percents are different numeral forms that may be used to name the same number. In computation, we find a use for both forms and need a method for changing from one to the other.

Exercises

1. Use the form $\dfrac{a}{b} = \dfrac{n}{100}$ and express each rational number as a percent.

(a) $\dfrac{3}{4}$.   (b) $\dfrac{7}{7}$.   (c) $\dfrac{8}{5}$.   (d) $3\dfrac{1}{2}$.

(e) $\dfrac{2}{5}$.   (f) 2.   (g) $\dfrac{1}{2}$.   (h) $\dfrac{7}{8}$.

2. Express each percent as a fraction in simplest form.

(a) 90%.   (b) 42%.   (c) 63%.   (d) $16\dfrac{2}{3}\%$.

(e) 130%.   (f) $\dfrac{1}{2}\%$.   (g) 1%.   (h) 100%.

3. Find 100% of 65.   **4.** Find 1% of 65.

5. Find $\dfrac{1}{2}$ of 10.   **6.** Find $\dfrac{1}{2}\%$ of 10.

7-3 Decimal Notation

Frequently in computational work decimal notation offers an advantage over fractional notation. It is important to note from previous discussions that decimal notation is merely an extension of our decimal system of numeration and not a new system. The place-value chart shows decimal representations both to the left and to the right of the decimal point.

In base ten notation the value of each place is ten times the value of the place to its right and one-tenth of the value of the place to its left. For example,

$$100 = 10 \times 10 \quad \text{and} \quad 100 = \frac{1}{10} \times 1{,}000.$$

Place-Value Chart

Thousands	Hundreds	Tens	Ones
$10 \times 10 \times 10$	10×10	10	1
10^3	10^2	10^1	10^0
$1{,}000$	100	10	1

We learned in Section 3-1 that two major characteristics of the decimal system of numeration are place value and a base of ten. Applying these characteristics, we represented whole numbers in expanded form. For example,

$$234 = (2 \times 100) + (3 \times 10) + (4 \times 1)$$
$$= (2 \times 10^2) + (3 \times 10^1) + (4 \times 10^0).$$

We may also use expanded notation to represent rational numbers that are not whole numbers. For example,

$$\frac{32,786}{1,000} = 32.786$$

$$32.786 = (3 \times 10) + (2 \times 1) + \left(7 \times \frac{1}{10}\right) + \left(8 \times \frac{1}{100}\right) + \left(6 \times \frac{1}{1,000}\right)$$
$$= (3 \times 10^1) + (2 \times 10^0) + (7 \times 10^{-1}) + (8 \times 10^{-2}) + (6 \times 10^{-3}).$$

When the number 32.786 is written in decimal notation, the decimal point locates the ones place, and the number is read "thirty-two *and* seven hundred eighty-six thousandths." Observe that the word "and" may designate the decimal point. Caution should be exercised when reading numerals to avoid careless use of the word "and."

We learned in Section 3-4 that, in general,

$$b^m \cdot b^n = b^{m+n},$$

$$b^m \div b^n = b^{m-n},$$

$$(b^m)^n = b^{m \cdot n}.$$

The idea of a negative exponent was introduced, and we agreed that, in general,

$$a^{-n} = \frac{1}{a^n}.$$

We should note that the procedures for working with multiplication, division, and powers of powers apply to both positive and negative exponents.

for Base Ten

Tenths	Hundredths	Thousandths	Ten-Thousandths
$\frac{1}{10}$	$\frac{1}{10 \times 10}$	$\frac{1}{10 \times 10 \times 10}$	$\frac{1}{10 \times 10 \times 10 \times 10}$
10^{-1}	10^{-2}	10^{-3}	10^{-4}
0.1	0.01	0.001	0.0001

For example,

$$\frac{1}{10} \times \frac{1}{10} = \frac{1}{100}$$

may also be expressed as

$$10^{-1} \times 10^{-1} = 10^{-2} = \frac{1}{10^2} = \frac{1}{100};$$

$$\frac{1}{100} \div \frac{1}{10} = \frac{1}{10}$$

may also be expressed as

$$10^{-2} \div 10^{-1} = 10^{-1} = \frac{1}{10};$$

$$\left(\frac{1}{10}\right)^2 = \frac{1}{10} \times \frac{1}{10} = \frac{1}{100}$$

may also be expressed as

$$(10^{-1})^2 = 10^{-2} = \frac{1}{10^2} = \frac{1}{100}.$$

Exercises

1. Write in decimal notation.
    (a) $(5 \times 10,000) + (7 \times 1,000) + (2 \times 100) + (9 \times 10) + (3 \times 1)$
       $+ \left(6 \times \frac{1}{10}\right) + \left(4 \times \frac{1}{100}\right) + \left(1 \times \frac{1}{1,000}\right).$
    (b) $(3 \times 10^2) + \left(7 \times \frac{1}{10^2}\right) + \left(4 \times \frac{1}{10^4}\right).$
    (c) $6 \times \frac{1}{10^5}.$
    (d) $(2 \times 10^{-1}) + (9 \times 10^{-2}) + (5 \times 10^{-3}) + (6 \times 10^{-4}).$

2. Write in expanded form.
    (a) 0.25.   (b) 694.851.   (c) 300.009.   (d) 5,320.7604.

3. Read each numeral in words.
    (a) 246.   (b) 2.46.   (c) 178.296.   (d) 0.9.

7-4 Rational Fractional Numerals and Decimal Numerals

Frequently it is more convenient to work with the decimal form of a rational number than it is to work with the fractional form. Since a rational number expressed in fractional form is the quotient of two integers, we can translate from the fractional form to the decimal form by performing the indicated division and expressing the quotient as a decimal numeral. For convenience in performing an indicated division, we observe that integers may be expressed as equivalent decimals. For example,

$$1 = 1.0 = 1.00 = 1.000 = 1.0000\ldots,$$
$$2 = 2.0 = 2.00 = 2.000 = 2.0000\ldots,$$
$$3 = 3.0 = 3.00 = 3.000 = 3.0000\ldots,$$
$$^-5 = {}^-5.0 = {}^-5.00 = {}^-5.000 = {}^-5.0000\ldots.$$

Consider the following examples of the conversion from a fractional numeral to a decimal numeral by the division process.

Example 1 Change $\frac{1}{2}$ to a decimal numeral.

$$
\begin{array}{r}
0.5 \\
2{\overline{)\,1.0}} \\
-1\,0 \\
\hline
0
\end{array}
$$
Thus, $\frac{1}{2} = 0.5$.

Example 2 Change $\frac{3}{5}$ to a decimal numeral.

$$
\begin{array}{r}
0.6 \\
5{\overline{)\,3.0}} \\
-3\,0 \\
\hline
0
\end{array}
$$
Thus, $\frac{3}{5} = 0.6$.

Example 3 Change $\frac{1}{8}$ to a decimal numeral.

$$
\begin{array}{r}
0.125 \\
8{\overline{)\,1.000}} \\
-8 \\
\hline
20 \\
-16 \\
\hline
40 \\
-40 \\
\hline
0
\end{array}
$$
Thus, $\frac{1}{8} = 0.125$.

Notice that in Examples 1, 2, and 3 the division process **terminates**; that is, the division process is continued until we have a remainder of 0. Notice also that in each case the divisor is a number that is expressible as a product of a power of 2 and a power of 5; that is, each divisor is a factor of a power of 10. Any whole number that is a factor of a power of 10 is expressible in the form $2^p \cdot 5^q$, where p and q are nonnegative integers. Division by a factor of a power of 10 always terminates.

With many rational numbers, however, the division process does *not* terminate. For example, examine the division process used to change $\frac{1}{3}$ to a decimal numeral:

$$
\begin{array}{r}
0.333\ldots \\
3\overline{)1.0000\ldots} \\
\underline{-9} \\
10 \\
\underline{-9} \\
10 \\
\underline{-9} \\
1
\end{array}
\qquad \text{Thus, } \frac{1}{3} = 0.333\ldots.
$$

Although the process of dividing does not terminate, we observe a repeating pattern in the quotient and in the differences (remainders). The numeral 3 is repeating in the quotient and the numeral 1 is repeating in the differences (remainders). The dots in $\frac{1}{3} = 0.333\ldots$ indicate that the threes continue without end in the quotient. A numeral of this type is referred to as a **repeating decimal** (also called a **periodic decimal**). The set of digits that repeats is called the **cycle**, and a bar is usually placed over the cycle to make it obvious. Thus, it is customary to write $0.333\ldots$ as $0.\overline{3}$.

To change the fraction $\frac{13}{55}$ to a decimal numeral, we may apply the division process:

$$
\begin{array}{r}
0.2363636\ldots \\
55\overline{)\,13.0000000\ldots} \\
\underline{-11\,0} \\
2\,00 \\
\underline{-1\,65} \\
350 \\
\underline{-330} \\
200 \\
\underline{-165} \\
350 \\
\underline{-330} \\
200 \\
\underline{-165} \\
350 \\
\underline{-330} \\
20
\end{array}
\qquad \text{Thus, } \frac{13}{55} = 0.2363636\ldots.
$$

Note the repeating pattern in the quotient and in the differences (remainders). In the quotient the two-digit numeral 36 is repeating, as indicated by the three-dot notation. The cycle 36 may be more clearly indicated by using the bar instead of the three dots, and we have $\frac{13}{55} = 0.2\overline{36}$. We also observe a repeating pattern in the differences (remainders) obtained at each step of the division process:

$$13, 20, 35, 20, 35, 20, 35, 20, \ldots.$$

It is important to understand that if we even once obtain a difference (remainder) in the division process such that the difference is equal to a previous difference, a cycle is repeating. Note also that only nonnegative remainders *less than the divisor* will be obtained; hence, a cycle must repeat in at most $n - 1$ steps when the divisor is represented by n. Thus, for any rational number $\dfrac{a}{b}$, the division process terminates if b is a factor of a power of 10 and, in general, the division process leads to a repetition of at most $b - 1$ digits.

Consider the examples below and observe the repeating pattern in each quotient.

Example 4 Change $\dfrac{1}{2}$ to a repeating decimal.

$$
\begin{array}{r}
0.500\ldots \\
2)\overline{1.000\ldots} \\
-1\,0 \\ \hline
00 \\
-\,0 \\ \hline
00 \\
-\,0 \\ \hline
0
\end{array}
$$

Thus, $\dfrac{1}{2} = 0.5\overline{0}$. Note that the division process terminates, since the divisor, 2, is a factor of a power of 10. Note also that the division process leads to a cycle of one digit in the quotient, since the divisor (n) is 2 and $n - 1$ is 1.

Example 5 Change $\dfrac{3}{5}$ to a repeating decimal.

$$
\begin{array}{r}
0.600\ldots \\
5)\overline{3.000\ldots} \\
-3\,0 \\ \hline
00 \\
-\,0 \\ \hline
00 \\
-\,0 \\ \hline
0
\end{array}
$$

Thus, $\dfrac{3}{5} = 0.6\overline{0}$. Note that the division process terminates, since the divisor, 5, is a factor of a power of 10. Note also that the division process leads to a cycle of at most four digits in the quotient, since the divisor (n) is 5 and $n - 1$ is 4. In this case the cycle is only one digit.

Example 6 Change $\dfrac{1}{8}$ to a repeating decimal.

$$
\begin{array}{r}
0.12500\ldots \\
8)\overline{1.00000\ldots} \\
-\ 8 \\ \hline
20 \\
-16 \\ \hline
40 \\
-40 \\ \hline
00 \\
-\,0 \\ \hline
00 \\
-\,0 \\ \hline
0
\end{array}
$$

Thus, $\dfrac{1}{8} = 0.125\overline{0}$. Note that the division process terminates, since the divisor, 8, is a factor of a power of 10. Note also that the division process leads to a cycle of at most seven digits in the quotient, since the divisor (n) is 8 and $n - 1$ is 7. In this case the cycle is only one digit.

In Examples 4, 5, and 6 we see that terminating decimals 0.5, 0.6, and 0.125 may also be represented as repeating decimals. Since a terminating decimal may be considered as a repeating decimal, we generalize that any rational number may be expressed as a repeating decimal.

We have discussed the procedure for changing from a rational fractional numeral to a decimal numeral. Now suppose we have the opposite situation; that is, we wish to change a decimal numeral to a rational fractional numeral. If the decimal numeral is a terminating one, the problem is simple. For example, 0.125 may be expressed as $\frac{125}{1,000}$ and then changed to simplest form. Then we have

$$0.125 = \frac{125}{1,000} = \frac{1}{8}.$$

If we have a repeating decimal, the problem of representing it as a rational fractional numeral is more difficult. For example, what is the rational number represented by $0.\overline{6}$? We shall write $0.\overline{6}$ as 0.66... and name it n; that is, $n = 0.66....$ We then multiply each member of the equality by 10, which gives us

$$10 \times n = 10 \times 0.66....$$

Completing the multiplication, we have

$$10n = 6.6....$$

If we subtract n from each side of the above equation (recall that $n = 0.66...$), we have $10n - n = 6.6... - 0.66...$, which is $9n = 6$, assuming that the repeated digits may be subtracted in the usual manner. Then $n = \frac{6}{9}$ and, in simplest form, $n = \frac{2}{3}$. Thus, we have determined that $0.\overline{6} = \frac{2}{3}$.

In general, to represent any repeating decimal as a rational fractional numeral, we multiply by the power of 10 whose exponent equals the number of digits in the cycle and then subtract the original number.

Example 7 Find a rational fractional numeral for $0.\overline{27}$.

We let $n = 0.\overline{27}$ and multiply each member of the equality by 10^2; that is, 100:

$$\begin{aligned} 100n &= 27.\overline{27} \\ -\ n &= \ \ 0.\overline{27} \\ \hline 99n &= 27 \end{aligned} \quad \text{and} \quad n = \frac{27}{99} = \frac{3}{11}.$$

Thus, $n = 0.\overline{27} = \frac{3}{11}$.

Exercises

1. Find the decimal numeral for each fractional numeral.

(a) $\frac{7}{10}$.   (b) $\frac{39}{50}$.   (c) $\frac{13}{20}$.   (d) $\frac{3}{8}$.

2. Use the division process to change each fraction to decimal form, and indicate the cycle by using a bar over one set of the repeated digits.

(a) $\frac{4}{7}$.   (b) $\frac{10}{15}$.   (c) $\frac{8}{11}$.   (d) $\frac{29}{37}$.

3. (a) Find the decimal numeral for $\frac{5}{13}$.

(b) Is the decimal numeral in Exercise 3(a) a repeating decimal?

4. Write a decimal numeral for each fraction.

(a) $\frac{2}{9}$.   (b) $\frac{25}{14}$.   (c) $\frac{47}{8}$.   (d) $11\frac{5}{6}$.

5. Change each decimal numeral to a rational fractional numeral.

(a) 0.23.   (b) 0.165.   (c) 3.0738.   (d) 0.009.

6. Find the rational number represented by each decimal numeral.

(a) $0.\overline{8}$.   (b) $0.\overline{47}$.   (c) $0.2\overline{35}$.   (d) $0.6\overline{2}$.

7-5 Operations with Numbers Expressed as Terminating Decimals

Any number represented by a terminating decimal may also be represented by an equivalent fraction of the form $\frac{a}{b}$, where b is some power of 10. Consequently, we may perform addition, subtraction, multiplication, and division on such numbers by changing the decimals to fractions and applying the computational principles and procedures that we studied with the set of rational numbers. For the sake of convenience, however, we have developed algorisms for performing the fundamental operations on numbers expressed as terminating decimals.

Addition and subtraction To add or subtract numbers expressed as terminating decimals, we arrange the numerals in vertical columns according to the concept of place value. We then add or subtract as if we were working with whole numbers. For example, the sum of 5.28 and 2.61 is illustrated below.

$$
\begin{array}{r}
5.28 \\
+2.61 \\
\hline
7.89
\end{array}
$$

Since $5.28 = \dfrac{528}{100}$ and $2.61 = \dfrac{261}{100}$, we may also find the sum by using fractions.

$$\frac{528}{100} + \frac{261}{100} = \frac{528 + 261}{100} = \frac{789}{100} = 7.89$$

The difference between 6.98 and 4.65 may be determined by either of these two procedures. In the decimal form we have

$$
\begin{array}{r}
6.98 \\
-4.65 \\
\hline
2.33
\end{array}
$$

and, in the fractional form,

$$\frac{698}{100} - \frac{465}{100} = \frac{698 - 465}{100} = \frac{233}{100} = 2.33.$$

Multiplication To multiply numbers expressed as terminating decimals, we temporarily disregard the decimal points and multiply as if we were working with whole numbers. Then we locate the decimal point in the product. The number of decimal places in the product is determined by adding the number of decimal places in each factor. The examples

$$\frac{3}{10} \times \frac{7}{10} = \frac{21}{100} \quad \text{and} \quad 0.3 \times 0.7 = 0.21$$

illustrate that products represented by decimal numerals are equivalent to the same products represented by fractional numerals. The parallel between multiplication of numbers expressed as fractions and multiplication of the same numbers expressed as decimals is excellent for developing an understanding of the multiplication procedures used with decimals. Study the following examples.

Example 1
$$
\begin{array}{r}
0.25 \\
\times\ 0.4 \\
\hline
0.100
\end{array}
$$

$$\frac{4}{10} \times \frac{25}{100} = \frac{4 \times 25}{10 \times 100} = \frac{100}{1,000}$$

Example 2
$$
\begin{array}{r}
2.341 \\
\times\ 0.07 \\
\hline
0.16387
\end{array}
$$

$$\frac{7}{100} \times 2\frac{341}{1,000} = \frac{7}{100} \times \frac{2,341}{1,000} = \frac{7 \times 2,341}{100 \times 1,000} = \frac{16,387}{100,000}$$

Example 3
$$
\begin{array}{r}
0.0123 \\
\times\ 0.5 \\
\hline
0.00615
\end{array}
$$

$$\frac{5}{10} \times \frac{123}{10,000} = \frac{5 \times 123}{10 \times 10,000} = \frac{615}{100,000}$$

Division To divide numbers expressed as terminating decimals, we temporarily disregard the decimal points and divide as if we were working with whole numbers. Then we locate the decimal point in the quotient. The examples

$$\frac{6}{10} \div \frac{3}{10} = 2 \quad \text{and} \quad 0.6 \div 0.3 = 2$$

illustrate that quotients represented by fractional numerals are equivalent to the same quotients represented by decimal numerals. The parallel between division of numbers expressed as decimals and division of the same numbers expressed as fractions is excellent for developing an understanding of the division procedures used with decimals. Study the examples below.

Example 1 $0.6 \div 0.03 = 20$ **Example 2** $0.06 \div 0.3 = 0.2$

$$\frac{6}{10} \div \frac{3}{100} = 20 \qquad\qquad \frac{6}{100} \div \frac{3}{10} = \frac{2}{10}$$

Example 3 $10 \div 0.25 = 40$

$$\frac{10}{1} \div \frac{25}{100} = 40$$

We may also use a standard division algorism to find the quotient of two numbers expressed as decimals. It is imperative that we understand why the division algorism works before we depend on it as an answer-producing procedure.

$$\begin{array}{r} 20. \\ 0.03)\overline{0.60.} \\ -\ 6 \\ \hline 00 \\ -00 \\ \hline 0 \end{array}$$

The arrows indicate that both 0.03 and 0.6 have been multiplied by 100; that is, $\dfrac{0.6 \times 100}{0.03 \times 100} = \dfrac{60}{3}$.

$$\begin{array}{r} 0.2 \\ 0.3)\overline{0.0.6} \\ -\ 6 \\ \hline 0 \end{array}$$

The arrows indicate that both 0.3 and 0.06 have been multiplied by 10; that is, $\dfrac{0.06 \times 10}{0.3 \times 10} = \dfrac{0.6}{3}$.

$$\begin{array}{r} 40. \\ 0.25)\overline{10.00.} \\ -10\ 0 \\ \hline 00 \\ -00 \\ \hline 0 \end{array}$$

The arrows indicate that both 0.25 and 10 have been multiplied by 100; that is, $\dfrac{10 \times 100}{0.25 \times 100} = \dfrac{1,000}{25}$.

Since any division problem may be expressed as a multiplication problem whose product and one factor are known, we may use the "missing factor" approach to find the quotient of two numbers expressed as terminating decimals. For example, $10 \div 0.25 = \square$ may be considered as $0.25 \times \square$ $= 10$, where the variable $\square$ represents the missing factor. Thus we need to determine what number multiplied by 0.25 yields a product of 10. Recall that we may multiply numbers expressed as decimals as if they were whole numbers, and then locate the decimal point in the numeral for the product. Our knowledge of multiplication facts might lead us to guess that the missing factor is 4; however, the product $25 \times 4 = 100$, and we have a total of two decimal places in the factors, which means that $0.25 \times 4 = 1.00$. This *trial and error* procedure should lead us to realize that the missing factor is 40, since $25 \times 40 = 1,000$, and when the decimal places are considered we have $0.25 \times 40 = 10.00$.

Thus, when we use the missing-factor approach to find the quotient of numbers expressed as decimals, we must consider the number of decimal places as we seek the factor that produces the indicated product.

Exercises

1. Work each of these in two ways, first by using decimals and then by using fraction equivalents of the decimals.
   (a) $7.8 + 2.75 + 6$.   (b) $0.123 + 1.1$.
   (c) $16.88 - 9.56$.   (d) $0.7 - 0.289$.

2. Find each product, first by using decimal numerals and then by using fractional numerals.
   (a) 4.07×0.3.   (b) 26.8×12.
   (c) 0.005×0.00009.   (d) 189.642×7.

3. Express each quotient as a fraction with a natural number as the denominator.
   (a) $0.65 \div 1.5$.   (b) $789 \div 0.0036$.
   (c) $4.7896 \div 22.31$.   (d) $59.2 \div 0.001$.

4. Find each quotient.
   (a) $0.65 \div 1.5$.   (b) $2.31 \div 1.4$.
   (c) $43.8 \div 0.08$.   (d) $0.0001568 \div 7$.

5. Express each decimal as a percent.
   (a) 0.09.   (b) 0.005.   (c) 2.78.   (d) 0.75.

6. Find the following.
   (a) 3 percent of 16.   (b) 100 percent of 97.
   (c) 1 percent of 28.   (d) $\frac{1}{2}$ percent of 28.

7-6 Scientific Notation

In the light of recent advances in science and technology it is essential that we develop a facility for working with very large and very small numbers. The decimal notation for numbers such as

$$2,850,000,000,000 \quad \text{and} \quad 0.000000000076$$

is somewhat cumbersome. These numbers may be represented by a simpler notation, as

$$2.85 \times 10^{12} \quad \text{and} \quad 7.6 \times 10^{-11}.$$

This form, representing numbers as the product of an appropriate power of 10 and a number that is greater than or equal to 1 but less than 10, is called **scientific notation.** Consider these illustrations of numbers represented in scientific notation:

$$36 = 3.6 \times 10^1,$$
$$793,000,000 = 7.93 \times 10^8,$$
$$10,000,000,000,000,000 = 1.0 \times 10^{16},$$
$$0.36 = 3.6 \times 10^{-1},$$
$$0.0091 = 9.1 \times 10^{-3},$$
$$0.00000067438 = 6.7438 \times 10^{-7}.$$

Scientific notation also makes certain calculations easier. For example, the product of

$$793,000,000 \quad \text{and} \quad 10,000,000,000,000,000$$

may be calculated as follows:

$$
\begin{aligned}
793,000,000 \times 10,000,000,000,000,000 &= (7.93 \times 10^8) \times (1.0 \times 10^{16}) \\
&= 7.93 \times 10^8 \times 1.0 \times 10^{16} \\
&= (7.93 \times 1.0) \times (10^8 \times 10^{16}) \\
&= 7.93 \times 10^{24}.
\end{aligned}
$$

Exercises

1. Represent each number in scientific notation.
   (a) 0.0000978. (b) 5,640,000. (c) 1.265.
   (d) 0.000000000000431. (e) 96,783,000. (f) 0.010005.

2. Express the factors in scientific notation, then determine each product and represent it in scientific notation.
   (a) $0.00001 \times 689,000,000.$ (b) $23,500,000 \times 800.$
   (c) $186,000 \times 86,400.$ (d) $0.000000234 \times 0.00056.$

3. Divide 693,100,000 by 0.000000025 and express the quotient in scientific notation.

4. Represent each number in ordinary decimal notation.
   (a) $7.23 \times 10^5.$ (b) $1.9 \times 10^{-6}.$ (c) $2.478 \times 10^{14}.$
   (d) $5.0 \times 10^{-14}.$ (e) $6.75 \times 10^{-8}.$ (f) $6.75 \times 10^8.$

chapter 8

Real Number System

In this chapter we extend our concept of number so that each point on a number line will have a number as its coordinate. These new numbers have most of the principles of rational numbers. From the discussion of the rational numbers in Chapter 6 we recall that the set of rational numbers is closed under the operations of addition, subtraction, multiplication, and division (except division by zero). Also, the operations of addition and multiplication are commutative and associative, and the operation of multiplication is distributive over the operation of addition. In the set of rational numbers there is an additive identity and a multiplicative identity; each rational number has a rational number as its additive inverse, and each nonzero rational number has a rational number as its multiplicative inverse.

8-1 Irrational Numbers

In Chapter 6 we discussed the representation of rational numbers on a number line. We noted that the set of rational numbers is dense; that is, there is a rational number between any two given rational numbers. Consider the number line between the graphs of 0 and 1. There are many rational numbers between 0 and 1; for example, there are the points with coordinates

$\frac{1}{2}$, $\frac{1}{3}$, $\frac{2}{3}$, $\frac{1}{4}$, $\frac{3}{4}$, $\frac{1}{6}$, and $\frac{5}{6}$ (Figure 8-1).

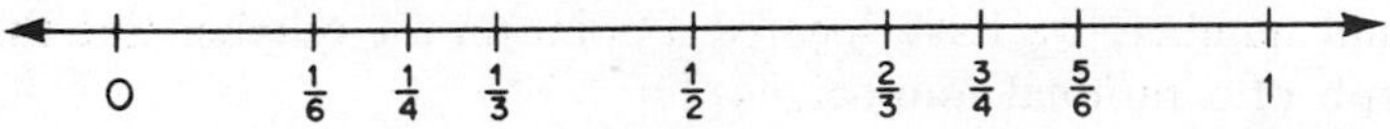

Figure 8-1

The graphs of rational numbers are spread throughout the number line. Any line segment, regardless of its length, contains an infinite number of graphs of rational numbers. In fact, one might think that every point on the number line is the graph of a rational number. *This is not so.* There are many points on the number line that are *not* graphs of rational numbers. For example, consider a square with sides of length 1 that has the line segment from 0 to 1 as a base (Figure 8-2).

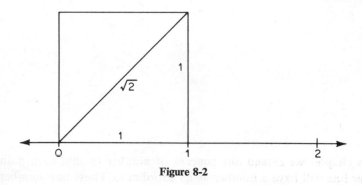

Figure 8-2

The length of the diagonal of the square may be represented by a number and, when the number is used as a factor two times, the product must be 2. We call the number $\sqrt{2}$ (read "square root of two"), and we can locate a point with coordinate $\sqrt{2}$ on the number line (Figure 8-3).

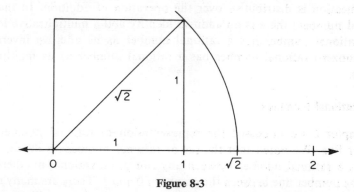

Figure 8-3

Notice that we have rotated the diagonal clockwise about the point with coordinate 0 until the other end of the diagonal marks the point on the number line with coordinate $\sqrt{2}$. Thus, if we can show that $\sqrt{2}$ is not a rational number, we have located a point on the number line that is not the graph of a rational number.

We shall assume that $\sqrt{2}$ is a rational number and use indirect reasoning to demonstrate that our original assumption is false. If $\sqrt{2}$ is a rational number, then we may express it in the form $\dfrac{a}{b}$, where a and b are integers, $b \neq 0$, and a and b are not both even. If $\dfrac{a}{b} = \sqrt{2}$, then

$$\frac{a}{b} \times \frac{a}{b} = 2 \quad \text{and} \quad \frac{a^2}{b^2} = 2.$$

Since a and b are integers, a^2 and b^2 are also integers, and $a^2 = 2b^2$. The integer $2b^2$ must be an even integer, because any integer is even if it is equal to the product of 2 and another integer. Remember that any integer is either even or odd. The product of two odd integers is an odd integer and the product $a \times a$ is even; therefore a cannot be odd. That is, a is an even integer. Thus, $a = 2k$, where k is an integer. Then the statement $a^2 = 2b^2$ may be written as

$$(2k)^2 = 2b^2 \quad \text{and} \quad (2k) \times (2k) = 2b^2$$

and as

$$k \times (2k) = b^2 \quad \text{and} \quad 2k^2 = b^2.$$

Thus b is an integer whose square is even, and b must be even. This is contrary to the assumption that a and b are not both even. Our assumption that there exists a rational number whose square is 2 has led to a contradiction, and so $\sqrt{2}$ is not a rational number.

The numbers that are coordinates of points on the number line and are not rational numbers are called **irrational numbers**. Some other examples of irrational numbers are

$$3\sqrt{2},\ 5\sqrt{2},\ \sqrt{3},\ \sqrt[3]{7},\ \sqrt[5]{19},\ \pi.$$

Exercises

1. List ten positive numbers less than 10 that do not appear to be rational numbers.

2. Assume that $\sqrt{3}$ is a rational number and use indirect reasoning to demonstrate that the original assumption is false and that therefore $\sqrt{3}$ is an irrational number. (*Note:* You may assume that, if d is an integer and d^2 is divisible by 3, then d is divisible by 3.)

8-2 Approximating $\sqrt{2}$ as a Decimal

We have learned that $\sqrt{2}$ is the name of a number whose square is 2. We have also demonstrated that there is a point on the number line with coordinate $\sqrt{2}$ and that there exist line segments of length $\sqrt{2}$. Now let us see whether we can represent $\sqrt{2}$ in decimal notation. We know from the definition of the number $\sqrt{2}$ that $(\sqrt{2})^2 = 2$. We then calculate the square of 1 and the square of 2 and quickly conclude that $\sqrt{2}$ is greater than 1 and less than 2, since $1^2 = 1$ and $2^2 = 4$. In other words, since

$$1^2 < (\sqrt{2})^2 < 2^2; \quad \text{that is, } 1 < 2 < 4,$$

we assume that

$$1 < \sqrt{2} < 2.$$

This statement, $1 < \sqrt{2} < 2$, is read "one is less than the square root of two and the square root of two is less than two." Now, to obtain a closer approximation, we find the squares of 1.1, 1.2, 1.3, 1.4, and so on, until we determine that $(1.5)^2$ is the first square that is greater than 2:

$$(1.1)^2 = 1.21,$$

$$(1.2)^2 = 1.44,$$

$$(1.3)^2 = 1.69,$$

$$(1.4)^2 = 1.96,$$

$$(1.5)^2 = 2.25.$$

An examination of these calculations should reveal that $\sqrt{2}$ is greater than 1.4 and less than 1.5, since $(1.4)^2 = 1.96$ and $(1.5)^2 = 2.25$:

$$(1.4)^2 < (\sqrt{2})^2 < (1.5)^2,$$

$$1.96 < 2 < 2.25,$$

$$1.4 < \sqrt{2} < 1.5.$$

We may extend this process and find an even closer decimal approximation of $\sqrt{2}$ by squaring 1.41, 1.42, 1.43, 1.44, and so on, until we determine that $(1.42)^2 > 2$. We then conclude that $\sqrt{2}$ is greater than 1.41 and less than 1.42, since $(1.41)^2 = 1.9881$ and $(1.42)^2 = 2.0164$:

$$(1.41)^2 < (\sqrt{2})^2 < (1.42)^2,$$

$$1.9881 < 2 < 2.0164,$$

$$1.41 < \sqrt{2} < 1.42.$$

The next extension of this process would reveal that $\sqrt{2}$ is greater than 1.414 and less than 1.415, since $(1.414)^2 = 1.999396$ and $(1.415)^2 = 2.002225$:

$$(1.414)^2 < (\sqrt{2})^2 < (1.415)^2,$$

$$1.999396 < 2 < 2.002225,$$

$$1.414 < \sqrt{2} < 1.415.$$

We can continue this process indefinitely by checking again and again to find two values that $\sqrt{2}$ lies between. In this manner we can determine an approximation for $\sqrt{2}$ to as many decimal places as we desire. If we had continued our procedure, we would have determined that the approximation of $\sqrt{2}$ to seven decimal places is 1.4142135. For most purposes we do not need so precise a value of $\sqrt{2}$. In fact, 1.414 is commonly used as an approximation of $\sqrt{2}$.

Special note should be made of the fact that we have been calculating *decimal approximations* for $\sqrt{2}$. The process used to determine the decimal approximation for $\sqrt{2}$ suggests that we write $\sqrt{2} = 1.4142135...$, where the three dots are used to indicate that the digits continue without terminating.

We recall that many rational numbers are represented as decimals with digits that continue without terminating. For example,

$$\frac{1}{3} = 0.333 \dots \quad \text{and} \quad \frac{13}{55} = 0.23636 \dots .$$

Then how can we tell the difference between a decimal representation of a rational number and a decimal representation of an irrational number? Fortunately, there is one special characteristic of the decimal representation of a rational number that aids in making a distinction. Each rational number may be expressed as a *repeating* (periodic) decimal, and if we continue to determine new digits in the decimal representation

$$\sqrt{2} = 1.4142135 \dots ,$$

we shall find that no digit or set of digits appear to repeat indefinitely. In general, each irrational number may be represented by a **nonrepeating decimal** that continues indefinitely.

Exercises

1. Find an expression for the number n such that
   (a) $n^2 = 5$.   (b) $n^2 = 7$.   (c) $n^2 = 13$.   (d) $n^2 = 16$.

2. We learned that $\sqrt{2}$ is between the integers 1 and 2; that is, $1 < \sqrt{2} < 2$. Between what two consecutive integers is
   (a) $\sqrt{3}$?   (b) $\sqrt{6}$?   (c) $\sqrt{12}$?   (d) $\sqrt{93}$?

3. Find to the nearest tenth the decimal approximation for each of the following.
   (a) $\sqrt{5}$.   (b) $\sqrt{8}$.   (c) $\sqrt{10}$.   (d) $\sqrt{29}$.

4. By definition, $(\sqrt{n})^2 = n$. Find a four-place decimal approximation for each.
   (a) $\sqrt{3}$.   (b) $\sqrt{6}$.

8-3 Real Numbers

Each number that we have studied thus far has been either rational or irrational. The union of the set of all rational numbers and the set of all irrational numbers is called the set of **real numbers**. We have learned that the rational and the irrational numbers are coordinates of points on the number line. In fact, every point on the number line is the graph of a real number; hence the number line is called the **real number line**. There is a one-to-one correspondence between the points on the real number line and the elements of the set of real numbers.

In Section 8-2 we stated that each rational number may be expressed as a repeating decimal and that each irrational number may be expressed as a nonrepeating decimal. Since the set consisting of all rational and irrational numbers is the set of real numbers, it follows that any real number may be expressed either as a repeating decimal or as a nonrepeating decimal. Conversely, any repeating decimal or nonrepeating decimal represents a real number.

A look at the diagram in Figure 8-4 may clarify the extensions used to develop the real number system.

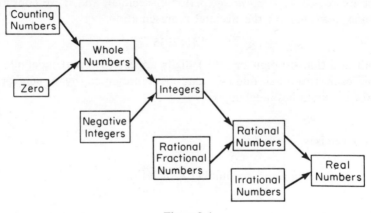

Figure 8-4

There are several ways of classifying real numbers. Each real number is

(1) positive, negative, or zero,
(2) a rational number or an irrational number,
(3) expressible as a repeating decimal or as a nonrepeating decimal.

Exercises

1. Which of these are rational numbers?

    (a) $\sqrt{3}$.   (b) $\sqrt{9}$.   (c) $\dfrac{17}{26}$.   (d) 0.172.

(e) π.   **(f)** $\frac{22}{7}$.   **(g)** $\sqrt{11}$.   **(h)** $\sqrt{16}$.

2. Which of the numbers in Exercise 1 are irrational numbers?

3. Which of the numbers in Exercise 1 are real numbers?

4. Represent each of the rational numbers in Exercise 1 as a repeating decimal.

5. Represent each of the irrational numbers in Exercise 1 as a nonrepeating decimal.

8-4 Principles of Real Numbers

The real numbers form a mathematical system with operations, relations, and principles. We can add, subtract, multiply, and divide real numbers. We can determine two real numbers as equal or unequal, and we have certain mathematical principles that apply to the real number system. These principles are as follows.

Principle of closure The real number system is closed under the operations of addition, subtraction, multiplication, and division (except division by zero).

Addition: If a and b are real numbers, then $a + b$ is a real number.

Subtraction: If a and b are real numbers, then $a - b$ is a real number.

Multiplication: If a and b are real numbers, then $a \times b$ is a real number.

Division: If a and b are real numbers and $b \neq 0$, then $a \div b$ is a real number.

Commutative principle In general for the real number system, addition and multiplication are commutative operations, whereas subtraction and division are not.

Addition: If a and b are real numbers, then $a + b = b + a$.

Subtraction: If a and b are real numbers, then $a - b \neq b - a$ when $a \neq b$.

Multiplication: If a and b are real numbers, then $a \times b = b \times a$.

Division: If a and b are real numbers different from zero, then $a \div b \neq b \div a$ when $a \neq b$.

Associative principle In general for the real number system, addition and multiplication are associative operations, whereas subtraction and division are not.

Addition: If a, b, and c are real numbers, then $(a + b) + c = a + (b + c)$.

Subtraction: If a, b, and c are real numbers, then in general $(a - b) - c \neq a - (b - c)$.

Multiplication: If a, b, and c are real numbers, then $(a \times b) \times c = a \times (b \times c)$.

Division: If a, b, and c are real numbers different from zero, then in general $(a \div b) \div c \neq a \div (b \div c)$.

Identities Zero is the identity element for the operations of addition and subtraction, and 1 is the identity element for the operations of multiplication and division.

Addition: If a is a real number, then $a + 0 = a$.
Subtraction: If a is a real number, then $a - 0 = a$.
Multiplication: If a is a real number, then $a \times 1 = a$.
Division: If a is a real number, then $a \div 1 = a$.

Distributive principle For the real number system, there are several instances where one operation may be distributed over another, and three cases may be considered: distributive from the left, distributive from the right, and distributive from both the left and the right. Some of the possibilities for consideration are as follows.

Multiplication over addition: If a, b, and c are real numbers, then $a \times (b + c) = (a \times b) + (a \times c)$.
Multiplication over subtraction: If a, b, and c are real numbers, then $a \times (b - c) = (a \times b) - (a \times c)$.
Division over addition: If a, b, and c are real numbers, then in general $a \div (b + c) \neq (a \div b) + (a \div c)$. If a, b, and c are real numbers and $c \neq 0$, then $(a + b) \div c = (a \div c) + (b \div c)$.
Division over subtraction: If a, b, and c are real numbers, then in general $a \div (b - c) \neq (a \div b) - (a \div c)$. If a, b, and c are real numbers and $c \neq 0$, then $(a - b) \div c = (a \div c) - (b \div c)$.

Inverses If a is a real number, then ^-a is a real number, called the additive inverse (negative) of a, such that $a + {}^-a = 0$. If a is a real number and $a \neq 0$, then $\dfrac{1}{a}$ is a real number, called the multiplicative inverse (reciprocal) of a, such that $a \times \dfrac{1}{a} = 1$.

Order The real number system is linearly ordered; that is, if a and b are *different* real numbers, then either $a > b$ or $a < b$.

Density The real number system is dense; that is, between any two distinct real numbers there is always another real number. Consequently, we can find an infinite number of real numbers between any two distinct real numbers.

Completeness The real number system is complete; that is, there is a real number for every point of the number line and, conversely, there is a point of the number line for every real number.

Exercises

1. Is the sum of two irrational numbers always an irrational number?
2. Is the product of two irrational numbers always an irrational number?
3. What is the additive inverse of

   (a) $\sqrt{3}$?   (b) $^-\sqrt{6}$?   (c) $\dfrac{1}{\sqrt{7}}$?   (d) $\sqrt{3} + \sqrt{2}$?

4. What is the multiplicative inverse of

   (a) $\sqrt{5}$?   (b) $^-\sqrt{2}$?   (c) $\dfrac{1}{\sqrt{11}}$?   (d) $\sqrt{6} + \sqrt{7}$?

5. If two positive real numbers are represented as infinite decimals, how can you tell which is the greater?

chapter 9

Nondecimal Systems
of Numeration

In Chapter 3 we learned that a system of numeration is a systematic method of naming numbers. In the decimal system of notation we can represent any number with only ten digits (0, 1, 2, 3, 4, 5, 6, 7, 8, 9) and the idea of place value. In this chapter we shall discuss systems of numeration with bases other than ten. The study of different number bases provides an opportunity for us to gain an appreciation of the features of our decimal system of numeration and our computational methods. We should develop a better understanding of the decimal system as a result of this study.

9-1 Collecting in Sets Other than Ten

Although the base is not specified, the idea of collecting in sets other than ten is frequently used in various kinds of measurements. For example, the idea of collecting in sets of two is used in the following dry measures (the symbol $\overset{m}{=}$ is read "is equal in measure to"):

$$2 \text{ cups} \overset{m}{=} 1 \text{ pint},$$

$$2 \text{ pints} \overset{m}{=} 1 \text{ quart},$$

$$2 \text{ quarts} \overset{m}{=} 1 \text{ half-gallon},$$

$$2 \text{ half-gallons} \overset{m}{=} 1 \text{ gallon}.$$

Base two, called the binary base, is used also in electronic computers.

Collecting objects by the dozen, gross, and great gross are illustrations of the use of twelve as a base. Other examples of this method of grouping are the number of months in a year and the number of inches in a foot.

The idea of base sixty is used in measuring time and angles. In the case of time,

$$60 \text{ seconds} \overset{m}{=} 1 \text{ minute,}$$

$$60 \text{ minutes} \overset{m}{=} 1 \text{ hour.}$$

In the case of angles,

$$60 \text{ seconds} \overset{m}{=} 1 \text{ minute,}$$

$$60 \text{ minutes} \overset{m}{=} 1 \text{ degree.}$$

9-2 Base Five Numeration

The base of any system of numeration establishes the method of grouping and the number of digits needed. In the base ten system we collect in sets of ten. In the base five system, we collect in sets of five, and we can represent any number with only five digits (0, 1, 2, 3, 4) and a positional notation. For example, consider the following illustrations of grouping in base five.

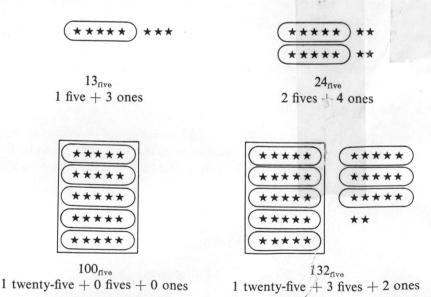

13_{five}
1 five + 3 ones

24_{five}
2 fives + 4 ones

100_{five}
1 twenty-five + 0 fives + 0 ones

132_{five}
1 twenty-five + 3 fives + 2 ones

It is important to note the subscript used in writing the numerals 13_{five}, 24_{five}, 100_{five}, and 132_{five}. The subscript "five" denotes the base, and the numeral 13_{five} is read "one three, base five." Any numeral written without a subscript will be assumed to be in base ten notation. Thus we have two names for the same number in each of the following:

$$13_{\text{five}} = 8,$$
$$24_{\text{five}} = 14,$$
$$100_{\text{five}} = 25,$$
$$132_{\text{five}} = 42.$$

Since counting is fundamental to the understanding of a system of numeration, we should study the table below, which gives the base ten and base five numerals for the numbers 1 through 26.

Base Ten		Base Five	
Numeral	*Meaning*	*Numeral*	*Meaning*
1	1 one	1_{five}	1 one
2	2 ones	2_{five}	2 ones
3	3 ones	3_{five}	3 ones
4	4 ones	4_{five}	4 ones
5	5 ones	10_{five}	1 five, 0 ones
6	6 ones	11_{five}	1 five, 1 one
7	7 ones	12_{five}	1 five, 2 ones
8	8 ones	13_{five}	1 five, 3 ones
9	9 ones	14_{five}	1 five, 4 ones
10	1 ten, 0 ones	20_{five}	2 fives, 0 ones
11	1 ten, 1 one	21_{five}	2 fives, 1 one
12	1 ten, 2 ones	22_{five}	2 fives, 2 ones
13	1 ten, 3 ones	23_{five}	2 fives, 3 ones
14	1 ten, 4 ones	24_{five}	2 fives, 4 ones
15	1 ten, 5 ones	30_{five}	3 fives, 0 ones
16	1 ten, 6 ones	31_{five}	3 fives, 1 one
17	1 ten, 7 ones	32_{five}	3 fives, 2 ones
18	1 ten, 8 ones	33_{five}	3 fives, 3 ones
19	1 ten, 9 ones	34_{five}	3 fives, 4 ones
20	2 tens, 0 ones	40_{five}	4 fives, 0 ones
21	2 tens, 1 one	41_{five}	4 fives, 1 one
22	2 tens, 2 ones	42_{five}	4 fives, 2 ones
23	2 tens, 3 ones	43_{five}	4 fives, 3 ones
24	2 tens, 4 ones	44_{five}	4 fives, 4 ones
25	2 tens, 5 ones	100_{five}	1 twenty-five, 0 fives, 0 ones
26	2 tens, 6 ones	101_{five}	1 twenty-five, 0 fives, 1 one

The value represented by each digit in a given base five numeral is determined by the position it occupies. For example, consider the numeral 32_{five}. The position of the 3 in this numeral indicates that it represents three sets of five whereas the 2 represents two sets of one.

The place values in the base five system are based on powers of five. Starting at the ones place and moving to the left, each place has a value five times as large as the value of the place to its right.

Place Values for Base Five

Six Hundred Twenty-fives	One Hundred Twenty-fives	Twenty-fives	Fives	Ones
$5 \times (5 \times 5 \times 5)$	$5 \times (5 \times 5)$	5×5	5×1	1
5^4	5^3	5^2	5^1	5^0

To change the notation for a number from base five to base ten, we express the number in terms of powers of five and simplify. Consider the examples below.

Example 1 Represent 432_{five} in base ten notation.

$$432_{\text{five}} = (4 \times 5^2) + (3 \times 5^1) + (2 \times 5^0)$$
$$= (4 \times 25) + (3 \times 5) + (2 \times 1)$$
$$= 100 + 15 + 2$$
$$= 117$$

Example 2 Represent $3{,}201_{\text{five}}$ in base ten notation.

$$3{,}201_{\text{five}} = (3 \times 5^3) + (2 \times 5^2) + (0 \times 5^1) + (1 \times 5^0)$$
$$= (3 \times 125) + (2 \times 25) + (0 \times 5) + (1 \times 1)$$
$$= 375 + 50 + 0 + 1$$
$$= 426$$

Example 3 Represent 123.42_{five} in base ten notation.

$$123.42_{\text{five}} = (1 \times 5^2) + (2 \times 5^1) + (3 \times 5^0) + (4 \times 5^{-1}) + (2 \times 5^{-2})$$
$$= (1 \times 25) + (2 \times 5) + (3 \times 1) + \left(4 \times \frac{1}{5}\right) + \left(2 \times \frac{1}{25}\right)$$
$$= (1 \times 25) + (2 \times 5) + (3 \times 1) + \left(4 \times \frac{2}{10}\right) + \left(2 \times \frac{4}{100}\right)$$
$$= 25 + 10 + 3 + \frac{8}{10} + \frac{8}{100}$$
$$= 38.88$$

Exercises

1. Illustrate with a diagram the grouping indicated by each of the following.
   (a) 12_{five}.   (b) 44_{five}.   (c) 113_{five}.   (d) 204_{five}.

2. List the base ten and base five numerals for the numbers 27 through 60.

3. Represent each number in terms of powers of five.
   (a) 413_{five}.   **(b)** $2,243_{\text{five}}$.   **(c)** 42.3_{five}.   **(d)** 1.32_{five}.

4. Represent each number in base ten notation.
   (a) 12_{five}.   **(b)** 44_{five}.   **(c)** 113_{five}.   **(d)** 204_{five}.
   (e) 342_{five}.   **(f)** $4,124_{\text{five}}$.   **(g)** $243,214_{\text{five}}$.   **(h)** 31.4_{five}.

9-3 Computation in Base Five Notation

Since the place values in base five follow the pattern of our denominations of money to a certain point, consider these illustrations of addition in base five in which pennies, nickels, and quarters are used.

Example 1 The sum of four pennies and three pennies is equal in value to one nickel and two pennies. This sum may be represented in base five notation as

$$4_{\text{five}} + 3_{\text{five}} = 12_{\text{five}},$$

where 12_{five} means 1 set of five (1 nickel) and 2 sets of one (2 pennies).

Example 2 If we add three nickels and four pennies to four nickels and three pennies, the sum is equal in value to one quarter, three nickels, and two pennies. This sum may be represented as

$$34_{\text{five}} + 43_{\text{five}} = 132_{\text{five}},$$

where 132_{five} means 1 set of twenty-five (1 quarter), 3 sets of five (3 nickels), and 2 sets of one (2 pennies).

Our understanding of addition in base five notation will be improved by an examination of the addition table for basic sums represented in base five notation.

Base Five Addition Table

+	0	1	2	3	4
0	0	1	2	3	4
1	1	2	3	4	10
2	2	3	4	10	11
3	3	4	10	11	12
4	4	10	11	12	13

Refer to the addition table to verify the sums obtained by computation in base five notation in Examples 3 and 4.

Example 3 Add 13_{five} and 22_{five}.

$$\overset{1}{1}3_{five}$$
$$+22_{five}$$
$$\overline{40_{five}}$$

Procedure: From the table we determine that

$$3_{five} + 2_{five} = 10_{five}$$

and then write 0 in the ones column and "carry" 1 set of five to the fives column. Next we determine from the table that

$$1_{five} + 2_{five} = 3_{five} \quad \text{and} \quad 3_{five} + 1_{five} = 4_{five}.$$

Thus, we have 4 sets of five, and we represent the sum of 13_{five} and 22_{five} as 40_{five}. We can check our result by converting the base five numerals to base ten numerals and adding.

$$13_{five} = (1 \times 5) + (3 \times 1) = 8$$
$$+22_{five} = (2 \times 5) + (2 \times 1) = 12$$
$$\overline{40_{five} = (4 \times 5) + (0 \times 1) = 20}$$

Example 4 Add 424_{five} and 323_{five}.

$$\overset{111}{4}24_{five}$$
$$+323_{five}$$
$$\overline{1{,}302_{five}}$$

Procedure: From the table we determine that

$$4_{five} + 3_{five} = 12_{five}$$

and then write 2 in the ones column and "carry" 1 set of five to the fives column. Next we determine from the table that

$$2_{five} + 2_{five} = 4_{five} \quad \text{and} \quad 4_{five} + 1_{five} = 10_{five};$$

then write 0 in the fives column and "carry" 1 set of twenty-five to the twenty-fives column. Next we determine from the table that

$$4_{five} + 3_{five} = 12_{five} \quad \text{and} \quad 12_{five} + 1_{five} = 13_{five};$$

then we write 3 in the twenty-fives column and "carry" 1 set of one hundred twenty-five to the one hundred twenty-fives column. So we represent the sum of 424_{five} and 323_{five} as $1{,}302_{five}$. We can check our result by converting the base five numerals to base ten numerals and adding.

$$424_{five} = (4 \times 5^2) + (2 \times 5) + (4 \times 1) = 114$$
$$+323_{five} = (3 \times 5^2) + (2 \times 5) + (3 \times 1) = 88$$
$$\overline{1{,}302_{five} = (1 \times 5^3) + (3 \times 5^2) + (0 \times 5) + (2 \times 1) = 202}$$

The table of addition facts also may be used to solve subtraction problems, since subtraction is the inverse operation of addition.

Example 5 Subtract 32_{five} from 42_{five}.

$$\begin{array}{r} 42_{\text{five}} \\ -32_{\text{five}} \\ \hline 10_{\text{five}} \end{array}$$

Procedure: Recall that a subtraction problem may be considered as an addition problem in which the sum and one addend are known. In this example we are trying to find the missing addend that produces a sum of 42_{five} when added to 32_{five}. From the addition table we determine that 0 is the number that must be added to 2 to produce the sum 2; thus, we write 0 in the ones column. Next we determine what number must be added to 3 to produce the sum 4 in the fives column:

$$1_{\text{five}} + 3_{\text{five}} = 4_{\text{five}}.$$

Thus we determine that 10_{five} is the missing addend and that

$$42_{\text{five}} - 32_{\text{five}} = 10_{\text{five}}.$$

We can check our result by converting the base five numerals to base ten numerals and subtracting.

$$\begin{array}{r} 42_{\text{five}} = (4 \times 5) + (2 \times 1) = 22 \\ -32_{\text{five}} = (3 \times 5) + (2 \times 1) = 17 \\ \hline 10_{\text{five}} = (1 \times 5) + (0 \times 1) = 5 \end{array}$$

Example 6 Subtract 14_{five} from 31_{five}.

$$\begin{array}{r} \overset{2\,1}{3\!\!\!1}_{\text{five}} \\ -14_{\text{five}} \\ \hline 12_{\text{five}} \end{array}$$

Procedure: From the addition table we determine that there is no number that may be added to 4 to produce 1; however, if we "borrow" 1 of the 3 sets of five, we determine that

$$4_{\text{five}} + 2_{\text{five}} = 11_{\text{five}}.$$

So we write a 2 in the ones column and understand that we have only 2 of the 3 given sets of five left. Next we determine what number must be added to 1 to produce 2 in the fives column:

$$1_{\text{five}} + 1_{\text{five}} = 2_{\text{five}}.$$

So we represent

$$31_{\text{five}} - 14_{\text{five}} \text{ as } 12_{\text{five}}.$$

We can check our result by converting the base five numerals to base ten numerals and subtracting.

$$31_{five} = (3 \times 5) + (1 \times 1) = 16$$
$$-14_{five} = (1 \times 5) + (4 \times 1) = \underline{9}$$
$$12_{five} = (1 \times 5) + (2 \times 1) = \overline{7}$$

To develop our understanding of multiplication in base five, a table of multiplication facts represented in base five notation is provided. The repeated-addition approach also may be used to perform multiplication in base five; see the table below.

Base Five Multiplication Table

×	0	1	2	3	4
0	0	0	0	0	0
1	0	1	2	3	4
2	0	2	4	11	13
3	0	3	11	14	22
4	0	4	13	22	31

Refer to the multiplication table to verify the products obtained by computation in base five notation in Examples 7 and 8.

Example 7 Multiply 34_{five} by 3_{five}.

$$\overset{2\,2}{34}_{five}$$
$$\times\ 3_{five}$$
$$\overline{212_{five}}$$

Procedure: From the table we determine that

$$3_{five} \times 4_{five} = 22_{five}$$

and then write 2 in the ones column and "carry" 2 sets of five to the fives column. Next we determine from the table that

$$3_{five} \times 3_{five} = 14_{five}$$

and add the 2 that we carried:

$$14_{five} + 2_{five} = 21_{five}.$$

We write 1 in the fives column and 2 in the twenty-fives column. So we represent the product of 3_{five} and 34_{five} as 212_{five}. We can check our result by converting the base five numerals to base ten numerals and multiplying.

$$34_{five} = \qquad\qquad (3 \times 5) + (4 \times 1) = 19$$
$$\times\ 3_{five} = \qquad\qquad (3 \times 1) = \underline{3}$$
$$\overline{212_{five}} = (2 \times 5^2) + (1 \times 5) + (2 \times 1) = \overline{57}$$

Example 8 Multiply 324_{five} by 12_{five}.

$$
\begin{array}{r}
\overset{1\,1\,1}{324}_{\text{five}} \\
\times\ \ 12_{\text{five}} \\
\hline
1\ 203 \\
3\ 24 \\
\hline
4{,}443_{\text{five}}
\end{array}
$$

Procedure: From the table we determine that

$$2_{\text{five}} \times 4_{\text{five}} = 13_{\text{five}}$$

and then write 3 in the ones column and "carry" 1 set of five to the fives column. Next we determine that

$$2_{\text{five}} \times 2_{\text{five}} = 4_{\text{five}}$$

and add the 1 that we carried:

$$4_{\text{five}} + 1_{\text{five}} = 10_{\text{five}}.$$

We write 0 in the fives column and "carry" 1 set of twenty-five to the twenty-fives column. Then we determine that

$$2_{\text{five}} \times 3_{\text{five}} = 11_{\text{five}}$$

and add the 1 that we carried:

$$11_{\text{five}} + 1_{\text{five}} = 12_{\text{five}}.$$

We write 2 in the twenty-fives column and 1 in the one hundred twenty-fives column. The partial product is then

$$2_{\text{five}} \times 324_{\text{five}} = 1{,}203_{\text{five}}.$$

We observe in the table that 1 is the multiplicative identity and that

$$1_{\text{five}} \times 324_{\text{five}} = 324_{\text{five}}.$$

The partial product 324_{five} is set one place to the left, as in decimal arithmetic, because we actually have the product

$$10_{\text{five}} \times 324_{\text{five}} = 3{,}240_{\text{five}}.$$

We add the partial products and obtain $4{,}443_{\text{five}}$. We can check this result by converting the base five numerals to base ten numerals and multiplying.

$$
\begin{array}{rll}
324_{\text{five}} = & (3 \times 5^2) + (2 \times 5) + (4 \times 1) = & 89 \\
\times\ 12_{\text{five}} = & (1 \times 5) + (2 \times 1) = & 7 \\
\hline
4{,}443_{\text{five}} = (4 \times 5^3) + (4 \times 5^2) + (4 \times 5) + (3 \times 1) = & 623
\end{array}
$$

The table of multiplication facts also may be used to solve division problems, since division is the inverse operation of multiplication.

Example 9 Divide 124_{five} by 3_{five}.

$$
\begin{array}{r}
23_{\text{five}} \\
3_{\text{five}})\overline{124_{\text{five}}} \\
-11_{\text{five}} \\
\hline
14_{\text{five}} \\
-14_{\text{five}} \\
\hline
\end{array}
$$

Procedure: Recall that a division problem may be considered as a multiplication problem in which the product and one factor are known. In this example we are trying to find the missing factor that produces a product of 124_{five} when multiplied by 3_{five}. From the multiplication table we determine that 2 is the number that we multiply by 3 to obtain a product that is as close to 12_{five} as we can get, such that the product is less than 12_{five}; that is,

$$3_{\text{five}} \times 2_{\text{five}} = 11_{\text{five}}.$$

So we write 2 in the fives place in the quotient, subtract 11_{five} from 12_{five}, bring down the next digit. Now we must find what number multiplied by 3_{five} will give 14_{five} and from the multiplication table we conclude that

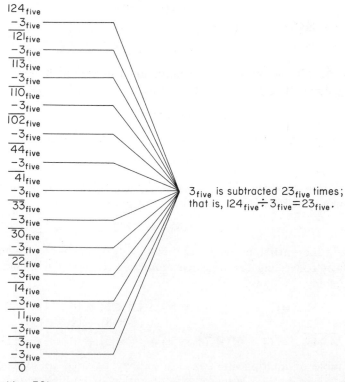

3_{five} is subtracted 23_{five} times; that is, $124_{\text{five}} \div 3_{\text{five}} = 23_{\text{five}}$.

Smith p. 301a

$$3_{\text{five}} \times 3_{\text{five}} = 14_{\text{five}}.$$

Thus we determine that 23_{five} is the missing factor and that

$$124_{\text{five}} \div 3_{\text{five}} = 23_{\text{five}}.$$

We can check the result by converting the base five numerals to base ten numerals and dividing.

$$124_{\text{five}} \div 3_{\text{five}} = [(1 \times 5^2) + (2 \times 5) + (4 \times 1)] \div 3$$
$$= 39 \div 3$$
$$= 13$$

$$\text{and} \quad 23_{\text{five}} = (2 \times 5) + (3 \times 1) = 13$$

We can also use a repeated-subtraction process (Section 5-14) to determine the quotient $124_{\text{five}} \div 3_{\text{five}}$. Consider the illustration of the repeated-subtraction process on page 184, and note that each subtraction is performed in base five notation.

Example 10 Divide $134{,}201_{\text{five}}$ by 23_{five}.

$$
\begin{array}{r}
3{,}202_{\text{five}} \\
23_{\text{five}} \overline{)\ 134{,}201_{\text{five}}} \\
-124_{\text{five}} \\
\hline
10\ 2_{\text{five}} \\
-10\ 1_{\text{five}} \\
\hline
101_{\text{five}} \\
-101_{\text{five}} \\
\hline
\end{array}
$$

Procedure: As observed in Example 9, we may divide numbers represented in base five notation by using the same computational patterns that we use to divide numbers represented in base ten; however, the operations of multiplication and subtraction are performed in base five notation. We can check the result by converting the base five numerals to base ten numerals and dividing.

$$134{,}201_{\text{five}} = (1 \times 5^5) + (3 \times 5^4) + (4 \times 5^3) + (2 \times 5^2)$$
$$+ (0 \times 5) + (1 \times 1) = 5{,}551$$

$$23_{\text{five}} = (2 \times 5) + (3 \times 1) = 13$$

$$3{,}202_{\text{five}} = (3 \times 5^3) + (2 \times 5^2) + (0 \times 5) + (2 \times 1) = 427$$

$$
\begin{array}{r}
427 \\
13 \overline{)\ 5{,}551} \\
-5\,2 \\
\hline
35 \\
-26 \\
\hline
91 \\
-91 \\
\hline
\end{array}
$$

Exercises

1. Find each sum in base five notation.

(a) 34_{five}
$+\ 3_{\text{five}}$

(b) 234_{five}
$+102_{\text{five}}$

(c) $1{,}234_{\text{five}}$
$+3{,}211_{\text{five}}$

(d) 101_{five}
124_{five}
$+432_{\text{five}}$

2. Convert the base five numerals in each part of Exercise 1 to base ten numerals and check the sum.

3. Find each difference in base five notation.

(a) 14_{five}
$-\ 3_{\text{five}}$

(b) 32_{five}
-23_{five}

(c) 421_{five}
-243_{five}

(d) $2{,}413_{\text{five}}$
$-1{,}014_{\text{five}}$

4. Convert the base five numerals in each part of Exercise 3 to base ten numerals and check the difference.

5. Find each product in base five notation.

(a) 40_{five}
$\times\ 4_{\text{five}}$

(b) 121_{five}
$\times\ 3_{\text{five}}$

(c) 413_{five}
$\times\ 42_{\text{five}}$

(d) $2{,}132_{\text{five}}$
$\times\ 21_{\text{five}}$

6. Convert the base five numerals in each part of Exercise 5 to base ten numerals and check the product.

7. Find each quotient in base five notation.

(a) $3_{\text{five}}\overline{)102_{\text{five}}}$

(b) $4_{\text{five}}\overline{)3{,}333_{\text{five}}}$

(c) $21_{\text{five}}\overline{)441_{\text{five}}}$

(d) $43_{\text{five}}\overline{)324{,}301_{\text{five}}}$

8. Convert the base five numerals in each part of Exercise 7 to base ten numerals and check the quotient.

9. We have learned that the symbols used in a system of numeration are man-made. In our discussion of base five numeration we have been using the conventional symbols 0, 1, 2, 3, and 4 as our five digits. Suppose we had chosen the letters E, F, G, H, and J for our five basic digits, as $E = 0$, $F = 1$, $G = 2$, $H = 3$, and $J = 4$. Complete the following tables of addition and multiplication facts, using the nonconventional symbols E, F, G, H, and J.

+	E	F	G	H	J
E					
F					
G					
H					
J					

×	E	F	G	H	J
E					
F					
G					
H					
J					

10. Compute, using the tables in Exercise 9.

 (a) JG   (b) GHJ   (c) HGJ   (d) $\overline{\text{J})\text{HG,HEJ}}$

  $+$HH $-$ JG $\times$ H

9-4 Change of Base

Translating from one base to another involves a regrouping process. As noted in Section 9-2, we change the notation for a number from base five to base ten by expressing the number in terms of powers of five and simplifying. For example,

$$
\begin{aligned}
3{,}214_{\text{five}} &= (3 \times 5^3) + (2 \times 5^2) + (1 \times 5^1) + (4 \times 5^0) \\
&= (3 \times 125) + (2 \times 25) + (1 \times 5) + (4 \times 1) \\
&= 375 + 50 + 5 + 4 \\
&= 434.
\end{aligned}
$$

Suppose we desire to represent the number 434 in base five notation, that is, in terms of powers of five. First, it is necessary to determine the highest power of five that we can subtract from 434. Since $5^4 = 625$ and $5^3 = 125$, we conclude that 5^3 is the highest power of five that is not greater than 434. Thus we can subtract 125 from 434 three times, leaving a difference of 59.

$$
\begin{array}{rl}
434 & \\
-125 & \quad (1 \times 5^3) \\
\hline
309 & \\
-125 & \quad (1 \times 5^3) \\
\hline
184 & \\
-125 & \quad (1 \times 5^3) \\
\hline
59 & \quad (3 \times 5^3)
\end{array}
$$

Our base five numeral begins to take form as

$$(3 \times 5^3) + (? \times 5^2) + (? \times 5^1) + (? \times 5^0).$$

Next we observe that the next lower power of five is 5^2, and $5^2 = 25$. Thus we can subtract 25 from 59 two times leaving a difference of 9.

$$
\begin{array}{rl}
59 & \\
-25 & \quad (1 \times 5^2) \\
\hline
34 & \\
-25 & \quad (1 \times 5^2) \\
\hline
9 & \quad (2 \times 5^2)
\end{array}
$$

We now have

$$(3 \times 5^3) + (2 \times 5^2) + (? \times 5^1) + (? \times 5^0).$$

The next lower power of five is 5^1, and we can subtract 5 from 9 one time, leaving a difference of 4.

$$\begin{array}{r} 9 \\ -5 \\ \hline 4 \end{array} \quad (1 \times 5^1)$$

We now have

$$(3 \times 5^3) + (2 \times 5^2) + (1 \times 5^1) + (? \times 5^0)$$

and, since $4 = 4 \times 5^0$, we conclude that

$$\begin{aligned} 434 &= (3 \times 125) + (2 \times 25) + (1 \times 5) + 4 \\ &= (3 \times 5^3) + (2 \times 5^2) + (1 \times 5^1) + (4 \times 5^0) \\ &= 3{,}214_{\text{five}}. \end{aligned}$$

To improve our understanding of the procedure for changing from base ten to base five we may study the following examples.

Example 1 Represent 8 in base five notation.

Since $5^2 = 25$ and $5^1 = 5$, the highest power of five that we can subtract from 8 is 5^1 and the difference is 3.

$$\begin{array}{r} 8 \\ -5 \\ \hline 3 \end{array}$$

Thus we have

$$\begin{aligned} 8 &= (1 \times 5) + 3 \\ &= (1 \times 5^1) + (3 \times 5^0) \\ &= 13_{\text{five}}. \end{aligned}$$

Example 2 Represent 173 in base five notation.

Since $5^4 = 625$ and $5^3 = 125$, the highest power of five that we can subtract from 173 is 5^3.

$$\begin{array}{r} 173 \\ -125 \\ \hline 48 \end{array}$$

Next we observe that $5^2 = 25$ and 5^2 may be subtracted from 48 one time.

$$\begin{array}{r} 48 \\ -25 \\ \hline 23 \end{array}$$

Finally, we subtract 5 from 23 four times and have a remainder of 3.

$$
\begin{array}{r}
23 \\
-\ 5 \\
\hline
18 \\
-\ 5 \\
\hline
13 \\
-\ 5 \\
\hline
8 \\
-\ 5 \\
\hline
3
\end{array}
$$

Thus we have

$$
\begin{aligned}
173 &= (1 \times 125) + (1 \times 25) + (4 \times 5) + 3 \\
&= (1 \times 5^3) + (1 \times 5^2) + (4 \times 5^1) + (3 \times 5^0) \\
&= 1{,}143_{\text{five}}.
\end{aligned}
$$

Exercises

1. Represent each number in base ten notation.
   (a) 123_{five}.   (b) $1{,}000_{\text{five}}$.   (c) $434{,}001_{\text{five}}$.   (d) $1{,}000{,}000_{\text{five}}$.
2. Represent each number in base five notation.
   (a) 29.   (b) 93.   (c) 785.   (d) 456.
   (e) 18.2.   (f) 5.6.   (g) 42.08.   (h) 0.48.

9-5 Base Nine Numeration

In the base nine system of numeration we group in sets of nine, and we can represent any number with nine digits (0, 1, 2, 3, 4, 5, 6, 7, 8) and a positional notation. We shall rely on our understanding of base ten and base five to develop the base nine system.

Exercises

1. Illustrate the grouping of each of these sets of objects in sets of nine by a diagram, and fill in the blanks to make each statement true.

   (a) 1 set of nine and —— ones, written 13_{nine}.   (b) ——sets of nine and —— ones, written ——$_{\text{nine}}$.

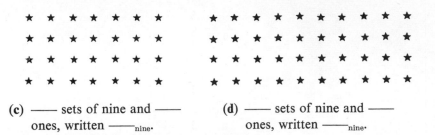

(c) —— sets of nine and ——
ones, written ——$_{nine}$.

(d) —— sets of nine and ——
ones, written ——$_{nine}$.

2. List the base ten and base nine numerals for the numbers 1 through 50.

3. Complete the place-value chart for base nine.

		Eighty-ones	*Nines*	*Ones*
	$9 \times (9 \times 9)$		9×1	1
9^4		9^2		9^0

4. Represent each number in base ten notation.

(a) 38_{nine}.   **(b)** 527_{nine}.   **(c)** 354_{nine}.   **(d)** $1{,}831_{nine}$.

5. Complete the following tables of addition and multiplication facts for base nine.

+	0	1	2	3	4	5	6	7	8
0									
1									
2									
3									
4									
5									
6									
7									
8									

×	0	1	2	3	4	5	6	7	8
0									
1									
2									
3									
4									
5									
6									
7									
8									

6. Find each sum in base nine notation.

(a) 76_{nine} $+12_{nine}$

(b) 38_{nine} $+46_{nine}$

(c) 657_{nine} $+302_{nine}$

(d) $2,485_{nine}$ $+5,406_{nine}$

7. Find each difference in base nine notation.

(a) 45_{nine} -23_{nine}

(b) 281_{nine} -144_{nine}

(c) 736_{nine} -546_{nine}

(d) $1,000_{nine}$ $-\ 888_{nine}$

8. Find each product in base nine notation.

(a) 82_{nine} $\times\ 5_{nine}$

(b) 674_{nine} $\times\ 8_{nine}$

(c) 78_{nine} $\times 43_{nine}$

(d) $8,765_{nine}$ $\times\ 167_{nine}$

9. Find each quotient in base nine notation.

(a) $6_{nine})\overline{323_{nine}}$

(b) $4_{nine})\overline{2,213_{nine}}$

(c) $57_{nine})\overline{7,117_{nine}}$

(d) $82_{nine})\overline{145,646_{nine}}$

10. Represent each number in base nine notation.

(a) 13.   (b) 97.   (c) 860.   (d) 12,789.

9-6 Base Two Numeration

Many electronic computing machines use a numeration system with a base of two. This system, often called the **binary system**, involves only two digits, 0 and 1. Consider the following table, which compares the base ten and base two numerals for the numbers 1 through 20.

Base Ten		Base Two	
Numeral	*Meaning*	*Numeral*	*Meaning*
1	1 one	1_{two}	1 one
2	2 ones	10_{two}	1 two, 0 ones
3	3 ones	11_{two}	1 two, 1 one
4	4 ones	100_{two}	1 four, 0 twos, 0 ones
5	5 ones	101_{two}	1 four, 0 twos, 1 one
6	6 ones	110_{two}	1 four, 1 two, 0 ones
7	7 ones	111_{two}	1 four, 1 two, 1 one
8	8 ones	$1,000_{two}$	1 eight, 0 fours, 0 twos, 0 ones
9	9 ones	$1,001_{two}$	1 eight, 0 fours, 0 twos, 1 one
10	1 ten, 0 ones	$1,010_{two}$	1 eight, 0 fours, 1 two, 0 ones
11	1 ten, 1 one	$1,011_{two}$	1 eight, 0 fours, 1 two, 1 one
12	1 ten, 2 ones	$1,100_{two}$	1 eight, 1 four, 0 twos, 0 ones
13	1 ten, 3 ones	$1,101_{two}$	1 eight, 1 four, 0 twos, 1 one
14	1 ten, 4 ones	$1,110_{two}$	1 eight, 1 four, 1 two, 0 ones
15	1 ten, 5 ones	$1,111_{two}$	1 eight, 1 four, 1 two, 1 one
16	1 ten, 6 ones	$10,000_{two}$	1 sixteen, 0 eights, 0 fours, 0 twos, 0 ones
17	1 ten, 7 ones	$10,001_{two}$	1 sixteen, 0 eights, 0 fours, 0 twos, 1 one
18	1 ten, 8 ones	$10,010_{two}$	1 sixteen, 0 eights, 0 fours, 1 two, 0 ones
19	1 ten, 9 ones	$10,011_{two}$	1 sixteen, 0 eights, 0 fours, 1 two, 1 one
20	2 tens, 0 ones	$10,100_{two}$	1 sixteen, 0 eights, 1 four, 0 twos, 0 ones

Since the binary system has only two digits, the tables of addition and multiplication facts are relatively simple, as shown.

Base Two Addition Table   Base Two Multiplication Table

+	0	1
0	0	1
1	0	10

×	0	1
0	0	0
1	0	1

Exercises

1. Represent each number in base ten notation.
   (a) $10,101_{two}$.
   (b) $11,111_{two}$.
   (c) $100,110_{two}$.
   (d) $100,000,010,000_{two}$.

2. Represent each number in base two notation.
   (a) 23.
   (b) 32.
   (c) 65.
   (d) 130.

3. Perform the indicated operation in base two notation.
   (a) $100_{two} + 101_{two}$.
   (b) $101_{two} \times 10,101_{two}$.
   (c) $1,110_{two} - 101_{two}$.
   (d) $11,001_{two} \div 101_{two}$.

(e) $10,110_{two}$
$\quad\ 1,001_{two}$
$\quad 10,110_{two}$
$+111,111_{two}$

(f) $10,000_{two}$
$\quad -\ 11_{two}$

9-7 Base Twelve Numeration

The base twelve system of numeration is often called the **duodecimal system.**
Our persent civilization contains several evidences that our ancestors col-
lected things in sets of twelve. For example, eggs are sold by the dozen,
twelve inches are equal in measure to one foot, and our calendar is based
on a twelve-month year.

The duodecimal system has several advantages over the decimal system.
Our of these is that the number twelve has more counting numbers as
factors than the number ten: twelve has 1, 2, 3, 4, 6, and 12 as factors, while
ten has only 1, 2, 5, and 10 as factors. Another advantage is that twelve is
more closely related to many of our common units of measure, such as
those mentioned in Section 9-1.

An interesting problem arises when we begin our consideration of a
numeration system in base twelve. We have already noted that any numeration system has the same number of digits as its base. Thus, the duodecimal
system must have twelve digits. If we use the standard decimal digits, 0, 1,
2, 3, 4, 5, 6, 7, 8, and 9, we have only ten digits, and it becomes necessary
to invent two new symbols to make the required total of twelve.

We shall use the letter T as a digit to represent the number ten and the
letter E as a digit to represent the number eleven; that is,

$$T_{twelve} = 10 \quad \text{and} \quad E_{twelve} = 11.$$

We should also note that 10_{twelve} is another name for the number twelve.
In the case of T_{twelve} and E_{twelve} we are using one-digit numerals to represent
numbers that we are accustomed to representing with two digits.

The place values in the base twelve system are based on powers of
twelve. Each place to the left of a given place has a value twelve times as
large as the value of the place on its right; each place to the right of a given
place has a value one-twelfth as large as the value of the place on its left.

Place Values for Base Twelve

One Thousand Seven Hundred Twenty-eights	One Hundred Forty-fours	Twelves	Ones	One-twelfths
$12 \times (12 \times 12)$	12×12	12×1	1	$\dfrac{1}{12}$
12^3	12^2	12^1	12^0	12^{-1}

Exercises

1. Represent each number in base ten notation.
   (a) 175_{twelve}.   (b) $1E_{\text{twelve}}$.   (c) $8,T90_{\text{twelve}}$.   (d) T,ETE_{twelve}.

2. Complete the following tables of addition and multiplication facts for base twelve.

+	0	1	2	3	4	5	6	7	8	9	T	E
0												
1												
2												
3												
4												
5												
6												
7												
8												
9												
T												
E												

×	0	1	2	3	4	5	6	7	8	9	T	E
0												
1												
2												
3												
4												
5												
6												
7												
8												
9												
T												
E												

3. Find each sum in base twelve notation.

   (a) 17_{twelve} (b) 36_{twelve} (c) $9E0_{twelve}$ (d) 238_{twelve}
   $+\ 4_{twelve}$ $+2E_{twelve}$ $+T59_{twelve}$ $T10_{twelve}$
                                                      67_{twelve}
                                             $+9E5_{twelve}$

4. Find each difference in base twelve notation.

   (a) $6T7_{twelve}$ (b) 100_{twelve} (c) 520_{twelve} (d) $72,431_{twelve}$
   $-3T8_{twelve}$ $-\ EE_{twelve}$ $-3E9_{twelve}$ $-\ E,T48_{twelve}$

5. Find each product in base twelve notation.

   (a) 23_{twelve} (b) 519_{twelve} (c) $4,34E_{twelve}$ (d) T,ETE_{twelve}
   $\times\ 5_{twelve}$ $\times\ 4T_{twelve}$ $\times\ 8T9_{twelve}$ $\times\ ET_{twelve}$

6. Find each quotient in base twelve notation.

   (a) $9_{twelve})\overline{76_{twelve}}$ (b) $57_{twelve})\overline{29,0T7_{twelve}}$

   (c) $T_{twelve})\overline{7T2_{twelve}}$ (d) $10_{twelve})\overline{8,9T6,5E0_{twelve}}$

7. Represent each number in base twelve notation.
   (a) 23.   (b) 109.   (c) 295.   (d) 3,467.

8. What base notation is used if
   (a) $2 + 3 + 1 = 12$?   (b) $35 + 64 = 132$?   (c) $34 + 56 + 27 = 141$?

9. Indicate whether each statement is true or false.

   (a) $0_{twelve} = 0_{two}$.   (b) $3_{seven} \times 5_{seven} = 21_{six}$.

   (c) $\dfrac{5_{twelve}}{10_{twelve}} = \dfrac{1}{2}$.   (d) $6_{eight} \times 15_{eight} > 4,526_{seven} \div 25_{seven}$.

10. Indicate whether each statement is true or false.
    (a) $403_{five} > 163$.   (b) $3,442_{five} < 379$.
    (c) $249_{twelve} < 101,110,111_{two}$.   (d) $1,200_{four} = 140_{eight}$.

chapter 10

Informal Geometry

Thousands of years ago people used geometry when they built temples and studied the motions of the stars and planets. The Greek geometers were the first of the great mathematicians. They considered geometry to be made up of ideas rather than physical things, and many of their mathematical ideas are still being used. The Egyptians and Babylonians also developed simple, practical uses for geometry.

Many ancient people thought that a stretched rope was a straight line, but the Greeks knew that a rope, no matter how small, could never be a line. The Greeks realized that a line was an idea and, consequently, no model such as a rope could ever be a line. They depended on their imagination to conceive relationships among such ideas as points and lines.

Geometry has rules like a game. To play the game of geometry, we agree that *points*, *lines*, *planes*, and *space* are the things we think about. We cannot see points, lines, planes, and space. Thus we use models to represent them and draw pictures of them. As we look at the models and pictures, we must remember that they represent abstract ideas that do not exist in a physical sense.

10-1 Points

One of the first ideas to think about in geometry is point. A **point** in geometry is an exact location in space. **Space** is the set of all locations. Thus space is made up of points. A point has no size and cannot be seen or measured.

In arithmetic we developed ideas about sets of objects, called these ideas numbers, and then invented symbols to represent the ideas. In geometry we use pictures to represent ideas, and we agree that the pictures do not prove anything about these ideas. Geometric relationships will be investigated in this text, but proofs will be left for your future study.

We use dots (as is done on maps to show locations) to represent points, since points are locations. The dots *are not* points but *are* pictures of points. We need a method of distinguishing one point from another in a set of points. Capital letters are used to name points. The capital letter may be written beside the dot to indicate which location (point) is represented by each dot. Thus a dot represents the point, and a capital letter identifies the individual point of a set of points. For example, the picture (drawing) below is the representation of a set of four points, *A*, *B*, *C*, and *D*.

A.

C.

B.

D.

Exercises

1. Can a point be moved from one location to another? Explain.

2. Can a dot be moved from one location to another? Explain.

3. Which of these two dots is the larger?

•A

•B

4. Which of these two points is the larger?

•A

•B

5. Indicate whether each statement is true or false.
   (a) A dot is a point.
   (b) Space is a set of dots.
   (c) A point may be represented by a dot.
   (d) Different points are named with different capital letters.

6. How many points are represented by the set of five dots named P, Q, R, S, T?

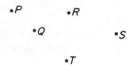

10-2 Line Segments, Lines, and Rays

Our physical world and the universe is a model of space. Objects such as marbles occupy space. In fact, a marble occupies more locations (points) than we can count.

Suppose we think of this side of this page as a set of points. Let A and B represent two different points of this set. We call the set of all points passed through in going from A to B a **path**, and we call A and B **endpoints** of the path (Figure 10-1).

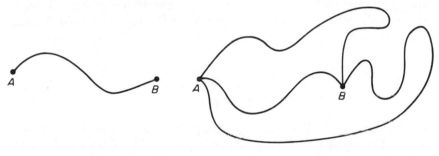

Figure 10-1   Figure 10-2

We must realize that there are many paths between A and B, as indicated in Figure 10-2. Each path connecting the endpoints A and B is called a **curve**.

If a piece of string is stretched taut so that A and B are directly under the string, then points directly under the string form a path between A and B. This path seems to be the most direct one connecting the endpoints A and B and is called a **straight path**. The straight path is a special case of a curve.

The set of all points contained in the straight path connecting two different points in space is called a **line segment**. We may denote the line segment consisting of the endpoints A and B and the straight path connecting these points either as $\overline{AB}$ or as $\overline{BA}$. The notation $\overline{AB}$ is read "the line segment AB" (Figure 10-3).

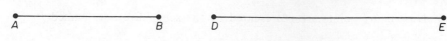

A   B   D   E

Figure 10-3   Figure 10-4

On a piece of paper we can draw a picture representing $\overline{DE}$ by using a pencil mark drawn along a side of a ruler connecting two dots representing points D and E (Figure 10-4).

Many line segments may be identified on any given line segment. For example, if we locate the point midway between D and E and call it H, we then have $\overline{DH}$ and $\overline{HE}$ on $\overline{DE}$ (Figure 10-5). By locating the point G mid-

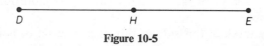

D   H   E

Figure 10-5

way between D and H and the point F midway between H and E we may form $\overline{DG}$, $\overline{GH}$, $\overline{HF}$, $\overline{FE}$, $\overline{DH}$, $\overline{DF}$, $\overline{GF}$, $\overline{GE}$, and $\overline{HE}$ on $\overline{DE}$ (Figure 10-6). Since it appears that we could continue indefinitely the process of finding a point midway between two points on a given line segment, we shall assume that a given line segment contains an infinite number of line segments.

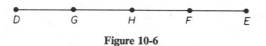

D   G   H   F   E

Figure 10-6

Now think about $\overline{GH}$. We may consider $\overline{HE}$ as an extension of it, forming a longer line segment, $\overline{GE}$. Imagine that we extend $\overline{GH}$ in this manner so that it extends to the right without end. We realize that this cannot be done on

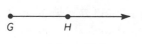

G   H

Figure 10-7

a sheet of paper; however, we can use our imagination to picture the idea. On paper, we may represent the original line segment, $\overline{GH}$, extend the drawing beyond the endpoint H, and use an arrowhead to indicate infinite extension in the direction of the arrowhead (Figure 10-7).

If we imagine a similar extension of $\overline{HG}$ to the left, it may be pictured as in Figure 10-8. This set of points is called a **line**. The line was determined by two points of a line segment that was extended without end in both directions. A line contains an infinite number of line segments, but a

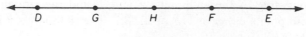

D   G   H   F   E

Figure 10-8

line does *not* have endpoints. A line may be named *by any two of its points.*
The line represented by the last picture may be named $\overleftrightarrow{GH}$, $\overleftrightarrow{HG}$, $\overleftrightarrow{DH}$, and
in other ways. The notation $\overleftrightarrow{GH}$ is read "the line *GH*."

It is important to note that an infinite number of lines may pass through
a single point (Figure 10-9). We should also note that only one line may
pass through two distinct points; in other words, two distinct points determine a unique line (Figure 10-10).

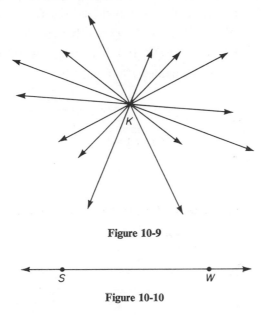

Figure 10-9

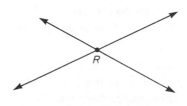

Figure 10-10

Another important property of lines is that the intersection of two
distinct lines is a single point (Figure 10-11).

Figure 10-11

Any point *P* on a line separates the line into three parts: the point *P*
and two **half-lines**, one on either side of *P*. Note that neither half-line includes the point *P* (Figure 10-12).

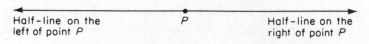

Half-line on the   P   Half-line on the
left of point P   right of point P

Figure 10-12

If we refer to the point P and all the points on the half-line that are on one side of P, we speak of a **ray**; thus, a ray is the union of a half-line and the point determining it. Point P is the endpoint of the ray, and we denote a ray by its endpoint and some other point on the ray. For example, we designate another point on the ray as Q and denote the ray as $\overrightarrow{PQ}$. The notation $\overrightarrow{PQ}$ is read "the ray PQ." If T is a point on $\overrightarrow{PQ}$ and is distinct from P, then $\overrightarrow{PQ}$ may also be named $\overrightarrow{PT}$ (Figure 10-13).

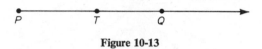

P   T   Q

Figure 10-13

Exercises

1. Consider the set of points A, B, C, and D as pictured.

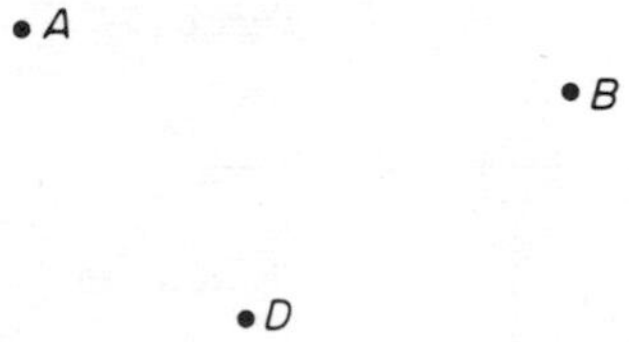

• A

• B

• C   • D

   (a) Draw a picture to represent all possible line segments determined by these points, each segment having two of the given points as end-points.
   (b) How many line segments are determined by these points?
   (c) Name each line segment indicated in part (a).

2. Given two different points M and N,
   (a) How many paths are there from M to N?
   (b) How many straight paths are there from M to N?
   (c) How many line segments are determined by M and N?
   (d) How many lines pass through M?
   (e) How many lines are determined by M and N?
   (f) How many rays pass through M and have N as endpoint?

3. Indicate whether each statement is true or false.
   (a) A line segment is a curve.
   (b) No point of a half-line is an endpoint of the half-line.
   (c) The endpoints of $\overleftrightarrow{XY}$ are X and Y.
   (d) $\overline{AB}$ is the same line segment as $\overline{BA}$.

4. Represent a point F on a sheet of paper.
  (a) Make a drawing to represent four rays with endpoint F.
  (b) How many rays are possible with endpoint F?

5. (a) Draw a picture to represent $\overrightarrow{JK}$.
  (b) How many rays are determined by endpoint J such that they pass through point K?
  (c) Is $\overline{JK}$ contained in $\overrightarrow{JK}$?

6. In each part of this exercise use two dots to represent points C and D, and draw a picture of

  (a) $\overleftrightarrow{CD}$.   (b) $\overrightarrow{CD}$.   (c) $\overrightarrow{DC}$.   (d) $\overline{DC}$.

10-3 Planes

Now let us consider the set of points suggested by a flat surface such as the top of a desk, a wall of a room, and a page in a book. Each of these flat surfaces suggests the idea of a part of a *plane* in geometry. If we think of extending the top of a desk indefinitely, we would have a better representation of a plane.

A plane is thought of as being unlimited in extent and may be represented by a picture of a flat surface. Note that a flat surface is *not* a plane. A plane cannot be drawn or constructed physically. A **plane** is a set of points in space suggested by a flat surface, which serves as a model of the plane. As illustrated in Figure 10-14, a picture of a part of a plane may be used to represent a plane. The picture of a plane may be named by the three letters for any three points of the plane that are not points of the same line. The picture in Figure 10-14 represents plane MNR.

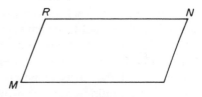

Figure 10-14

A plane contains an infinite number of points and each point of the plane is said to be on the plane. Since two distinct points determine a line, a plane contains an infinite number of lines. To illustrate this we may use a sheet of paper as a model for a plane and mark two dots on the paper to represent points A and B (Figure 10-15).

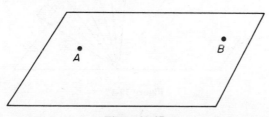

Figure 10-15

Now we may fold the paper in such a way that the crease falls on the dots. The crease represents a line in the plane passing through A and B, and there are infinitely many points on the crease. If C is a point that is not on the crease, then each of the points of the crease may be used with C to determine another line of the plane (Figure 10-16). Thus there are infinitely many lines on the plane that contain C. Of course, there are also infinitely many lines on the plane that do not contain C!

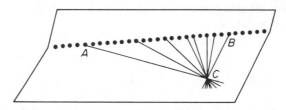

Figure 10-16

It is important to note (as we have assumed) that two distinct points on a plane may determine a line, every point of which is on the plane. In Figure 10-16 $\overleftrightarrow{AB}$ is said to lie in the plane, and the plane is said to contain $\overleftrightarrow{AB}$.

Consider the folded sheet of paper again as a model. We observe that the two parts of the folded paper could represent two planes, and $\overleftrightarrow{AB}$ is then contained in each of the two planes. Further use of our imagination should lead us to the conclusion that a line may be contained in many planes. For example, think of many sheets of paper fastened together along a common edge as a model of a line in many planes (Figure 10-17). Thus we note that two distinct points in space determine a line, and the line may lie in an infinite number of planes.

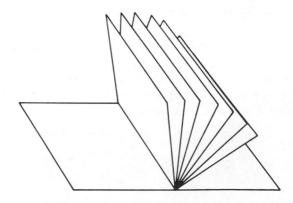

Figure 10-17

Next, let us think about three points in space and name these points D, E, and F. We know that points D and E determine $\overleftrightarrow{DE}$. Is the point F on $\overrightarrow{DE}$? With a little thought, we should conclude that F may or may not be on $\overrightarrow{DE}$. From the set of all points (space), there are many points on $\overleftrightarrow{DE}$, and there are many points not on $\overleftrightarrow{DE}$. We shall consider the case in which F is not on $\overleftrightarrow{DE}$. Then, of the uncountable number of planes that contain $\overleftrightarrow{DE}$, how many also contain F? We may think of a revolving door, its axis fastened at the top and bottom, and let the points D and E be represented by the connections of the axis at the top and bottom of the door. We may imagine the axis extended through D and E, as a representation of

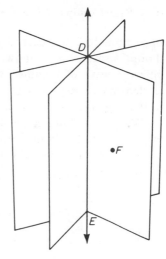

Figure 10-18

$\overleftrightarrow{DE}$. The many positions of the revolving door suggest planes that contain $\overleftrightarrow{DE}$. If point F is not on $\overleftrightarrow{DE}$, then exactly one of the many planes represented by the revolving door contains the point F (Figure 10-18).

It is important to note that three points not on the same line determine a unique plane. If three points are on the same line, then the line determined by two of the points also contains the third point, and this line is contained in an infinite number of planes.

Exercises

1. Two distinct points in space are contained in how many planes?

2. Indicate whether each statement is true or false.
   (**a**) One point in space is contained in more than one plane.
   (**b**) Three points in space always determine a plane.
   (**c**) A plane is a flat surface.
   (**d**) A plane contains only a finite number of points.

3. (**a**) How many different lines may be determined by three distinct points not on the same line?
   (**b**) Do all of the lines indicated in part (a) lie in the same plane?

4. Draw a picture of each of the following.
   (**a**) A plane and a line in the plane.
   (**b**) A plane and two intersecting lines in the plane.
   (**c**) Three planes containing the same line, $\overleftrightarrow{AB}$.
   (**d**) Three planes containing the same point, C.

10-4 Relationships of Lines and Planes

In Section 10-2 we learned that two lines may intersect in one point. We should also realize that two lines may not intersect at all. Think of the different ways of holding two pencils and imagine that each pencil is extended indefinitely in both directions. Are there ways to hold the pencils so that the lines represented by the pencils do not intersect?

We observed in Section 10-3 that we could represent the intersection of two planes by a fold in a piece of paper. We also noted that the intersection of two planes is a line; this is illustrated in Figure 10-19, where the planes FGH and JKL intersect in $\overleftrightarrow{AB}$.

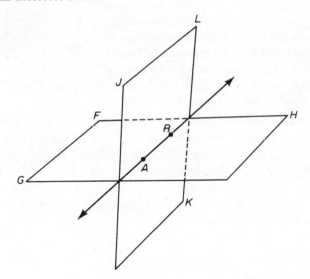

Figure 10-19

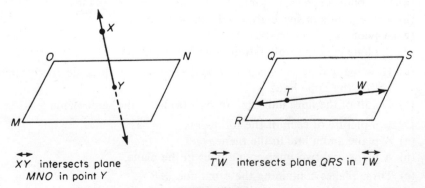

$\overleftrightarrow{XY}$ intersects plane
MNO in point Y

$\overleftrightarrow{TW}$ intersects plane QRS in $\overleftrightarrow{TW}$

Figure 10-20

Now let us consider the intersection of a line and a plane. If a line and a plane intersect, then either the intersection is a single point or the entire line lies in the plane and the intersection is the set of points forming the line (Figure 10-20).

If two lines lie in the same plane and do not intersect, they are **parallel lines**. It is also possible that two lines do not intersect and yet are not parallel. Such lines are **skew lines**. They never lie in the same plane. Figure 10-21 shows the lines along the edges of the top and bottom of an ordinary rectangular box or along the floor and ceiling of an ordinary room. In this drawing $\overleftrightarrow{AB}$ and $\overleftrightarrow{DH}$ are skew lines whereas $\overleftrightarrow{AB}$ and $\overleftrightarrow{DC}$ are parallel lines; there are also other skew lines and other parallel lines. Notice that any two distinct lines on a plane are either parallel (have no point in common) or intersect in exactly one point.

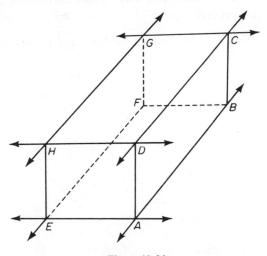

Figure 10-21

If two planes do not intersect, they are **parallel planes**. In Figure 10-21, planes ABF and DCG are parallel planes. The floor and ceiling of an ordinary room may be considered a model of parallel planes. A line and a plane may also be parallel. In the drawing $\overleftrightarrow{DH}$ is parallel to plane ABF.

Exercises

1. Indicate whether each statement is true or false.
   (a) Two lines either intersect or are parallel.
   (b) Two planes either intersect or are parallel.
   (c) A line and a plane either intersect or are parallel.
   (d) Two distinct lines may intersect in more than one point.

2. Consider the following drawing.

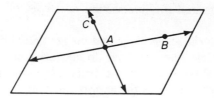

    (a) Is it true that $\overleftrightarrow{AC}$ intersects $\overrightarrow{AB}$ in only one point; that is, that $\overleftrightarrow{AC}$
    $\cap\ \overrightarrow{AB} = A$?

    (b) Is it true that $\overleftrightarrow{AC}$ intersects every plane containing $\overleftrightarrow{AB}$ in the one
    point, A?

3. Consider this drawing and think of the lines and planes suggested.

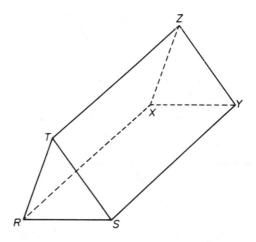

    From the drawing, name the following.
    (a) Two lines that are skew.
    (b) Two lines that are parallel.
    (c) Two lines that intersect in a point.
    (d) Two planes that are parallel.
    (e) Two planes that intersect in a line.
    (f) A line and a plane that intersect in a point.
    (g) A line and a plane that intersect in a line.
    (h) A line and a plane that do not intersect.
    (i) Three lines that intersect in a point.
    (j) Three planes that intersect in a point.

10-5 Plane Curves

In Section 10-2 we discussed the idea of *paths* joining two points on a plane. We noted that each path connecting two points is a *curve*. A curve may be located anywhere in space; that is, a curve is not restricted to one plane. In this section, we shall impose a restriction and discuss only those curves consisting of sets of points that lie in the same plane. Such curves are called **plane curves**. Each of the drawings in Figure 10-22 is a picture of a plane curve. We have noted that a line segment is a special case of a plane curve.

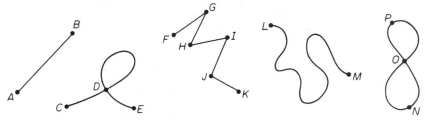

Figure 10-22

We should also observe that there exist many different kinds of curves and that curves may or may not contain portions that are straight. One of the kinds of curves is called a **closed curve**; the curve *PONOP* is an example of a closed curve. A closed curve is a plane curve consisting of a path that begins at a point and comes back to the same point. Consider the examples of closed curves in Figure 10-23. The curves with points R and S are simple closed curves.

Figure 10-23

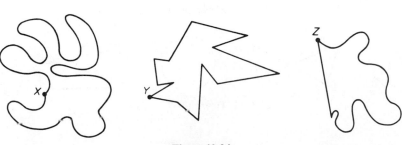

Figure 10-24

If a closed curve does not intersect itself, it is called a **simple closed curve.** Consider the examples of simple closed curves in Figure 10-24.

There are also curves that are simple but not closed and curves that are neither simple nor closed, as shown in the drawings in Figure 10-25.

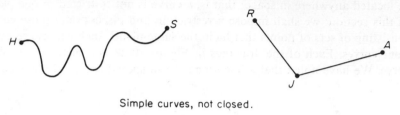

Simple curves, not closed.

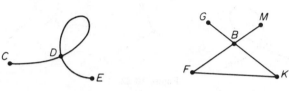

Curves, neither simple nor closed.

Figure 10-25

The most direct path between two points in a plane is called a line segment. If a simple closed curve is the union of three or more line segments, it is called a **polygon.** Note that a curve can be the union of three or more line segments without being a polygon; that is, without being simple or without being closed. Each of the drawings in Figure 10-26 represents a polygon. Each of the drawings in Figure 10-27 does not represent a polygon. (Why?)

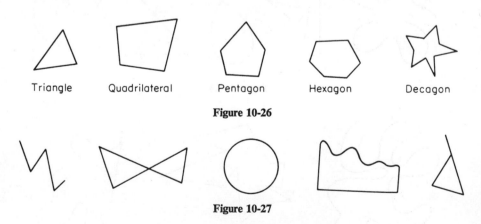

| Triangle | Quadrilateral | Pentagon | Hexagon | Decagon |

Figure 10-26

Figure 10-27

The endpoints of the segments of a polygon are called the **vertices** of the polygon, and the line segments are called the **sides** of the polygon. For example, the vertices of the octagon in Figure 10-28 are A, B, C, D, E, F, G, and H, and the sides are $\overline{AB}$, $\overline{BC}$, $\overline{CD}$, $\overline{DE}$, $\overline{EF}$, $\overline{FG}$, $\overline{GH}$, and $\overline{HA}$.

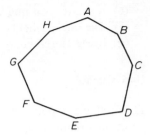

Figure 10-28

Exercises

1. Indicate which of the drawings below represent closed curves.

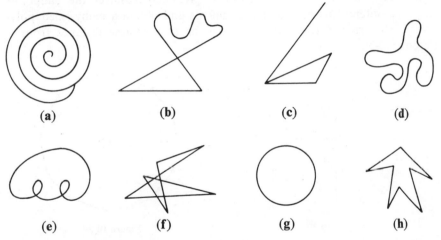

(a)   (b)   (c)   (d)

(e)   (f)   (g)   (h)

2. Indicate which of the drawings in Exercise 1 represent simple closed curves.

3. Indicate which of the drawings in Exercise 1 represent plane curves.

4. Indicate which of the drawings in Exercise 1 represent polygons.

5. We denote the name of a triangle with vertices A, B, and C in symbol form as $\triangle ABC$. Draw a picture of $\triangle ABC$ and name the sides.

6. Indicate whether each statement is true or false.
    (a) A polygon cannot have less than three sides.
    (b) A rectangle is not a polygon.
    (c) Every polygon has the same number of sides as it has vertices.
    (d) In naming a triangle the order of writing the letters makes no difference.

(e) A square is a quadrilateral.

(f) The line segments of a polygon are called the vertices of the polygon.

(g) Every closed curve is a simple curve.

10-6 Circles

Think about a polygon of many sides. We shall begin by representing a point on a plane by a dot on a piece of paper. We name the point C. Next, we represent a line segment with C as one endpoint and R as the other. Then we represent a large number of different line segments of the same length as $\overline{CR}$ and with C as one endpoint (Figure 10-29).

If the representation of each line segment were erased except for the endpoints, we would have point C and a set of points such that each point was the same distance from C. We may connect the endpoints that are different from C by line segments and obtain a many-sided polygon. Each vertex of this polygon would be at the same distance from C (Figure 10-30).

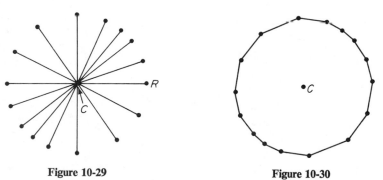

Figure 10-29   Figure 10-30

Imagine a process in which we return to the set of line segments, each having C as an endpoint, and locate another such segment between each pair; suppose we do this over and over again. If every time we had done so we constructed a picture of the polygon like the preceding drawings, we would find that the number of sides of the polygon was increasing and that the length of each side was decreasing. As the process continued, it would suggest the set of *all* points that are at a given distance (length of $\overline{CR}$) from a point (C) in a plane.

Thus we accept the existence of a simple closed curve consisting of a set of points in a plane such that each point is at a given distance from a given point in the plane. This simple closed curve is called a **circle**. The given point (C in the previous illustration) is called the **center** of the circle. It is important to note that the center is *not* an element of the set of points forming the circle. Any line segment with one endpoint on the circle and the other endpoint at the center of the circle is called a **radius** of the circle. The given distance (length of $\overline{CR}$ in the previous illustration) is the measure of a radius of the circle. A radius of a circle is not a point and thus is not a part of the circle. Only the point R of $\overline{CR}$ is a point of the circle. We should also note that a circle is a plane curve; that is, a set of points on a plane.

We may use a compass to draw a model of a circle with any point as center and any line segment as a radius. Remember, we cannot actually draw a circle, because a circle is an idea that we represent by a model.

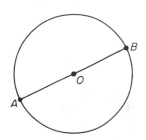

A line segment that passes through the center of a circle and has both endpoints on the circle is called a **diameter** of the circle. We observe in Figure 10-31 that the length of the diameter, $\overline{AB}$, of the circle is twice the length of the radius, $\overline{AO}$, of the same circle (since the radii $\overline{AO}$ and $\overline{OB}$ have the same length). Notice that the diameter is not a part of the circle. Only the points A and B of $\overline{AB}$ are points of the circle.

Figure 10-31

Recall (Section 10-2) that a path is a particular set of points passed through in going from one point to another. On a circle a path is called an **arc**. In other words, an arc is the set of points on a circle that are passed through in going from one point on the circle to another point on the circle. In Figure 10-32, the arc DXE is represented in heavier ink than the arc DYE. The notation $\overset{\frown}{DXE}$ may be used to represent arc DXE.

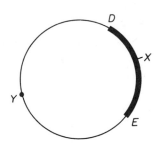

Figure 10-32

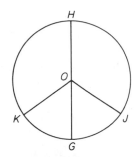

Figure 10-33

The special case of an arc of a circle with endpoints the same as the endpoints of a diameter of the circle is called a **semicircle**. The semicircle does not include any points of the diameter except the endpoints. In Figure 10-33 $\overset{\frown}{GKH}$ is a semicircle, $\overset{\frown}{GJH}$ is a semicircle, $\overline{GH}$ is a diameter of the circle, $\overline{GO}$, $\overline{KO}$, $\overline{JO}$, and $\overline{HO}$ are radii of the circle O.

Exercises

1. Consider the circle represented below with the center at point S.

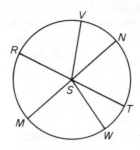

(a) Name three radii of the circle.
(b) Name four different arcs with endpoint R.
(c) Name two diameters of the circle.
(d) Name five points on the circle.

2. Refer to the drawing for Exercise 1.
(a) Is point S on the circle?
(b) Is the length of $\overline{RS}$ equal to the length of $\overline{VS}$?
(c) Is $\overset{\frown}{VMW}$ a semicircle?
(d) Is point R on $\overset{\frown}{VMW}$?

3. Indicate whether each statement is true or false.
(a) All radii of the same circle have the same length.
(b) A line segment with both endpoints on the circle is always called a diameter.
(c) All diameters have the same length.
(d) An arc of a circle is a line segment whose endpoints are also endpoints of a diameter of the circle.
(e) All diameters of the same circle intersect at the center of the circle.
(f) A semicircle is half of a circle.
(g) A circle is a plane curve.
(h) A circle is a polygon.

4. Use a compass for the following.
(a) Draw a model of a circle with center at point P and with $\overline{PR}$ as a radius of length $\frac{1}{2}$ inch.
(b) On the same drawing made for part (a), draw a model of a circle with R as center and $\overline{PR}$ as a radius.
(c) Determine how many points are common to the two circles.
(d) Draw a model of a circle with center at one of the points of intersec-

tion of the two circles pictured in part (b) and with a radius of the same length as $\overline{PR}$.

(e) Determine whether points P and R are on the circle suggested in part (d).

5. Is it possible to construct a model of a circle such that it contains
   (a) One given point?   (b) Two given points?   (c) Three given points?

10-7 Regions

In Section 10-2 we discussed the idea that each point P on a line separates the line into two sets of points called *half-lines*. The point P does not belong to either half-line. If A is any point on one half-line and B is any point on the other half-line, then the line segment AB must contain the separating point P (Figure 10-34).

Half-line on the   Half-line on the
left of point P.   right of point P.

Figure 10-34

In a similar manner, we could develop the idea that any plane separates space into two sets of points called **half-spaces**. The points on the separating plane do not belong to either half-space. Two points A and B that are not points of the separating plane are in different half-spaces if the line segment AB does contain a point of the separating plane; the points A and B are in the same half-space if $\overline{AB}$ does not contain a point of the separating plane.

Now think about a plane and a line in the plane. Does the line divide the plane into two sets of points? A study of Figure 10-35 should lead us to the idea that any line DF on the plane XYZ separates the plane into two sets of points called **half-planes**.

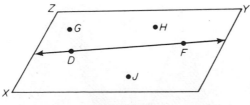

Figure 10-35

The separating line DF does not lie in either of the half-planes determined by it. In the preceding drawing, points G and H are in the same half-plane since $\overleftrightarrow{GH}$ does not intersect $\overleftrightarrow{DF}$, and points H and J are in different half-planes since $\overline{HJ}$ does intersect $\overleftrightarrow{DF}$.

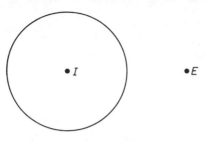

Figure 10-36

Consider the relationship of a simple closed curve to the plane containing it (Figure 10-36). Does the simple closed curve separate the plane into different sets of points? How many different sets of points are formed in the plane by the simple closed curve?

A study of the drawing should lead us to the idea that a simple closed curve separates the plane into two sets of points, one set of points inside the curve, called the **interior** of the curve, and another set of points outside the curve, called the **exterior** of the curve. Actually, a third set of points exists, since the points on the curve are neither inside nor outside the curve. Notice that every line that contains an interior point of the curve also contains an exterior point; some lines that contain exterior points contain only exterior points.

In the preceding drawing, can we connect points I and E by a curve in the plane such that the curve does not intersect the simple closed curve in at least one point? A study of this drawing and similar ones should lead us to the idea that we can never connect an exterior point E to an interior point I by a curve (in the plane of the given simple closed curve) that does not intersect the given simple closed curve.

The union of the interior of a simple closed curve and the curve is called a **region**. The curve is called the **boundary** of the region, and we should note that the boundary of the region *is part of* the region.

To picture the idea of a simple closed curve, its interior, exterior, and region, we may use shading as in the drawings in Figure 10-37. Note that the boundary of a set of points is represented by dashed marks when the boundary is not contained in the set of points.

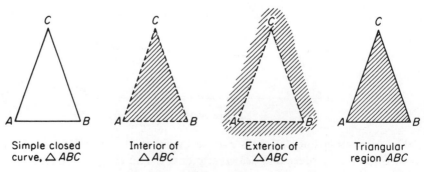

| Simple closed curve, △ABC | Interior of △ABC | Exterior of △ABC | Triangular region ABC |

Figure 10-37

Exercises

1. Consider the adjacent drawing and
   the indicated points.
   (a) Does the drawing represent a
       simple closed curve?
   (b) Name the points that are interior
       to the curve.
   (c) Name the points that are exterior
       to the curve.

2. Draw a model of a simple closed
   curve and shade to represent the following.
   (a) Exterior points.
   (b) Interior points.
   (c) Region.

3. Indicate whether each statement is true or false.
   (a) If a ray has its endpoint interior to a simple closed curve and is
       located in the plane of the curve, it will always intersect the simple
       closed curve.
   (b) If a plane separates space into two half-spaces, every curve in space
       will intersect the separating plane.
   (c) A half-line and a ray are the same idea.
   (d) If a line separates a plane into two half-planes, then every line in the
       plane either intersects the separating line or is parallel to the sepa-
       rating line.

4. Sometimes elementary school children are told to draw and color a
   triangle. How should these instructions be stated?

10-8 Plane Angles

In Section 10-2 we learned that a ray is the union of a half-line and the
point determining the half-line; that is, a ray is the union of a point on
a line and all the points on the line that are in one direction from the given

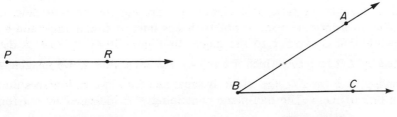

Figure 10-38   Figure 10-39

point. In Figure 10-38 we name the ray, $\overrightarrow{PR}$, where P is the endpoint of the ray and R is any other point on the ray.

Consider Figure 10-39, in which the two rays have a common endpoint. Any figure formed by two rays that have a common endpoint is called a **plane angle.** The common endpoint is the **vertex** of the angle, and the rays are the **sides** of the angle. Thus, B is the vertex, $\overrightarrow{BA}$ and $\overrightarrow{BC}$ are the sides, and the angle may be named either $\angle ABC$ or $\angle CBA$, where we agree to write the letter corresponding to the vertex between the other two letters. Thus,

$$\angle ABC = \angle CBA,$$
$$\angle ABC = \overrightarrow{BA} \cup \overrightarrow{BC}.$$

Are plane angles formed by the sides of a triangle? Remember that the sides of a triangle are line segments. Thus, we should realize that each side of a triangle is only part of a ray. We may extend the sides of a triangle from a particular vertex to form rays and thus associate a plane angle with each vertex of the triangle. For example, we may extend $\overline{XZ}$ to obtain $\overrightarrow{XZ}$, extend $\overline{XY}$ to $\overrightarrow{XY}$, and thus associate $\angle ZXY$ with vertex X of $\triangle XYZ$ (Figure 10-40). Since the points of the extended segments $\overrightarrow{XZ}$ and $\overrightarrow{XY}$ are not points of $\triangle XYZ$, we must agree that $\angle ZXY$ is not a part of $\triangle XYZ$. We do agree to call $\angle ZXY$ *an angle* of $\triangle XYZ$. However, we realize that the angle consists of points that are not points of the triangle, and thus we actually think of the angle as determined by the sides of the triangle.

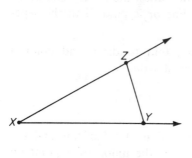

Figure 10-40

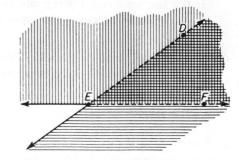

Figure 10-41

A plane angle separates the plane into two sets of points if its sides are distinct rays. If the sides of a plane angle are not on the same line, it is possible to determine a set of points that is interior to the angle and a set of points that is exterior to the angle. In Figure 10-41, $\angle DEF$ is determined by $\overrightarrow{ED}$ and $\overrightarrow{EF}$, which are not on the same line. If we imagine $\overrightarrow{ED}$ extended to form $\overleftrightarrow{ED}$, the plane is separated into two half-planes and F is in one of them. The half-plane containing F is indicated by horizontal shading. Next we imagine $\overrightarrow{EF}$ extended to form $\overleftrightarrow{EF}$ and indicate the half-plane containing D by vertical shading. The **interior points** of $\angle DEF$ are indicated by the double shading (shaded both horizontally and vertically). The rays are depicted by dashed marks that indicate that the points on the angle are neither interior nor exterior to the angle. All points of the plane that are neither interior points nor points of the rays are **exterior points** of $\angle DEF$.

We should note that it is not always possible to determine the interior and exterior of an angle. In the case in which the two rays forming the angle also form a straight line, we have two half-planes and either half-plane may be thought of as the interior of the angle. Since we cannot determine which half-plane to choose, we do not define interior for such angles. Such is the case in Figure 10-42, where K represents the vertex of $\angle JKL$.

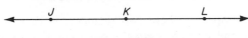

Figure 10-42

Exercises

1. Consider the drawing below and name the following.

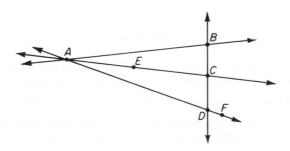

(a) $\overrightarrow{AB} \cap \overrightarrow{DC}$.   (b) $\overrightarrow{AB} \cap \overrightarrow{CD}$.   (c) $\overleftrightarrow{AF} \cap \overleftrightarrow{BC}$.   (d) $\overleftrightarrow{AC} \cap \overleftrightarrow{DF}$.

(e) $\overline{AE} \cap \overline{BD}$.   (f) $\overrightarrow{BA} \cup \overrightarrow{BC}$.   (g) $\overline{AE} \cup \overline{CE}$.   (h) $\overrightarrow{EA} \cup \overrightarrow{EC}$.

2. Refer to the preceding drawing and name the following.
   (a) Three different triangles.
   (b) A line segment that is not the side of a triangle.
   (c) A point of the exterior of $\triangle ABD$.
   (d) A point of the interior of $\angle ABD$.
   (e) A point of the exterior of $\angle ABD$.
   (f) A point of the exterior of $\angle AEC$.
   (g) A point of the interior of $\angle AEC$.

10-9 Congruence of Line Segments

An interesting aspect of geometry is the comparison of geometric figures. Consider the problem of comparing the two line segments pictured in

Figure 10-43. In our comparison we must agree that only one of the following three possibilities is true:

$\overline{AB}$ is longer than $\overline{CD}$,

$\overline{AB}$ is shorter than $\overline{CD}$, or

$\overline{AB}$ is the same length as $\overline{CD}$.

One method of comparing these two segments is to use a compass and copy a picture of one segment onto the representation of a ray formed by extending the second line segment indefinitely in one direction. In Figure 10-44 we extend $\overline{CD}$ through D to form $\overrightarrow{CD}$, so that we may copy $\overline{AB}$ onto $\overrightarrow{CD}$.

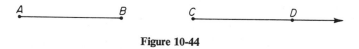

Figure 10-44

If the compass is set so that the metal tip is on A and the pencil point is on B, then the line segment between the metal tip and the pencil point represents $\overline{AB}$. To copy $\overline{AB}$ onto $\overrightarrow{CD}$, we place the metal tip of the compass on C and then mark on the picture of $\overrightarrow{CD}$ the location of the pencil point. If the mark of the pencil point is on the extension of $\overline{CD}$ (that is, beyond point D), then $\overline{AB}$ is longer than $\overline{CD}$. If the mark is between C and D, then $\overline{AB}$ is shorter than $\overline{CD}$. If the mark is on D, then $\overline{AB}$ **is congruent to** $\overline{CD}$; that is, $\overline{AB}$ and $\overline{CD}$ have the same length.

From the pictures of $\overline{AB}$ and $\overline{CD}$ we may conclude that $\overline{AB}$ is congruent to $\overline{CD}$, and we represent this idea in symbol form as $\overline{AB} \cong \overline{CD}$. Note that the symbol $\cong$ does not have the same meaning as the symbol $=$. The symbol $=$ is used only when we wish to indicate that we have two different names for the *same* thing; that is, $\overline{AB} = \overline{BA}$ means that we have two different names for the same line segment. The statement $\overline{AB} \cong \overline{CD}$ means that we can copy one line segment onto the other so that the endpoints of the two segments match exactly; that is, the two line segments have exactly the same length.

Exercises

1. Indicate whether each statement is true or false.
   (a) If $\overline{GH} = \overline{JK}$, then $\overline{GH} \cong \overline{JK}$.
   (b) If $\overline{LM} \cong \overline{RS}$, then $\overline{LM} = \overline{RS}$.
   (c) If $\overline{PQ} \cong \overline{EF}$ and $\overline{EF} \cong \overline{XY}$, then $\overline{PQ} \cong \overline{XY}$.
   (d) Every line segment is congruent to itself.

2. Use a compass to determine which of the line segments pictured below
   are congruent, and then state your conclusion in symbol form.

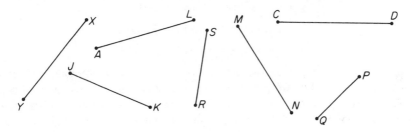

3. Indicate whether each statement is true or false.
   (a) All radii of the same circle are congruent line segments.
   (b) All diameters of the same circle are congruent line segments.
   (c) Any two congruent line segments are equal.
   (d) If two line segments are not equal, then one segment is either longer
       or shorter than the other.

4. Extend one of the line segments given below through an endpoint to
   form a ray, and then copy a picture of the other line segment onto the
   representation of the ray. Determine whether $\overline{FG}$ is longer than, shorter
   than, or congruent to $\overline{BC}$.

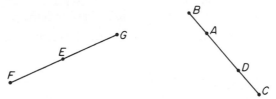

10-10 Congruence of Plane Angles

We can compare two plane angles in much the same way that we compared
line segments. Recall (Section 10-8) that a plane angle is defined as any
figure formed by two rays with a common endpoint. Consider the two plane
angles pictured in Figure 10-45.

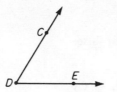
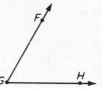

Figure 10-45

In making a comparison of these two angles we must agree that only one of the following three possibilities is true:

$\angle CDE$ is larger than $\angle FGH$,

$\angle CDE$ is smaller than $\angle FGH$, or

$\angle CDE$ is the same size as $\angle FGH$.

One method of comparing these two angles is to use a compass and copy a picture of one angle onto the representation of the other angle. To copy $\angle CDE$ onto $\angle FGH$ we set the compass to any convenient radius, place the metal tip on D, and draw with the pencil point an arc that intersects $\angle CDE$ in two points, X and Y. We retain the same compass opening (length of $\overline{DY}$), place the metal tip on G, and draw with the pencil point an arc that intersects $\angle FGH$ in two points, X' and Y' (Figure 10-46).

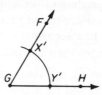

Figure 10-46

Next we set the compass so that the metal tip is on Y and the pencil point is on X, place the metal tip on Y', and draw with the pencil point an arc (in the same half-plane as X' relative to $\overleftrightarrow{GH}$) that intersects $\widehat{X'Y'}$ (Figure 10-47).

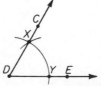

Figure 10-47

If the arc intersects $\widehat{X'Y'}$ in the exterior of $\angle FGH$, then $\angle CDE$ is larger than $\angle FGH$. If the arc intersects $\widehat{X'Y'}$ in the interior of $\angle FGH$, then $\angle CDE$ is smaller than $\angle FGH$. If the arc intersects $\widehat{X'Y'}$ at X', then $\angle CDE$

is congruent to $\angle FGH$, and we write $\angle CDE \cong \angle FGH$. Consider the drawings in Figure 10-48, which picture the three possible cases.

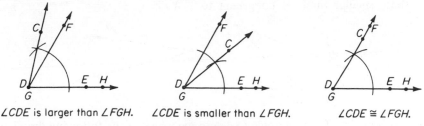

∠CDE is larger than ∠FGH.   ∠CDE is smaller than ∠FGH.   ∠CDE ≅ ∠FGH.

Figure 10-48

Again it is important to note that we use the symbol = only when we have two different names for the same thing; that is, $\angle CDE = \angle EDC$ means that we have two different names for the same angle. The statement $\angle CDE \cong \angle FGH$ means that we can copy one angle onto the other so that the vertex and rays of one angle lie on the vertex and rays of the other, and that the two angles are exactly the same size.

Consider the picture of two congruent angles, $\angle RJK$ and $\angle SJK$ in Figure 10-49. This drawing represents a special case of congruent angles. Observe that $\overrightarrow{JR}$ and $\overrightarrow{JS}$ form $\overleftrightarrow{RS}$ with R and S on opposite sides of J. Observe also that K is not on $\overleftrightarrow{RS}$ and, thus, $\overrightarrow{JK}$ intersects $\overleftrightarrow{RS}$ and forms two congruent angles. Each of the angles formed in this

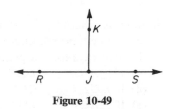

Figure 10-49

manner is called a **right angle**. Models of right angles exist all about us. The corner of a page in this book is a model of a right angle, the hands of a clock at exactly nine o'clock represent a right angle, and the printed letter ∟ is often a model of a right angle.

Exercises

1. Determine which of the angles pictured below are congruent, and then state your conclusion in symbol form.

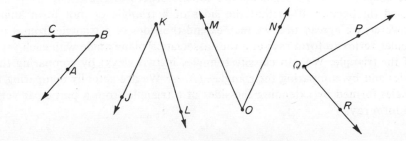

2. Represent one of the angles given below and then copy a picture of the other angle onto the representation, to determine whether $\angle DEF$ is larger than, smaller than, or congruent to $\angle XYZ$.

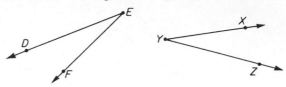

3. Use a model of a right angle to determine which of the following drawings of angles represent right angles.

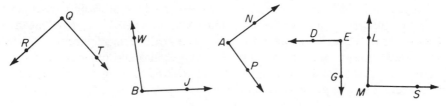

4. Indicate whether each statement is true or false.
  (a) Two congruent angles always form a right angle.
  (b) Two rays form a plane angle.
  (c) If $\angle ABC = \angle DEF$, then $\angle ABC \cong \angle DEF$.
  (d) If $\angle GHJ \cong \angle KLM$, then $\angle GHJ = \angle KLM$.
  (e) If $\angle NOP \cong \angle QRS$ and $\angle QRS \cong \angle TUX$, then $\angle NOP \cong \angle TUX$.
  (f) Every angle is congruent to itself.
  (g) Any two right angles are congruent.
  (h) If two angles are not equal, then one angle is either larger or smaller than the other.

10-11 Classification of Triangles and Quadrilaterals

We learned in Section 10-5 that a triangle is a polygon that is the union of three line segments. These line segments are called sides of the triangle, and the endpoints of the segments are called vertices of the triangle. We also noted (in Section 10-8) that the sides of a triangle do not form angles; however, we agreed that we may extend the sides of a triangle from a particular vertex to form rays and thus associate a plane angle with each vertex of the triangle. We can classify triangles in two ways: by comparing their sides and by comparing their angles. (*Note:* We are actually comparing the angles formed by extending the sides of a triangle from a particular vertex to form rays.)

First, we shall consider the classification of triangles by comparing the sides of a triangle (Figure 10-50). A triangle with three sides congruent is called an **equilateral triangle**. A triangle with at least two sides congruent is called an **isosceles triangle**. A triangle with no two sides congruent is called a **scalene triangle**. The symbol $\not\cong$ means "is not congruent to."

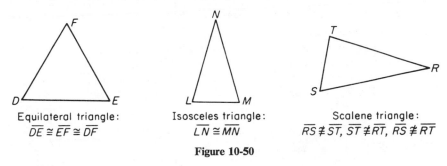

Equilateral triangle: Isosceles triangle: Scalene triangle:
$\overline{DE} \cong \overline{EF} \cong \overline{DF}$ $\overline{LN} \cong \overline{MN}$ $\overline{RS} \not\cong \overline{ST},\ \overline{ST} \not\cong \overline{RT},\ \overline{RS} \not\cong \overline{RT}$

Figure 10-50

Now consider the classification of triangles by comparing the angles of a triangle (Figure 10-51). A triangle with a right angle is called a **right triangle**. A triangle with each angle smaller than a right angle is called an **acute triangle**. A triangle with one angle larger than a right angle is called an **obtuse triangle**.

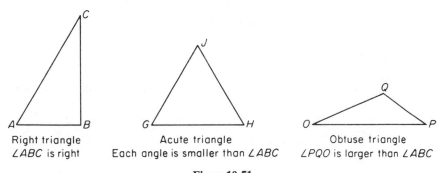

Right triangle   Acute triangle   Obtuse triangle
$\angle ABC$ is right   Each angle is smaller than $\angle ABC$ $\angle PQO$ is larger than $\angle ABC$

Figure 10-51

We should recall (Section 10-5) that a quadrilateral is a polygon that is the union of four line segments. Quadrilaterals can also be classified by comparing either their sides or their angles (Figure 10-52). A quadrilateral with no two sides congruent is called a **scalene quadrilateral**. A quadrilateral with opposite (nonintersecting) sides that are parallel line segments is called a **parallelogram**. The opposite sides of a parallelogram are also congruent. A parallelogram with all four angles congruent is called a **rectangle**. Each of the four angles of a rectangle is a right angle. A rectangle with all four sides congruent is called a **square**. In formal geometry courses some of these definitions are replaced by simpler ones.

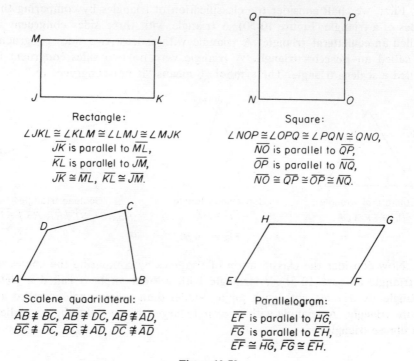

Rectangle:

∠JKL ≅ ∠KLM ≅ ∠LMJ ≅ ∠MJK
$\overline{JK}$ is parallel to $\overline{ML}$,
$\overline{KL}$ is parallel to $\overline{JM}$,
$\overline{JK} \cong \overline{ML}$, $\overline{KL} \cong \overline{JM}$.

Square:

∠NOP ≅ ∠OPQ ≅ ∠PQN ≅ QNO,
$\overline{NO}$ is parallel to $\overline{QP}$,
$\overline{OP}$ is parallel to $\overline{NQ}$,
$\overline{NO} \cong \overline{QP} \cong \overline{OP} \cong \overline{NQ}$.

Scalene quadrilateral:

$\overline{AB} \not\cong \overline{BC}$, $\overline{AB} \not\cong \overline{DC}$, $\overline{AB} \not\cong \overline{AD}$,
$\overline{BC} \not\cong \overline{DC}$, $\overline{BC} \not\cong \overline{AD}$, $\overline{DC} \not\cong \overline{AD}$

Parallelogram:

$\overline{EF}$ is parallel to $\overline{HG}$,
$\overline{FG}$ is parallel to $\overline{EH}$,
$\overline{EF} \cong \overline{HG}$, $\overline{FG} \cong \overline{EH}$.

Figure 10-52

Exercises

1. Classify each of the triangles pictured below by comparing their sides.

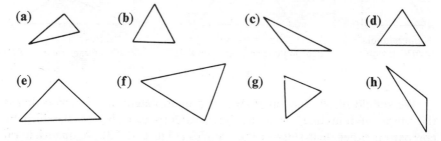

(a)   (b)   (c)   (d)

(e)   (f)   (g)   (h)

2. Classify each of the triangles pictured in Exercise 1 by comparing their angles.

3. Draw a picture of a triangle that is
    (a) Obtuse and scalene.   (b) Acute and scalene.
    (c) Right and scalene.   (d) Obtuse and isosceles.
    (e) Acute and isosceles.   (f) Right and isosceles.

4. Can you draw a picture of a triangle that is
   (a) Obtuse and equilateral?   **(b)** Acute and equilateral?
   (c) Right and equilateral?

Mathematical Symbols
and Abbreviations

SYMBOL	MEANING
$+$	Plus; add; also used to indicate positive direction, as in $^+2$ (read "positive two").
$-$	Minus; subtract; also used to indicate negative direction, as in $^-2$ (read "negative two").
$\times$, $\cdot$	Times; multiply, as in $a \times b$, $a \cdot b$, and ab (read "a times b").
$\div$, $-$	Divide, as in $a \div b$, $\dfrac{a}{b}$ (read "a is divided by b").
$:$	Ratio, as in $a : b$ (read "a is to b").
$\ldots$	The three-dot notation means to complete, as in $1, 2, 3, \ldots, 12$, or to continue indefinitely in the same manner, as in $1, 2, 3, \ldots$.
$=$	Is equal to, as in $a = b$ (read "a is equal to b").
$\neq$	Is not equal to, as in $a \neq b$ (read "a is not equal to b").
$>$	Is greater than, as in $a > b$ (read "a is greater than b").
$<$	Is less than, as in $a < b$ (read "a is less than b").

SYMBOL	MEANING
$\geq$	Is greater than or equal to, as in $a \geq b$ (read "a is greater than or equal to b").
$\leq$	Is less than or equal to, as in $a \leq b$ (read "a is less than or equal to b").
$\cong$	Is congruent to, as in $a \cong b$ (read "a is congruent to b").
$\not\cong$	Is not congruent to, as in $a \not\cong b$ (read "a is not congruent to b").
$\leftrightarrow, \sim$	Is equivalent to, as in $R \leftrightarrow S, R \sim S$ (read "set R is equivalent to set S" or "set R has the same number of elements as set S").
$\sqrt{\ }, \sqrt[3]{\ }, \sqrt[5]{\ }$	Square root, cube root, fifth root, respectively.
$\overset{m}{=}$	Is equal in measure to.
(), [], {}	Symbols of inclusion, called parentheses, brackets, and braces, respectively.
$\{x, y\}$	The set whose elements are x and y.
$\in$	Is an element of, as in $a \in A$ (read "the element a is a member of set A").
$\subseteq$	Is a subset of, as in $A \subseteq B$ (read "set A is a subset of set B"). Each element of A is an element of B.
$\subset$	Is a proper subset of, as in $D \subset E$ (read "set D is a proper subset of set E"). Each element of D is an element of E and there is at least one element of E that is not an element of D.
$\nsubseteq$	Is not a subset of, as in $F \nsubseteq G$.
$\not\subset$	Is not a proper subset of, as in $J \not\subset K$.
$\cup$	Union, as in $A \cup B$ (read "set A union set B"). $A \cup B$ is the set of all elements that are elements of at least one of the two given sets.
$\cap$	Intersection, as in $D \cap E$ (read "set D intersection set E"). $D \cap E$ is the set of all elements in both D and E.
$\{\}, \emptyset$	The empty (null) set.
U	The universal set.
$\{1, 2, 3, 4, \ldots\} = C$	The set of counting (natural) numbers.
$\{0, 1, 2, 3, 4, \ldots\} = W$	The set of whole numbers.

SYMBOL	MEANING
$n(T)$	The number of elements of set T.
A'	The complement of set A.
$\square = 3 + 2$	An example of an open number sentence; the symbol $\square$ is a placeholder (also referred to as a variable).
a^n	The letter a represents the base of a power, the letter n an exponent, and a^n represents a power.
π	Pi, $\pi = 3.14159.\ldots$
$\%$	Percent; by the hundred.
10_{five}	The subscript "five" indicates the base of the system of numeration.
$0.\overline{6}$	A repeating decimal; the digit 6 is repeated indefinitely.
$\overline{AB}$	Line segment with endpoints A and B.
$\overrightarrow{AB}$	Ray with endpoint A, extending in the direction of B from A.
$\overleftrightarrow{AB}$	Line determined by the points A and B.
$\overarc{CD}$	Arc with endpoints C and D.
$\triangle ABC$	Triangle with vertices at A, B, and C.
$\angle ABC$	Angle with vertex at point B and sides $\overrightarrow{BA}$ and $\overrightarrow{BC}$.
L.C.M.	Least common multiple.
G.C.F.	Greatest common factor.

Glossary of
Mathematical Terms

The purpose of this glossary is to provide a convenient and useful explanation of mathematical words and phrases used in this book. This list is by no means complete and the explanations given are not intended to be precise definitions. Additional discussion of these terms as well as examples and illustrations may be found in the book by referring to the index.

Abstract—That which exists in the mind, as opposed to that which is concrete and physically in existence.

Acute triangle—A triangle with each angle smaller than a right angle.

Addend—The name given to each of the numbers to be added.

Addition—The process of finding the cardinal number of a set formed by the union of two disjoint sets; also a binary operation defined for numbers.

Additive identity—The number zero is the additive identity because the sum of any number and zero is always the original number; that is, for every number a, $a + 0 = a$. The additive identity is also called the identity element for addition.

Additive inverse of a number—The unique number which produces a sum of 0 when added to a given number; that is, for every number a there is a unique number ^-a such that $a + {^-a} = 0$. The additive inverse of a number is often called the negative of the number.

Additive system of numeration—A system of numeration in which the number represented by a particular set of symbols is the sum of the numbers represented by the symbols in the set.

Algorism—A computational procedure; in general, an algorism is a method of arranging numerals in such a way as to reduce the number of steps necessary to determine a correct answer to a particular problem.

Arbitrary—Fixed at the discretion of an individual without reference to any established pattern.

Arc—The set of points on a circle that are passed through in going along the circle from one point on the circle to another point on the circle.

Array—An arrangement of symbols, often in columns and rows.

Associative principle of addition—For every three numbers to be added together the sum is not affected by grouping the numbers differently (without changing their order); that is, for all numbers a, b, and c, $(a + b) + c = a + (b + c)$.

Associative principle of multiplication—For every three numbers to be multiplied together the product is not affected by grouping the numbers differently (without changing their order); that is, for all numbers a, b, and c, $(a \cdot b) \cdot c = a \cdot (b \cdot c)$.

Assumption—Any statement that is accepted without proof in order to provide a basis for discussion.

Base of a power—A number used a given number of times as a factor; the product is called the power, and the repeated factor is the base of the power.

Base of a system of numeration—A number that establishes the method of grouping and the number of digits needed for a particular system of numeration.

Between—A particular order relation; specifically, for three different numbers a, b, and c, the number a is between the numbers b and c if $b > a > c$ or $c > a > b$.

Binary operation—A rule that assigns to two given elements a third element.

Borrowing—A colloquial term used to describe the renaming (regrouping) of a number that is sometimes necessary in order to subtract one number from another. Generally, it is suggested that the term *renaming* (or regrouping) be taught instead of the term *borrowing*.

Boundary of a region—A simple closed curve.

Braces, { , }—Symbols used in this book to indicate sets of elements. The members of a set are represented within the braces.

Brackets, [,]—Symbols used to indicate that the enclosed numerals or symbols should be considered together.

Cardinal number—A number used to indicate how many elements are contained in a set, irrespective of the order in which the elements are arranged.

Carrying—A colloquial term used to describe the renaming (regrouping) of a number that is sometimes necessary in order to add two or more numbers together. Generally, it is suggested that the term *renaming* (or regrouping) be taught instead of the term *carrying*.

Center of a circle—The point in the plane of the circle that is the same distance from every point on the circle.

Check—Verify the correctness of a solution.

Circle—A simple closed curve consisting of a set of points in a plane such that each point is at a given distance from a given point in the plane.

Circular region—The union of the interior of a circle and the circle; that is, the set of all points inside and on a circle.

Closed curve—A plane curve consisting of a path that begins at a point and comes back to the same point.

Closure principle of addition—For every two elements of a given set of numbers the sum of the two elements also is an element of the given set.

Closure principle of multiplication—For every two elements of a given set of numbers the product of the two elements also is an element of the given set.

Column—A vertical arrangement of symbols.

Common factors—Factors of each of two or more given numbers.

Common multiples—Multiples of each of two or more given numbers.

Commutative principle of addition—For every two numbers the sum is not affected by the order of addition; that is, for every number a and every number b, $a + b = b + a$.

Commutative principle of multiplication—For every two numbers the product is not affected by the order of multiplication; that is, for every number a and every number b, $a \cdot b = b \cdot a$.

Compass—An instrument used to draw pictures of circles and arcs; also used to make comparisons of geometric figures.

Complement of a set—If A is a subset of a universal set, then the complement of A with respect to the universal set is the set of all elements in the universal set that are not elements of A.

Completeness—A property of the set of real numbers. The real numbers are complete, because there is a real number for every point of the number line; conversely, there is a point of the number line for every real number.

Composite number—A whole number greater than 1 that is not prime; that is, a whole number greater than 1 that has whole numbers other than 1 and the number itself as factors.

Congruent—Two geometric figures are congruent if they have the same measurements; that is, they can be matched exactly. In such cases one figure can be copied onto the other and the two figures are exactly the same.

Consecutive—Following one after the other in a regular order.

Coordinate of a point—The number that is associated with a particular point on a number line.

Correspondence—A matching (that is, pairing) of the elements of one set with the elements of another set.

Counting—A procedure whereby the counting numbers beginning with 1 are matched in order with the elements of a set, to determine that the set contains as many elements as the last number named.

Counting number—Any element of the set $\{1, 2, 3, 4, 5, 6, \ldots\}$. The set of counting numbers is also called the set of natural numbers.

Curve—The set of points of a path.

Cycle—The set of digits that repeats in a periodic decimal.

Decagon—A polygon with ten sides.

Decimal—A numeral in decimal notation.

Decimal notation—A notation which extends the base ten place-value system to the right of the ones place by making use of a decimal point to separate the ones place from the tenths place immediately to the right of the ones place.

Decimal point—A dot used in decimal notation to separate the ones place from the tenths place.

Decimal system of numeration—A system of numeration that uses the number ten as a base and requires ten digits. The decimal system is also called the base ten system of numeration.

Denominator—The number that is represented by b in a fractional number expressed in the form $\frac{a}{b}$, where $b \neq 0$.

Dense—A set of numbers is dense if there is always at least one number between any two different numbers of the set.

Diameter of a circle—A line segment that passes through the center of the circle and has both endpoints on the circle.

Difference—The result obtained when one number is subtracted from another.

Digit—Any one of the single symbols that is used to write a numeral in a system based on place value. The ten decimal digits are 0, 1, 2, 3, 4, 5, 6, 7, 8, and 9.

Directed line segment—A line segment pictured with an arrowhead at one endpoint to indicate the direction associated with the line segment. Although the choice of directions for positive and negative is arbitrary, on the number line we generally represent a positive number by a line segment directed to the right and a negative number by a line segment directed to the left.

Disjoint sets—Any two sets with no elements in common; that is, two sets whose intersection is the empty set.

Distinct—Not the same.

Distributive principle of multiplication over addition—For all numbers a, b, and c, $a \times (b + c) = (a \times b) + (a \times c)$.

Division—The process of finding the quotient of two numbers. Division is the inverse of multiplication; division may be considered as repeated subtraction.

Division by zero—A meaningless operation that is excluded from consideration in our number system.

Divisor—Any one of the numbers that are multiplied to form a product. A divisor of a number is also called a factor of the number. In a division problem the number that we divide by is the divisor.

Dot—A small mark that is used to picture a point.

Element of a set—An object contained in a set. An element of a set is also called a member of the set.

Empty set—A set containing no elements. An empty set is also called a null set.

Endpoint—Either of the two points that are connected by a path; also the initial point of a ray.

Equality—A relation between two numbers that are exactly the same. The symbol = is written between two numerals to indicate that both numerals represent the same number; it is also used in other cases to indicate that different names are being used for the same thing.

Equation—A number sentence expressing the relation of equality. The statement may involve specified numbers, or numbers represented by variables, or both.

Equilateral triangle—A triangle with three sides congruent.

Equivalent fractions—Two or more fractions that name the same number.

Equivalent sets—Two sets whose elements can be placed in one-to-one correspondence.

Even number—Any element of the set $\{\ldots, ^-8, ^-6, ^-4, ^-2, 0, 2, 4, 6, 8, \ldots\}$.

Expanded form of a numeral—A form of a numeral that clearly illustrates the place value of each digit making up the numeral. For example, the expanded form of 321 is $(3 \times 10^2) + (2 \times 10^1) + (1 \times 10^0)$.

Exponent (positive integral)—A number represented by a small numeral written above and to the right of another numeral representing the base. The exponent indicates how many times the base is to be used as a factor.

Exterior of a plane curve (or angle)—One of the sets of points into which the curve (or angle) separates the plane in which it lies. Generally, the set of points is considered to be "outside" the curve (or angle).

Factor—Any one of the two or more numbers that may be multiplied to form a product. A factor of a product is also called a divisor of the product.

Finite set—A set with a whole number as its cardinal number.

Fraction—A numeral that names a fractional number. A fraction is also called a fractional numeral.

Fractional number—Any number that can be expressed in the form $\frac{a}{b}$ where the numerator a and the denominator b are any numbers and $b \neq 0$.

Fractional numeral—A numeral that names a fractional number. A fractional numeral is also called a fraction.

Fundamental Theorem of Arithmetic—Every composite number can be expressed as a product of prime numbers which is unique except for the order of the factors. The Fundamental Theorem of Arithmetic is also called the Unique Factorization Theorem.

Geometry—The part of mathematics that deals with the study of points, lines, planes, and space.

General—Not specific; covering all known special cases.

Graph of a number—The point on a number line that is associated with a particular number.

Greatest common factor (greatest common divisor)—The largest natural number that is a common factor (divisor) of two or more given numbers.

Greater than—An order relation of numbers. For any two numbers a and b, a is greater than b (written $a > b$) if $a - b$ is a positive number.

Half-line—One of the sets of points that is formed when a point separates a line. A point separates a line into two half-lines, neither one of which contains the point.

Half-plane—One of the sets of points that is formed when a line separates a plane. A line separates a plane into two half-planes, neither one of which contains the line.

Half-space—One of the two sets of points that is formed when a plane separates space. A plane separates space into two half-spaces, neither one of which contains the plane.

Hexagon—A polygon with six sides.

Hindu-Arabic system of numeration—A name associated with the decimal system of numeration.

Identical sets—Two sets whose elements are exactly the same. Identical sets are also called equal sets.

Identity element—A number that does not change the value of a given number when a certain operation is performed on the two numbers. Zero is the identity element for addition and subtraction because, for every number a, $a + 0 = a$ and $a - 0 = a$. The number 1 is the identity element for multiplication and division because, for every number a, $a \times 1 = a$ and $a \div 1 = a$.

Inequality—A relation between two numbers that are not the same. Each of the symbols $\neq$ (is not equal to), $<$ (is less than), and $>$ (is greater than) represents an inequality relation when written between two numerals.

Inequation—A number sentence expressing an inequality. The statement may involve specified numbers, or numbers represented by variables, or both.

Infinite decimal—A decimal that does not terminate; that is, the digits continue indefinitely.

Infinite set—A set that does not have a whole number as its cardinal number.

Informal geometry—A study of geometric concepts that makes no attempt to substantiate the concepts by formal proof. This approach to the study of geometry is dependent upon intuition, experimentation, observation, reasoning by analogy, and reasoning by induction.

Integer—Any element of the set $\{\ldots, {}^-3, {}^-2, {}^-1, 0, 1, 2, 3, \ldots\}$.

Integral—Having the property of being an integer.

Interior of a plane curve (or angle)—One of the sets of points into which the curve (or angle) separates the plane in which it lies. Generally, the set of points is considered to be "inside" the curve (or angle).

Intersect—To have a point, a nonempty set of points, or other elements in common.

Intersection of sets—The intersection of two sets M and N is the set consisting of the elements that are common to both M and N.

Inverse operations—Two operations that are such that one operation undoes what

the other operation does; that is, the net effect of performing the two operations is the same as that of not having performed either operation.

Irrational number—Any real number that cannot be expressed in the form $\frac{a}{b}$, where a and b are integers and $b \neq 0$, that is, the numbers that are coordinates of points on the real number line and are not rational numbers. Each irrational number may be expressed as an infinite nonrepeating decimal.

Isosceles triangle—A triangle with at least two congruent sides.

Least common denominator—The least common multiple of the denominators under consideration.

Least common multiple—The smallest of the common multiples of two or more numbers.

Less than—An order relation of numbers. For any two numbers a and b, a is less than b (written $a < b$) if $b - a$ is a positive number.

Like fractions—Fractions whose numerals representing denominators are identical.

Line (straight line)—A set of points that can be thought of informally as a line segment that is extended in both directions without end.

Line segment—The set of all points contained in the straight path connecting two points.

Lowest terms—A fractional number is expressed in lowest terms when the greatest common factor of its numerator and denominator is 1. A fractional number in lowest terms is also said to be in simplest form.

Match—To pair an element of one set with an element of another set.

Mathematical system—A set of elements, one or more binary operations, one or more relations, and some rules which the elements, operations, and relations satisfy.

Member of a set—An object contained in a set. A member of a set is also called an element of the set.

Missing addend—A name given to the number to be determined when one number is subtracted from another.

Missing factor—A name given to the number to be determined when one number is divided by another.

Mixed numeral—A numeral which includes representations of both an integer and a rational fractional number.

Model (geometric)—A representation of an abstract geometrical idea.

Modern mathematics—An approach to the study of mathematics that emphasizes the importance of concepts, patterns, and mathematical structure, as well as the development of mathematical skills.

Multiple of a number—Any number that is obtained by multiplying a given number by a positive integer.

Multiplication—The process of finding the product of two numbers. Multiplication may be considered as repeated addition.

Multiplication principle of zero—For every number a, $a \times 0 = 0$.

Multiplicative identity—The number 1 is the multiplicative identity, because the product of any number and 1 is always the original number; that is, for every number a, $a \times 1 = a$. The multiplicative identity is also called the identity element for multiplication.

Multiplicative inverse of a number other than zero—The unique number which produces a product of 1 when multiplied by a given number (other than 0); that is, if $a \times b = 1$, then b is the multiplicative inverse of a and a is the multiplicative inverse of b. Two numbers whose product is 1 are also called reciprocals of each other.

Natural number—Any element of the set {1, 2, 3, 4, 5, 6, . . .}. The set of natural numbers is also called the set of counting numbers.

Negative integer—Any element of the set {⁻1, ⁻2, ⁻3, ⁻4, ⁻5, . . .}.

Negative number—Any number less than zero. On a number line the negative numbers are generally represented to the left of zero.

Nondecimal system of numeration—A system of numeration in which a number other than 10 is used as a base.

Nonnegative number—Any number that is not negative; that is, any number greater than or equal to zero.

Nonrepeating decimal—An infinite decimal with no digit or set of digits that repeats indefinitely.

Notation—Any systematic convention for expressing ideas, operations, relations, etc. by means of symbols.

Null set—A set containing no elements. A null set is also called an empty set.

Number—An abstract idea of quantity.

Number line—A representation of numbers by points on a line. The line is usually pictured horizontally and is thought of as extending, without end, both to the left and to the right.

Number sentence—A statement in symbols describing a relation between two or more numbers. The relation may be an equality or an inequality, and it may be either true or false.

Numeral—A symbol used to represent a number.

Numeration system—An organized procedure for arranging a set of symbols so that they can be used effectively to name numbers.

Numerator—The number that is represented by a in a fractional number expressed in the form $\frac{a}{b}$, where $b \neq 0$.

Obtuse triangle—A triangle with one angle larger than a right angle.

Octagon—A polygon with eight sides.

Odd number—Any element of the set {. . . , ⁻7, ⁻5, ⁻3, ⁻1, 1, 3, 5, 7, . . .}. The odd numbers may be obtained by adding 1 to each element of the set of even numbers.

One-to-one correspondence—An arrangement whereby the elements of two sets are matched so that each element of the first set is matched to one and only

one element of the second set, and each element of the second set is matched to one and only one element of the first set.

Open number sentence—A number sentence containing one or more variables.

Order—A set of numbers is ordered if, for any two numbers in the set, one is less than, greater than, or equal to the other; that is, for every pair of numbers a and b in a given set exactly one of the relations $a > b$, $a < b$, $a = b$ must hold.

Ordered pair—A pair of elements which have been assigned a specific order; that is, one element is designated as the first element and the other is designated as the second element.

Ordinal number—A natural number used to indicate a particular position of an element in a set.

Parallel lines—Lines in the same plane that do not intersect.

Parallel planes—Planes that do not intersect.

Parallelogram—A quadrilateral with opposite sides parallel.

Parentheses, (,)—Symbols used to indicate that the enclosed numerals or symbols should be considered together.

Partial product—Part of a product, as illustrated below.

$$
\begin{array}{r}
123 \\
\times\,321 \\
\hline
123 \\
2\ 46 \\
36\ 9 \\
\hline
39{,}483
\end{array}
$$

Each of these numbers is a partial product.

Path—A set of points in space that are passed through in going from one point to another.

Pentagon—A polygon with five sides.

Percent—A numeral form that means by the hundred; that is, 8 percent means $\frac{8}{100}$.

Periodic decimal—Any decimal in which a single digit or set of digits repeats indefinitely. A periodic decimal is also called a repeating decimal.

Place value—A notation wherein the value represented by each digit in a given numeral is determined by the position it occupies. Place value is also referred to as positional notation.

Placeholder—A symbol used to represent an unspecified number. A placeholder is also called a variable.

Plane—A set of points in space that can be thought of as an indefinite extension of a flat surface.

Plane angle—The union of two rays that have a common endpoint.

Plane curve—A curve consisting of a set of points that lie in the same plane.

Point—An exact location in space. A point has no size because it is only an idea.

Polygon—A simple closed curve that is the union of three or more line segments.

Positional notation—A notation wherein a value is assigned to each position in a numeral; thus, the positional value of each digit in a numeral can be determined by multiplying the value of the digit by the value assigned to the particular place it occupies. Positional notation is also called place value.

Positive integer—Any element of the set $\{1, 2, 3, 4, 5, \ldots\}$.

Positive number—Any number greater than zero. On a number line positive numbers are generally represented to the right of zero.

Power—Any product in which all the factors are the same; the common factor is the base, and the number of such factors is indicated by the exponent. For example, 2^4 is the fourth power of the base 2, and $2^4 = 2 \times 2 \times 2 \times 2$.

Prime number—A whole number greater than 1 which has only itself and 1 as whole number factors.

Product—The result obtained when two or more numbers are multiplied.

Proof—A deductive mathematical procedure used to establish the validity of a statement. The procedure is based on undefined terms, definitions, assumptions, and previously proved statements.

Proper subset—A proper subset of set K is any subset of K that is not the entire set K; that is, there is at least one element of set K that is not an element of a proper subset of K.

Proportion—A statement that two ratios are equal.

Quadrilateral—A polygon with four sides.

Quotient—The result obtained when a number is divided by another number different from zero.

Radius of a circle (plural, radii)—A line segment with the center of the circle as one endpoint and a point on the circle as the other endpoint.

Ratio—A comparison of two numbers by division.

Rational number—Any number that can be expressed in the form $\frac{a}{b}$, where the numerator a and the denominator b are integers and $b \neq 0$. Each rational number may be expressed as a repeating decimal.

Ray—The union of a half-line and the point determining the half-line.

Real number—A coordinate of a point on the number line. Any real number is either a rational number or an irrational number.

Reciprocal—One of a pair of numbers whose product is 1. The reciprocal of a number is also called the multiplicative inverse of the number.

Rectangle—A parallelogram with four right angles.

Rectangular region—The union of the interior of a rectangle and the rectangle; that is, the set of all points inside and on a rectangle.

Reduce—Change the name of a fractional number by dividing both the numerator and the denominator by the same number (usually a natural number). The value of a fractional number is not changed when its name is changed in this manner.

Region—The union of the interior of a simple closed curve and the curve.

Relation—A statement of the association between two or more numbers, ideas, operations, etc.

Repeating decimal—Any decimal in which a single digit or set of digits repeats indefinitely. A repeating decimal is also called a periodic decimal.

Repeats—Continues on and on; that is, the same element (or set of elements) appears over and over again in some pattern.

Right angle—Either of the two angles formed when a ray extends from a point on a line in such a way that the two angles are congruent.

Right triangle—A triangle with a right angle.

Row—A horizontal arrangement of symbols.

Rule—A defined method of performing some operation.

Scalene quadrilateral—A quadrilateral with no two sides congruent.

Scalene triangle—A triangle with no two sides congruent.

Scientific notation—A form for representing any given number as the product of an appropriate power of 10 and some number that is greater than or equal to 1 but less than 10.

Semicircle—An arc of a circle such that the endpoints of the arc are the endpoints of a diameter of the circle.

Separate—A geometric concept that means to divide a given set of points into two disjoint subsets such that the dividing point (or set of points) is not a member of either subset and any path with one endpoint in each of the two disjoint subsets contains the separating point (or a point of the separating set of points).

Set—Any well-defined collection, class, or aggregate of objects or ideas.

Sides of a polygon—The line segments forming the polygon.

Signed number—A directed number, that is, a number whose direction is indicated by a + or − sign prefixed to the numeral that names the number.

Simple closed curve—A closed curve that does not intersect itself.

Simplest form—A fractional number is expressed in simplest form when the greatest common factor of its numerator and denominator is 1. A fractional number that is expressed in simplest form is said to be in lowest terms.

Simplify—To transform a given expression into a simpler form that is equal in value to the given expression.

Skew lines—Lines that do not intersect and are not parallel. Skew lines are not on the same plane.

Solution—The set of numbers that make an open number sentence true.

Space—The set of all points.

Square—A rectangle with all four sides congruent.

Square of a number—The number obtained by multiplying a number by itself; that is, the second power of the number.

Straight path—The most direct path from one point to another.

Subset—A subset of A is a set B such that each element of B is an element of A.

Subscript—A word, numeral, or letter that is written below and (in this text) to the right of a symbol to distinguish it from other symbols.

Substitution—A process of replacing one symbol by another symbol representing the same thing; the symbols may represent numbers, or variables, or both.

Subtraction—The process of finding the difference between two numbers; subtraction is the inverse of addition.

Sum—The result obtained when two or more numbers are added.

Symbol—A mark of any sort that represents a number, an operation, a relation, etc.

Terminates—Comes to an end; the division process is said to terminate when the division continues until there is a remainder of 0.

Terminating decimal—A decimal in which the digit 0 repeats indefinitely; that is, since the digit 0 repeats indefinitely in the numeral, we may terminate the decimal with the last digit prior to the repeating 0.

Triangle—A polygon with three sides.

Union of sets—The union of two sets is the set of elements that are elements of at least one of the two given sets.

Unique—One and only one.

Unique Factorization Theorem—Every composite number can be expressed as a product of prime numbers which is unique except for the order of the factors. The Unique Factorization Theorem is also called the Fundamental Theorem of Arithmetic.

Uniqueness principle for an operation—When an operation is performed on two elements of a set, there is one and only one result produced. The result is said to be the unique result of the operation.

Universal set—The set from which all subsets under discussion are derived. The universal set is also referred to as the universe.

Unlike fractions—Fractions whose numerals representing denominators are not the same.

Variable—A symbol used to represent an unspecified number. A variable is also called a placeholder.

Venn diagram—A picture illustrating relations and operations on sets. Usually, a rectangular region is used to represent a universal set and circular regions are used to represent subsets of the universal set.

Vertex of an angle—The common endpoint of the two rays forming the angle.

Vertices of a polygon—The endpoints of the line segments forming the polygon. Each endpoint is a vertex of the polygon.

Whole number—Any element of the set $\{0, 1, 2, 3, 4, 5, \ldots\}$.

Zero—The number designated by the numeral 0; the cardinal number of the empty set; the identity element for addition and subtraction; the integer that is neither positive nor negative; the point on the real number line that separates the positive real numbers and the negative real numbers.

Bibliography

Anderson, Richard D., *Concepts of Informal Geometry, Studies in Mathematics,* Vol. V. Yale University: School Mathematics Study Group, 1960.

Banks, J. Houston, *Elements of Mathematics.* Boston, Mass.: Allyn and Bacon, 1961.

Bell, Clifford, Clela Hammond, and Robert Herrera, *Fundamentals of Arithmetic for Teachers.* New York: Wiley, 1962.

Brumfiel, Charles, Robert Eicholz, and Merrill Shanks, *Fundamental Concepts of Elementary Mathematics.* Reading, Mass.: Addison-Wesley, 1962.

Brumfiel, Charles, *et al., Principles of Arithmetic.* Reading, Mass.: Addison-Wesley, 1963.

Crouch, Ralph, and George Baldwin, *Mathematics for Elementary Teachers.* New York: Wiley, 1964.

Freitag, Herta and Arthur, *The Number Story.* Washington, D. C.: National Council of Teachers of Mathematics, 1960.

Johnson, Donovan, and William Glenn, *Sets, Sentences, and Operations.* St. Louis, Mo.: Webster, 1960.

Johnson, Donovan, and William Glenn, *Understanding Numeration Systems.* St. Louis, Mo.: Webster, 1960.

Meserve, Bruce, and Max Sobel, *Introduction to Mathematics.* Englewood Cliffs, N. J.: Prentice-Hall, 1964.

Meserve, Bruce, and Max Sobel, *Mathematics for Secondary School Teachers.* Englewood Cliffs, N. J.: Prentice-Hall, 1962.

National Council of Teachers of Mathematics, *23rd Yearbook, Insights Into Modern Mathematics.* Washington, D. C.: NCTM, 1957.

National Council of Teachers of Mathematics, *24th Yearbook, The Growth of Mathematical Ideas, Grades K-12.* Washington, D. C.: NCTM, 1959.

National Council of Teachers of Mathematics, *25th Yearbook, Instruction in Arithmetic.* Washington, D. C.: NCTM, 1960.

National Council of Teachers of Mathematics, *27th Yearbook, Enrichment Mathematics for the Grades.* Washington, D. C.: NCTM, 1963.

Osborn, Roger, *et al., Extending Mathematics Understanding.* Columbus, Ohio: Charles E. Merrill, 1961.

Peterson, John, and Joseph Hashisaki, *Theory of Arithmetic.* New York: Wiley, 1963.

Schaaf, William L., *Basic Concepts of Elementary Mathematics.* New York: Wiley, 1960.

School Mathematics Study Group, *Number Systems, Studies in Mathematics,* Vol. VI. Yale University, 1961.

School Mathematics Study Group, *A Brief Course in Mathematics for Elementary School Teachers, Studies in Mathematics,* Vol. IX. Stanford University, 1963.

Shipp, Donald, and Sam Adams, *Developing Arithmetic Concepts and Skills.* Englewood Cliffs, N. J.: Prentice-Hall, 1964.

Smith, David, *Number Stories of Long Ago.* Washington, D. C.: NCTM, 1962.

Smith, David, and Jekuthiel Ginsburg, *Numbers and Numerals.* Washington, D. C.: NCTM, 1953.

Swain, Robert, *Understanding Arithmetic.* New York: Holt, Rinehart & Winston, 1962.

Ward, Morgan, and Clarence Hardgrove, *Modern Elementary Mathematics.* Reading, Mass.: Addison-Wesley, 1964.

Webber, G. Cuthbert, and John A. Brown, *Basic Concepts of Mathematics.* Reading, Mass.: Addison-Wesley, 1963.

Williams, Sammie, *et al., Modern Mathematics in the Elementary and Junior High Schools.* Syracuse, N. Y.: Singer, 1961.

Answers for
Odd-Numbered Exercises

CHAPTER 1—BASIC MATHEMATICAL CONCEPTS

1-2 Concept of Sets

1. (a) $A = \{0, 2, 4, 6, 8, 10, 12, 14\}$.
   (b) $B = \{1, 3, 5, 7, 9, 11, 13\}$.
   (c) $C = \{$March, May$\}$.
   (d) $D = \{$Sunday, Monday, Tuesday, Wednesday, Thursday, Friday, Saturday$\}$.
3. (a) Well defined; {January, March, May, July, August, October, December}.
   (b) Not well defined. (c) Not well defined. (d) Not well defined. In (b), (c), and (d) the words "interesting," "great," and "good" mean different things to different people.

1-3 Empty Set

1. $\{\}$.
3. Among the many correct answers are: the set of ten-foot-tall basketball players in the United States; the set of natural numbers less than zero.

1-4 One-to-One Correspondence

1. (a) Yes.　　　　　　　(b) No.　　　　　　　(c) Yes.

3. (a) One.   (b) Among the many correct diagrams are
   (c) No.

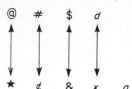

1-7 Whole Numbers

1. There is no largest whole number.   **3.** 0.
5. There is no largest counting number.

1-9 Ordinal Numbers

1. (a) Cardinal.   (b) Ordinal.
   (c) Cardinal, ordinal.   (d) Cardinal, cardinal.
3. (a) Ordinal.   (b) Cardinal.
   (c) Cardinal.   (d) Ordinal.

1-10 Distinction between Number and Numeral

1. The number 7.
3. (a), (d), and (f) are all names for the number two.

1-11 Finite and Infinite Sets

1. Infinite.   **3.** Finite.   **5.** Finite (also empty).
7. Infinite.   **9.** Finite.

1-12 Equal and Equivalent Sets

1. (a) Equal and equivalent.   (b) Neither.   (c) Equivalent.
   (d) Neither.   (e) Equivalent.
3. (a) Yes. (b) No. (c) No. (d) Yes.
5. $Y = \{$John, Ruth, Bob$\}$.

1-13 Relations of Equality and Inequality

1. (a) $21 > 18$.   (b) $16 < 35$.   (c) $a = b$.
   (d) $R = \{r, s, t\}$.   (e) $c \neq d$.
3. $6 + n < 7 + n$.   **5.** $6 \times n < 7 \times n$.
7. $2 < 4$.   **9.** $4 \times 8 < 5 \times 9$.

1-14 Number Sentences

1. (a) $<$. (b) $>$. (c) $=$. (d) $>$. (e) $<$. (f) $<$.

3. (a) Not open; true.   (b) Not open; false.   (c) Open.
(d) Open.   (e) Not open; true.   (f) Not open; true.

1-15 Number Line

1. The graph of the smaller number is located at the left of the graph of the larger on the number line.

3. (a) N. (b) P. (c) T. (d) R. (e) M. (f) Q.

CHAPTER 2—WORKING WITH SETS

2-1 Sets and Subsets

1. (a) $\{8, 10, 12, 14, 16, 18\}$.   (b) $\{7, 9, 11, 13, 15, 17\}$.
(c) Among the many correct answers are $\{7, 8, 9\}$, $\{16, 17, 18\}$, $\{7, 10, 16\}$, $\{14, 13, 15\}$, and $\{9, 16, 11\}$.

3. The cardinal number of the set A is less than the cardinal number of the set C. If $A \subset C$, then there is at least one element of C that is not an element of A. Therefore, the number of elements in A is less than the number of elements in C.

5.

Set	Subsets	Number of Elements in the Original Set	Number of Subsets
$\{d\}$	$\{d\}, \{\ \}$	1	2
$\{d, e\}$	$\{d\}, \{e\}, \{d, e\}, \{\ \}$	2	4
$\{d, e, f\}$	$\{d\}, \{e\}, \{f\}, \{d, e\}, \{d, f\},$ $\{e, f\}, \{d, e, f\}, \{\ \}$	3	8
$\{d, e, f, g\}$	$\{d\}, \{e\}, \{f\}, \{g\}, \{d, e\}, \{d, f\},$ $\{d, g\}, \{e, f\}, \{e, g\}, \{f, g\},$ $\{d, e, f\}, \{d, e, g\}, \{d, f, g\},$ $\{e, f, g\}, \{d, e, f, g\}, \{\ \}$	4	16

2-2 Universal Set

1. Among the many correct answers are
(a) The set of all automobiles.
(b) The set of all students at George Wythe High School.
(c) The set of all whole numbers.

3. Among the many correct answers are
  (a) The set consisting of the first American astronaut to orbit the earth.
  (b) The set of equilateral triangles.
  (c) The set of natural numbers less than seven.

2-3 Union of Sets

1. $G \cup H = \{1, 2, 3, 4, 5, 6\}$, $n(G \cup H) = 6$.
3. $R \cup S = \{\%, @, \#, c, \&\}$, $n(R \cup S) = 5$.
5. $E \subseteq D$.

2-4 Intersection of Sets

1. $A \cap B = \{b, c\}$, $n(A \cap B) = 2$.   **3.** $G \cap H = \{\ \}$, $n(G \cap H) = 0$.
5. $M = N$.   **7.** $D = E$.
9. **(a)** $\{0, 1, 2, 3, 4, 5, 6, 7, \ldots\}$; that is, A. **(b)** $\{10, 20, 30, \ldots\}$.
  (c) $\{1, 3, 5, 7, \ldots\}$; that is, C.   **(d)** $\{\ \}$.
  (e) $\{5, 10, 15, 20, \ldots\}$; that is, D. **(f)** $\{5, 15, 25, 35, \ldots\}$.

2-5 Disjoint Sets

1. Not disjoint.   **3.** Disjoint.

2-6 Complement of a Set

1. $A' = \{1, 3\}$.
3. **(a)** $\{1, 2, 3\}$; that is, A.   **(b)** $\{1, 2, 3, 4, 5, 6, 7, 8, 9\}$; that is, U.
  (c) $\{1, 2, 4, 6, 8\}$; that is, B'.   **(d)** $\{1, 2, 4, 6, 8\}$; that is, B'.
  (e) $\{1, 2, 3, 4, 5, 6, 7, 8, 9\}$; that is, U. **(f)** $\{1, 2, 4\}$; that is, $(B \cup C)'$.
  (g) $\{1, 2, 3, 4, 5, 6, 7, 8, 9\}$; that is, U. **(h)** $\{1, 2, 4\}$; that is, $B' \cap C'$.

2-7 Venn Diagrams

1. **(a)**

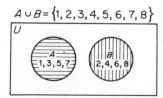

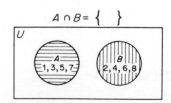

Set A is shaded horizontally and set B is shaded vertically; $A \cup B$ is the subset of U, which is shaded in either or both directions.

Set A is shaded horizontally, and set B is shaded vertically; $A \cap B$ is the subset of U, which is shaded both horizontally and vertically.

(b)

$M \cup N = \{$Ann, Louise, Lucille$\}$

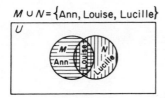

$M \cap N = \{$Louise$\}$

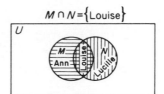

Set M is shaded horizontally and set N is shaded vertically; $M \cup N$ is the subset of U, which is shaded in either or both directions.

Set M is shaded horizontally and set N is shaded vertically; $M \cap N$ is the subset of U, which is shaded both horizontally and vertically.

3. (a)

$P \cup Q$

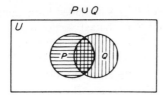

(b)

$P \cap Q$

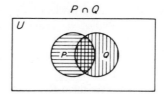

Set P is shaded horizontally and set Q is shaded vertically; $P \cup Q$ is the subset of U, which is shaded in either or both directions.

Set P is shaded horizontally and set Q is shaded vertically; $P \cap Q$ is the subset of U, which is shaded both horizontally and vertically.

5. (a)

$G \cup H = G = H$

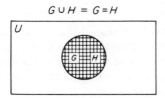

(b)

$G \cap H = G = H$

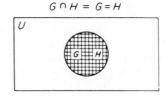

Set G is shaded horizontally and set H is shaded vertically; $G \cup H$ is the subset of U, which is shaded in either or both directions.

Set G is shaded horizontally and set H is shaded vertically; $G \cap H$ is the subset of U, which is shaded both horizontally and vertically.

7. (a)

$R \subset S$

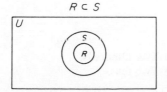

(b)

$A \subset B, B \subset E$

(c) $X \subset Y, Z \subset Y, X \cap Z = \{\ \}$

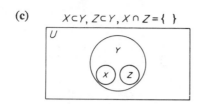

9. (a)   **(b)**

$R \cup (S \cup T)$ $(R \cup S) \cup T$

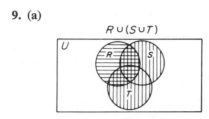   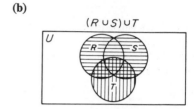

Set R is shaded horizontally and set $S \cup T$ is shaded vertically; the union of these sets is the subset of U, which is shaded in either or both directions.

Set $R \cup S$ is shaded horizontally and set T is shaded vertically; the union of these sets is the subset of U, which is shaded in either or both directions.

Note in the diagrams for Exercises 9(a) and 9(b) that the final result is the same. Thus we have $R \cup (S \cup T) = (R \cup S) \cup T$.

(c)   **(d)**

$R \cap (T \cup S)$ $R \cap (T \cap S)$

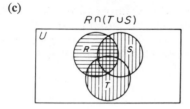   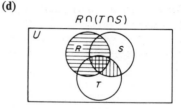

Set R is shaded horizontally and set $T \cup S$ is shaded vertically; the intersection of these sets is the subset of U, which is shaded both horizontally and vertically.

Set R is shaded horizontally and set $T \cap S$ is shaded vertically; the intersection of these sets is the subset of U, which is shaded both horizontally and vertically.

CHAPTER 3—SYSTEMS OF NUMERATION

3-1 Characteristics of Decimal Notation

1. Place value and a base of ten.

3-2 Place Value

1. (a) Two thousands.   (b) Two hundreds.
   (c) Two ones.   (d) Two tens.

3-3 Powers of Numbers

1. (a) 9^3.   (b) 7^4.   (c) 3^2.   (d) 5^3.
3. The exponent and the number of zeros is the same; for example, $10^2 = 100$ and $10^3 = 1,000$.
5. (a) The base is 3, the exponent is 6, and the power is 3^6.
   (b) The base is 7, the exponent is 2, and the power is 7^2.

3-4 Multiplication and Division of Powers

1. (a) 2^7. (b) 3^3. (c) 6^5. (d) 4^8. (e) 1. (f) 5^{12}.
3. (a) 3^{14}.   (b) 3^9.   (c) 25^2.
   (d) 4^{-6}.   (e) $2^6 \div 2 = 2^5$.   (f) $\dfrac{1}{21^6} = 21^{-6}$.

5. (a) One-tenth.   (b) One-hundredth.
   (c) One-thousandth.   (d) One-ten-thousandth.

3-5 Base of a System of Numeration

1. (a) $(3 \times 10^2) + (2 \times 10^1) + (8 \times 10^0)$.
   (b) $(9 \times 10^3) + (6 \times 10^2) + (5 \times 10^1) + (7 \times 10^0)$.
   (c) $(2 \times 10^5) + (6 \times 10^4) + (3 \times 10^3) + (7 \times 10^2) + (8 \times 10^1) + (4 \times 10^0)$.
   (d) $(6 \times 10^0) + (1 \times 10^{-1}) + (7 \times 10^{-2}) + (5 \times 10^{-3})$.
3. (a) One set of ten and eight more   (b) One set of twelve and six more

   (c) Three sets of five and three more   (d) Two sets of seven and four more

        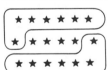

5. (a) Ten.   (b) Twelve.   (c) Five.   (d) Seven.
   (e) Nine.   (f) Eight.   (g) Six.   (h) Two.

3-6 Early Egyptian Numerals

1. (a) ∩||||| (b) ∩∩∩∩∩∩∩∩∩||

   (c) 𐦀𐦀𐦀𐦀𐦀99∩||||| (d) ⪽⪽𐦀𐦀||

3. (a) 107.   (b) 207,218.   (c) 5,308.   (d) 5,231.

5. $\overset{\sim}{\text{I}}$ ϙϙϙ∩∩∩∩∩∩∩.

7. We have two names for the same number.

3-7 Early Babylonian Numerals

1. (a) ▼▼▼
▼▼▼
▼▼▼

(b) ◄◄▼▼▼
◄◄▼▼▼

(c) ▼ ▼▼
▼▼

(d) ▼▼▼◄◄◄▼

3. (a) 55.   **(b)** 296.   **(c)** 111.   **(d)** 74.

3-8 Roman Numerals

1. (a) XII.   **(b)** LXXXIII.   **(c)** XCV.   **(d)** MCMLXIV.
3. (a) 95.   **(b)** 2,059.   **(c)** 178.   **(d)** 107.
5. CMXCVI.
7. We have two names for the same number.

CHAPTER 4—OPERATIONS: ADDITION AND SUBTRACTION

4-1 Addition of Whole Numbers

1. $n(A \cup B) = 6.$ **3.** $n(E \cup F) = 5.$
5. (a) No.   **(b)** Yes.   **(c)** No.   **(d)** Yes.

4-2 Closure and Uniqueness

1. (a) Closed.   **(b)** Not closed.   **(c)** Not closed.   **(d)** Closed.
  (e) Closed.   **(f)** Not closed.   **(g)** Closed.

4-3 The Commutative Principle of Addition

1. (a) Not commutative.   **(b)** Commutative.
  (c) Commutative.   **(d)** Not commutative.
3. (a) $1 + 2 = 2 + 1.$ **(b)** $19 + 6 = 6 + 19.$
  (c) $27 + 63 = 63 + 27.$ **(d)** $108 + 325 = 325 + 108.$

4-4 The Associative Principle of Addition

1. (a) $(15 + 3) + 42 = 18 + 42 = 60.$
        $15 + (3 + 42) = 15 + 45 = 60.$
  (b) $(22 + 7) + 18 = 29 + 18 = 47.$
        $22 + (7 + 18) = 22 + 25 = 47.$
  (c) $(109 + 23) + 11 = 132 + 11 = 143.$
        $109 + (23 + 11) = 109 + 34 = 143.$

(d) $(237 + 165) + 35 = 402 + 35 = 437.$
$237 + (165 + 35) = 237 + 200 = 437.$

3. (a) $27 + (36 + 13) + 64 = 27 + (13 + 36) + 64 = (27 + 13) + (36 + 64)$
$= 40 + 100 = 140.$

   (b) $135 + (81 + 15) + 9 = 135 + (15 + 81) + 9 = (135 + 15) + (81 + 9)$
$= 150 + 90 = 240.$

   (c) $58 + (24 + 32) + 16 = 58 + (32 + 24) + 16 = (58 + 32) + (24 + 16)$
$= 90 + 40 = 130.$

   (d) $19 + (17 + 11) + 83 = 19 + (11 + 17) + 83 = (19 + 11) + (17 + 83)$
$= 30 + 100 = 130.$

5. (a) False.   (b) True.   (c) True.   (d) False.

4-5   Identity Element for Addition

1. (a) 0.   (b) 8.   (c) 27.   (d) 0.

4-6 The Addition Table

1. (a) One-more pattern. (b) One-more pattern. (c) Two-more pattern. (d) Each block in a particular diagonal row contains the same numeral. (e) One-less pattern.

3. A line drawn diagonally through the table from the upper left-hand corner to the lower right-hand corner divides the table into two parts. The corresponding blocks in the two parts of the table contain the same numeral; that is, $9 + 1 = 1 + 9, 7 + 2 = 2 + 7$, etc.

4-7 Understanding the Addition Algorism

1. (a) $\overset{1}{4}56$ (b) $\overset{1}{6}80$ (c) $\overset{11}{1}08$ (d) $\overset{111}{3}33$
   $+324$ $+227$ $+\ 94$ $+777$
   $\overline{780}$ $\overline{907}$ $\overline{202}$ $\overline{1,110}$

4-8 Subtraction of Whole Numbers

1. (a) $13 - 7 = 6$ or $13 - 6 = 7.$ (b) $59 - 21 = 38$ or $59 - 38 = 21.$
   (c) $5 - 4 = 1$ or $5 - 1 = 4.$ (d) $m - k = h$ or $m - h = k.$

3. (a) $5 - 2 = 3.$

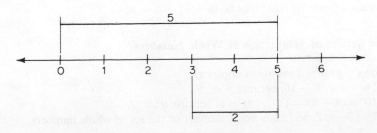

(b) 2 + 3 = 5.

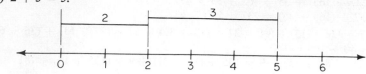

(c) 7 − 4 = 3.

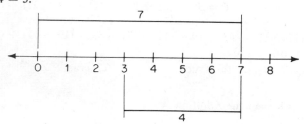

(d) 4 + 3 = 7.

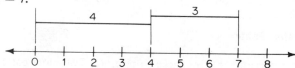

(e) 9 + 2 = 11.

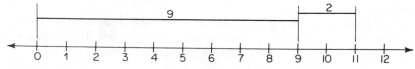

(f) 11 − 9 = 2.

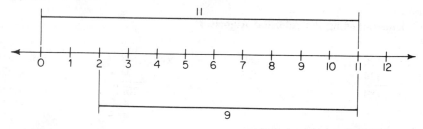

4-9 Inverse Operations

1. (a) Opening a door.   **(b)** Withdrawing $6.00 from the bank.
   (c) Taking off your shoes.   **(d)** Removing a pie from the oven.

3. Subtract 6 from the sum; that is, $(n + 6) − 6 = n$.

4-10 Principles of Subtraction of Whole Numbers

1. Among the many possible examples are
   (a) $16 − 7 \neq 7 − 16$, because $9 \neq {}^-9$.
   (b) $10 − (9 − 8) \neq (10 − 9) − 8$, because $9 \neq {}^-7$.
   (c) $7 − 9 = {}^-2$, and ${}^-2$ is not a member of the set of whole numbers.

4-11 Understanding the Subtraction Algorism

1. **(a)** $\overset{5\,1}{\cancel{6}7}$ **(b)** $\overset{4\,1}{\cancel{5}0}$ **(c)** $\overset{1\,12\,1}{2\cancel{3}6}$ **(d)** $\overset{3\,13\,1}{4\cancel{4}4}$
$\underline{-\ 19}$ $\underline{-\ 13}$ $\underline{-158}$ $\underline{-355}$
    48   37   78   89

3. Yes.   The limitations are that we must have closure for the particular subtraction problem; that is, the difference between the two whole numbers must be a whole number.

4-12 The Set of Integers

1. Positive four plus positive nine is equal to positive thirteen.
3. Negative six plus positive eight is equal to positive two.
5. Zero plus negative fourteen is equal to negative fourteen.
7. Positive seven minus positive five is equal to positive two.
9. Negative three minus positive five is equal to negative eight.
11. Negative six minus negative eleven is equal to positive five.
13. Positive seven minus zero is equal to positive seven.
15. Zero minus negative nineteen is equal to positive nineteen.
17. Positive five plus negative four is equal to positive one.
19. Positive sixteen plus positive eight is equal to positive twenty-four.
21. Negative eleven minus negative thirty-one is equal to positive twenty.

4-13 Additive Inverse

1. **(a)** $^+3$; that is, 3.   **(b)** $^-5$.   **(c)** $^-17$.   **(d)** $^+26$; that is, 26.   **(e)** 0.

4-14 Addition of Integers

1. **(a)** $5 + {}^-4 = 1$.

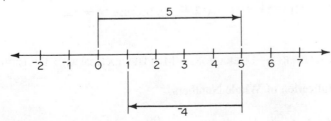

(b) $^-1 + {}^-3 = {}^-4$.

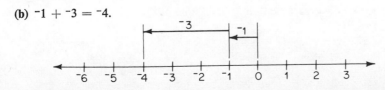

(c) $^-6 + 5 = {}^-1$.

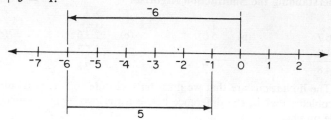

(d) $^-2 + 2 = 0$.

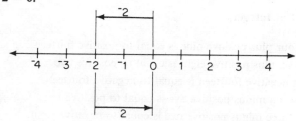

3. The sum of two positive integers is a positive integer.
The sum of a positive integer and a negative integer is a positive integer if the line segment representing the positive integer is longer than the line segment representing the negative integer. The sum of a positive integer and a negative integer is a negative integer if the line segment representing the negative integer is longer than the line segment representing the positive integer.
The sum of two negative integers is a negative integer.

4-15 Subtraction of Integers

1. (a) $^+6$. **(b)** ^-x. **(c)** $^-4$. **(d)** $^+1$. **(e)** $^-(a + b)$. **(f)** $^-(4 + {}^-3)$; that is, $^-1$. **(g)** $^-({}^-13 + {}^-4)$; that is, $^+17$. **(h)** $^-({}^-a + 2)$; that is, $a + {}^-2$.
3. (a) $^-6$. **(b)** 0. **(c)** $^-5$. **(d)** 5.
5. Yes.
7. No; $(^+1 - {}^+2) - {}^+3 \neq {}^+1 - (^+2 - {}^+3)$, because $^-4 \neq {}^+2$.

CHAPTER 5—OPERATIONS—MULTIPLICATION AND DIVISION

5-1 Multiplication of Whole Numbers

1. (a) • • • • •
• • • • •

(b) • •
• •
• •
• •
• •

(c) A 4 × 0 array is the empty set.   (d) • • • • • • • •

3. (a) 4 × 2 = 8.

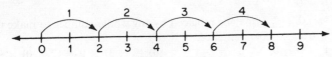

(b) 2 × 4 = 8.

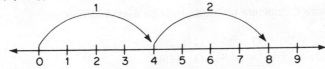

(c) 3 × 4 = 12.

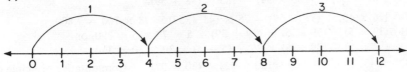

(d) 5 × 1 = 5.

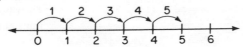

5-2 Closure and Uniqueness

1. (a) Closed.   (b) Closed.   (c) Closed.   (d) Not closed.
    (e) Closed.   (f) Not closed.   (g) Closed.

5-3 The Commutative Principle of Multiplication

1. (a) 5 × 3 = 3 × 5.   (b) 7 × 9 = 9 × 7.
    (c) 143 × 10 = 10 × 143.   (d) 999 × 4 = 4 × 999.

5-4 The Associative Principle of Multiplication

1. (a) (2 × 5) × 46 = 10 × 46 = 460; 2 × (5 × 46) = 2 × 230 = 460.
    (b) (3 × 6) × 9 = 18 × 9 = 162; 3 × (6 × 9) = 3 × 54 = 162.
    (c) (50 × 20) × 7 = 1,000 × 7 = 7,000; 50 × (20 × 7) = 50 × 140 = 7,000.
    (d) (4 × 8) × 25 = 32 × 25 = 800; 4 × (8 × 25) = 4 × 200 = 800.

3. (a) False.   (b) False.   (c) True.   (d) True.

5-5 Identity Element for Multiplication

1. (a) 16 × 1 = 16.   (b) 1 × d = d.
    (c) 8 × 1 = 8.   (d) 1 × 1 = 1.

5-6 Principle of Multiplication by Zero

1. (a) $8 \times \underline{0} = 0$.
 (b) The variable ____ may be replaced by any whole number to make $0 \times$ ____
    $= 0$ a true number sentence.
 (c) $7 \times 8 \times 0 = \underline{0}$.   (d) $(2 \times 3) \times \underline{0} = (7 \times 0) \times 9$.

5-7 Distributive Principle of Multiplication over Addition

1. (a) $7 \times (8 + 29) = (7 \times \underline{8}) + \underline{(7} \times 29)$.
 (b) $(5 \times 3) + (5 \times \underline{26)} = 5 \times \underline{(3} + 26)$.
 (c) $128 \times (64 + 216) = \underline{(128} \times \underline{64)} + (128 \times \underline{216)}$.
 (d) $(785 \times 38) + (785 \times 59) = \underline{785} \times \underline{(38} + \underline{59)}$.

3. (a) $(78 \times 43) + (78 \times 57) = 78 \times (43 + 57) = 78 \times 100 = 7{,}800$.
 (b) $(39 \times 5) + (39 \times 5) = (39 + 39) \times 5 = 78 \times 5 = 390$, or
    $(39 \times 5) + (39 \times 5) = 39 \times (5 + 5) = 39 \times 10 = 390$.

5. $(30 \times 13) + (37 \times 30) = (30 \times 13) + (30 \times 37)$ Commutative principle of
                                                                multiplication

                              $= 30 \times (13 + 37)$ Distributive principle of
                                                         multiplication over addi-
                                                         tion

                              $= 30 \times 50$ Addition
                              $= 1{,}500$ Multiplication

5-8 The Multiplication Table

1. The principle of multiplication by zero.
3. Row: 0, 700, 1400, 2100; column: 0, 700, 1400, 2100.
5. The differences between these consecutive squares form a pattern.

$$1 - 0 = 1$$
$$4 - 1 = 3$$
$$9 - 4 = 5$$
$$16 - 9 = 7$$
$$25 - 16 = 9$$
$$36 - 25 = 11$$
$$49 - 36 = 13$$
$$64 - 49 = 15$$
$$81 - 64 = 17$$

These differences are consecutive odd whole numbers. The next five numbers
represented on the main diagonal would be as follows.

First:	$81 + 19 = 100$
Second:	$100 + 21 = 121$
Third:	$121 + 23 = 144$
Fourth:	$144 + 25 = 169$
Fifth:	$169 + 27 = 196$

7. A line drawn diagonally through the table from the upper left-hand corner to the lower right-hand corner divides the table into two parts. The corresponding blocks in the two parts of the table contain the same numeral; that is, $9 \times 8 = 8 \times 9$, $6 \times 5 = 5 \times 6$, and so on.

5-9 Understanding the Multiplication Algorism

1. (a)
$$\begin{array}{r} \overset{5}{29} \\ \times\ 6 \\ \hline 174 \end{array}$$

(b)
$$\begin{array}{r} \overset{4}{37} \\ \times 16 \\ \hline 222 \\ 37 \\ \hline 592 \end{array}$$

5-10 Prime Numbers

1. 101, 103, 107, 109, 113, 127, 131, 137, 139, 149, 151, 157, 163, 167, 173, 179, 181, 191, 193, 197, 199.

3. No. The fact that $n \times 0 = 0$ for every whole number n tells us that every whole number is a factor of 0. Thus, zero is excluded from the set of prime numbers because it has more than two factors.

5-11 Fundamental Theorem of Arithmetic

1. (a) $42 = 6 \times 7 = 2 \times 3 \times 7$. (b) $99 = 9 \times 11 = 3 \times 3 \times 11$.
   (c) $148 = 2 \times 74 = 2 \times 2 \times 37$.
   (d) $375 = 5 \times 75 = 3 \times 5 \times 25 = 3 \times 5 \times 5 \times 5$.

3. (a) 1, 2, 3, 4, 6, 9, 12, 18, 36. (b) 4, 6, 9, 12, 18, 36.
   (c) 2, 3.

5. 2×9; 3×6; $2 \times 3 \times 3$.

5-12 Least Common Multiple

1. (a) 2×2. (b) $2 \times 3 \times 3$. (c) $2 \times 2 \times 5$.
   (d) $2 \times 2 \times 2 \times 2 \times 2$. (e) $2 \times 2 \times 3 \times 3 \times 11$.

3. Because it is a multiple of 2 and also a multiple of 3.

5. (a) $9 = 3 \times 3$,
   $12 = 2 \times 2 \times 3$,
   L.C.M. of 9 and 12 is $2 \times 2 \times 3 \times 3$; that is, 36.
   (b) $10 = 2 \times 5$,
   $11 = 1 \times 11$,
   $12 = 2 \times 2 \times 3$,
   L.C.M. of 10, 11, and 12 is $1 \times 2 \times 2 \times 3 \times 5 \times 11$; that is, 660.

(c) $21 = 3 \times 7,$
$35 = 5 \times 7,$
$15 = 3 \times 5,$
L.C.M. of 21, 35, and 15 is $3 \times 5 \times 7$; that is, 105.

(d) $57 = 3 \times 19,$
$98 = 2 \times 7 \times 7,$
$121 = 11 \times 11,$
L.C.M. of 57, 98, and 121 is $2 \times 3 \times 7 \times 7 \times 11 \times 11 \times 19$; that is, 675,906.

5-13 Greatest Common Factor

1. (a) 16.   (b) 8.   (c) 18.   (d) 1.
3. The G.C.F. of any two prime numbers is always 1.
5. (a) 4.   (b) 5.   (c) 3.   (d) 6.
7. (a) Yes; $30 \times 5 = 10 \times 15$, because $150 = 150$.
    (b) Yes; $180 \times 3 = 12 \times 45$, because $540 = 540$.
9. 1.   **11.** No.

5-14 Division of Whole Numbers

1.
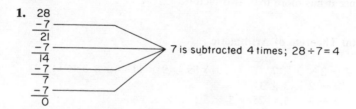

3. (a) $51 \div 17 = d$ or $51 \div d = 17.$ (b) $39 \div b = g$ or $39 \div g = b.$
    (c) $n \div 13 = 26$ or $n \div 26 = 13.$ (d) $t \div s = r$ or $t \div r = s.$

5-15 Inverse Operations

1. (a) True.   (b) True.   (c) False.   (d) True.
3. Multiply the quotient by 23; that is, $(n \div 23) \times 23 = n.$

5-16 Principles of Division of Whole Numbers

1. Among the many correct answers are
    (a) $25 \div 5 \neq 5 \div 25.$ (b) $48 \div (16 \div 8) \neq (48 \div 16) \div 8.$
    (c) $1 \div 3 \neq n$, where n is any whole number.

5-17 Division by Zero

1. (a) True.   **(b)** True.   **(c)** False, since $\frac{0}{0}$ is undefined.

5-18 Understanding the Division Algorism

1. (a)

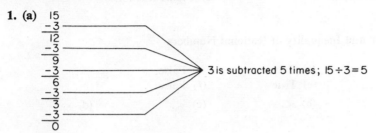

```
 15
 -3
 12
 -3
  9
 -3
  6
 -3
  3
 -3
  0
```
3 is subtracted 5 times; $15 \div 3 = 5$

(b)

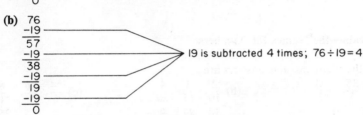

```
 76
-19
 57
-19
 38
-19
 19
-19
  0
```
19 is subtracted 4 times; $76 \div 19 = 4$

(c)

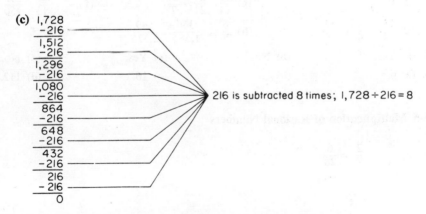

```
 1,728
  -216
 1,512
  -216
 1,296
  -216
 1,080
  -216
   864
  -216
   648
  -216
   432
  -216
   216
  -216
     0
```
216 is subtracted 8 times; $1,728 \div 216 = 8$

5-19 Multiplication and Division of Integers

1. The product of two positive integers is a positive integer.

The product of a positive integer and a negative integer is a negative integer.

The product of two negative integers is a positive integer.

3. (a) ⁻6.   **(b)** ⁺4.   **(c)** ⁻4.   **(d)** Undefined.   **(e)** 0.   **(f)** 54.

CHAPTER 6—RATIONAL NUMBER SYSTEM

6-2 Fractional Numbers and Fractional Numerals

1. (a) Unlike fractions.   (b) Like fractions.
   (c) Like fractions.   (d) Unlike fractions.

6-3 Equality and Inequality of Rational Numbers

1. (a) True.   (b) False.   (c) False.
   (d) True.   (e) True.   (f) False.

3. (a) $>$.   (b) $<$.   (c) $<$.   (d) $=$.

5. Yes.

6-4 Numerals—the Names for Numbers

1. Among the many possible answers are

   (a) $\frac{14}{2}$, $\frac{35}{5}$, $\frac{-21}{-3}$.   (b) $\frac{2}{10}$, $\frac{3}{15}$, $\frac{4}{20}$.   (c) $\frac{-4}{6}$, $\frac{-6}{9}$, $\frac{8}{-12}$.

   (d) 0, $\frac{0}{9}$, $\frac{0}{-6}$.   (e) $\frac{18}{14}$, $\frac{27}{21}$, $\frac{9}{7}$.   (f) $\frac{5}{3}$, $\frac{25}{15}$, $\frac{250}{150}$.

   (g) $\frac{13}{-2}$, $\frac{-26}{4}$, $\frac{52}{-8}$.   (h) $\frac{61}{264}$, $\frac{366}{1,584}$, $\frac{549}{2,376}$.

3. (a) Yes.   (b) No.   (c) Yes.   (d) No.

5. (a) 6.   (b) 1.   (c) 16.   (d) 112.

6-5 Multiplication of Rational Numbers

1. (a) $\frac{3}{4} \times \frac{2}{7} = \frac{6}{28}$.

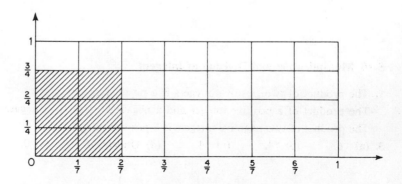

(b) $\frac{1}{2} \times \frac{2}{3} = \frac{2}{6}$.

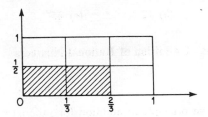

6-6 Principles of Multiplication of Rational Numbers

1. (a) $\frac{1}{15} \times \frac{3}{8} = \frac{3}{120} = \frac{1}{40}$.　　　　　**(b)** $\frac{1}{3} \times \frac{3}{40} = \frac{3}{120} = \frac{1}{40}$.

3. Associative principle of multiplication of rational numbers.

5. One.

7. (a) $\square = \frac{7}{6}$.　　　　　**(b)** $\square = \frac{14}{-13}$.　　　　　**(c)** $\square = 0$.

　　(d) There is no rational number as a replacement for the variable $\square$ such that $0 \times \square = 1$.

9. Zero.

6-7 Addition of Rational Numbers

1. (a) $\frac{4}{3} + \frac{2}{3} = \frac{6}{3}$.

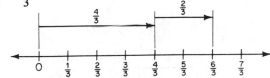

(b) $\frac{2}{7} + \frac{4}{7} = \frac{6}{7}$.

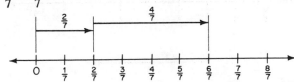

(c) $\frac{5}{6} + \frac{-4}{6} = \frac{1}{6}$.

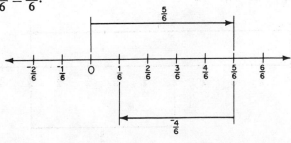

3. (a) 24.   (b) 12.   (c) 45.

6-8 Principles of Addition of Rational Numbers

1. (a) $\dfrac{81}{91}$.   (b) $\dfrac{81}{91}$.

3. Commutative principle of addition for rational numbers.

5. Zero.   **7.** The answers are the same.

9. (a) $\dfrac{5}{3}$.   (b) $\dfrac{3}{4}$.   (c) $\dfrac{63}{136}$.   (d) $\dfrac{63}{136}$.   (e) $\dfrac{63}{136}$.

6-9 Subtraction of Rational Numbers

1. (a) $\dfrac{6}{7} - \dfrac{2}{7} = \dfrac{6}{7} + \dfrac{-2}{7} = \dfrac{4}{7}$.

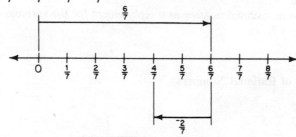

(b) $\dfrac{-2}{5} - \dfrac{-4}{5} = \dfrac{-2}{5} + \dfrac{4}{5} = \dfrac{2}{5}$.

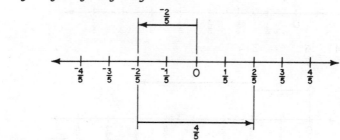

(c) $\dfrac{9}{4} - \dfrac{5}{4} = \dfrac{9}{4} + \dfrac{-5}{4} = \dfrac{4}{4}$.

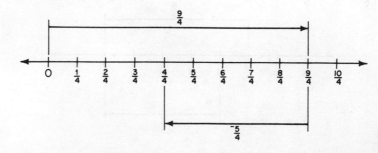

3. (a) $\frac{7}{24}$. (b) $\frac{13}{4}$. (c) $\frac{0}{9} = 0$.

(d) $\frac{16}{91}$. (e) $\frac{-1}{30}$. (f) $\frac{-1}{96}$.

6-10 Principles of Subtraction of Rational Numbers

1. (a) $n = \frac{5}{14}$. (b) $n = \frac{-5}{14}$. (c) No. (d) No.

3. (a) $\frac{7}{8}$. (b) $\frac{0}{5} = 0$. (c) $\frac{3}{7}$. (d) 0.

5. (a) True. (b) False. (c) False. (d) False.

6-11 Division of Rational Numbers

1. (a) $\frac{5}{2}$. (b) 1. (c) $\frac{121}{169}$.

(d) $\frac{eh}{fg}$. (e) $\frac{1}{7}$. (f) $\frac{26}{5}$.

3. (a) Yes. (b) Yes.

6-12 Principles of Division of Rational Numbers

1. (a) True. (b) True. (c) True. (d) True.

(e) True. (f) False. (g) False. (h) False.

6-13 Mixed Numerals and Computation

1. (a) $9\frac{11}{12}$. (b) $4\frac{9}{40}$. (c) $14\frac{1}{42}$. (d) $27\frac{1}{3}$.

3. (a) $29\frac{3}{4}$. (b) $41\frac{1}{8}$. (c) $1\frac{2}{9}$. (d) $53\frac{61}{95}$.

6-14 Density of the Rational Numbers

1. No. Notice that there is an integer between integers such as 2 and 7, but there is no integer between the integers 2 and 3.

3. An infinite number; consider $\frac{1}{2}$, $\frac{1}{3}$, $\frac{1}{4}$, $\frac{1}{5}$, $\cdots$ among many others.

5. It is impossible to determine the smallest positive rational number.

CHAPTER 7—RATIO, PERCENT, AND DECIMALS

7-1 Ratio and Proportion

1. (a) $\frac{4}{9}$. (b) $\frac{30}{55}$. (c) $\frac{32}{56}$. (d) $\frac{53}{17}$.

3. (a) $\frac{1}{3}$. (b) $\frac{1}{6}$. (c) $\frac{3}{2}$. (d) $\frac{1}{50}$.

5. (a) 45. (b) 39. (c) $\frac{5}{8}$. (d) $\frac{7}{3}$.

7. (a) False. (b) True. (c) False. (d) True.

7-2 Percent

1. (a) 75%. (b) 100%. (c) 160%. (d) 350%.
   (e) 40%. (f) 200%. (g) 50%. (h) $87\frac{1}{2}$%.

3. 65.   5. 5.

7-3 Decimal Notation

1. (a) 57,293.641. (b) 300.0704.
   (c) 0.00006. (d) 0.2956.

3. (a) Two hundred forty-six.
   (b) Two and forty-six hundredths.
   (c) One hundred seventy-eight and two hundred ninety-six thousandths.
   (d) Nine tenths.

7-4 Rational Fractional Numerals and Decimal Numerals

1. (a) 0.7. (b) 0.78. (c) 0.65. (d) 0.375.

3. (a) $0.\overline{384615}$. (b) Yes. The cycle is 384615.

5. (a) $\frac{23}{100}$. (b) $\frac{165}{1,000}$; that is, $\frac{33}{200}$.

   (c) $3\frac{738}{10,000}$; that is, $3\frac{369}{5,000}$. (d) $\frac{9}{1,000}$.

7-5 Operations with Numbers Expressed as Terminating Decimals

1. (a) 7.8
       2.75
       +6.
       ───
       16.55
   $\frac{780}{100} + \frac{275}{100} + \frac{600}{100} = \frac{780 + 275 + 600}{100}$
   $= \frac{1,655}{100} = 16.55.$

   (b) 0.123
       +1.1
       ────
       1.223
   $\frac{123}{1,000} + \frac{1,100}{1,000} = \frac{123 + 1,100}{1,000} = \frac{1,223}{1,000} = 1.223.$

(c) 16.88
     -9.56
     ___
     7.32

$\dfrac{1{,}688}{100} - \dfrac{956}{100} = \dfrac{1{,}688 - 956}{100} = \dfrac{732}{100} = 7.32.$

(d) 0.700
     -0.289
     ___
     0.411

$\dfrac{700}{1{,}000} - \dfrac{289}{1{,}000} = \dfrac{700 - 289}{1{,}000} = \dfrac{411}{1{,}000} = 0.411.$

3. (a) $\dfrac{6.5}{15}.$ (b) $\dfrac{7{,}890{,}000}{36}.$ (c) $\dfrac{478.96}{2{,}231}.$ (d) $\dfrac{59{,}200}{1}.$

5. (a) 9%. (b) 0.5%. (c) 278%. (d) 75%.

7-6 Scientific Notation

1. (a) $9.78 \times 10^{-5}.$ (b) $5.64 \times 10^{6}.$ (c) $1.265 \times 10^{0}.$
   (d) $4.31 \times 10^{-13}.$ (e) $9.6783 \times 10^{7}.$ (f) $1.0005 \times 10^{-2}.$

3. $2.7724 \times 10^{16}.$

CHAPTER 8—REAL NUMBER SYSTEM

8-1 Irrational Numbers

1. Among the many positive irrational numbers are $\sqrt[3]{2}, \sqrt{5}, \sqrt{6}, \sqrt{7}, \sqrt[3]{11},$
   $3\sqrt{8}, \dfrac{2}{3}\sqrt{2}, 2\pi, \sqrt[6]{10}, \sqrt[5]{3}.$

8-2 Approximating $\sqrt{2}$ as a Decimal

1. (a) $\sqrt{5}.$ (b) $\sqrt{7}.$ (c) $\sqrt{13}.$ (d) $\sqrt{16} = 4.$
3. (a) 2.2. (b) 2.8. (c) 3.2. (d) 5.4.

8-3 Real Numbers

1. (b), (c), (d), (f), and (h) represent rational numbers.
3. All of the numbers in Exercise 1 are real numbers.
5. $\sqrt{3} = 1.7320\ldots;$ $\pi = 3.1415926\ldots;$ $\sqrt{11} = 3.31662\ldots.$

8-4 Principles of Real Numbers

1. No; $\sqrt{2} + {}^{-}\sqrt{2} = 0,$ and 0 is not an irrational number.
3. (a) ${}^{-}\sqrt{3}.$ (b) $\sqrt{6}.$ (c) $\dfrac{-1}{\sqrt{7}}.$ (d) ${}^{-}(\sqrt{3} + \sqrt{2}).$

5. Consider a and b as two positive real numbers represented as infinite decimals.
   If $a - b$ is positive, then $a > b$; if $a - b$ is negative, then $a < b$; if $a - b$ is
   zero, then $a = b.$

CHAPTER 9—NONDECIMAL SYSTEMS OF NUMERATION

9-2 Base Five Numeration

1. (a)

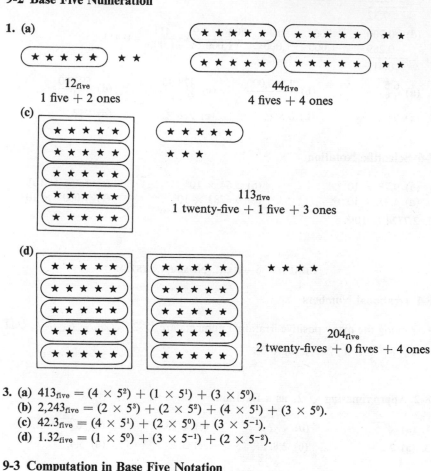

12_{five}
1 five + 2 ones

44_{five}
4 fives + 4 ones

(c)

113_{five}
1 twenty-five + 1 five + 3 ones

(d)

204_{five}
2 twenty-fives + 0 fives + 4 ones

3. (a) $413_{\text{five}} = (4 \times 5^2) + (1 \times 5^1) + (3 \times 5^0)$.
   (b) $2,243_{\text{five}} = (2 \times 5^3) + (2 \times 5^2) + (4 \times 5^1) + (3 \times 5^0)$.
   (c) $42.3_{\text{five}} = (4 \times 5^1) + (2 \times 5^0) + (3 \times 5^{-1})$.
   (d) $1.32_{\text{five}} = (1 \times 5^0) + (3 \times 5^{-1}) + (2 \times 5^{-2})$.

9-3 Computation in Base Five Notation

1. (a) 42_{five}.   (b) 341_{five}.   (c) $10,000_{\text{five}}$.   (d) $1,212_{\text{five}}$.
3. (a) 11_{five}.   (b) 4_{five}.   (c) 123_{five}.   (d) $1,344_{\text{five}}$.
5. (a) 310_{five}.   (b) 413_{five}.   (c) $34,001_{\text{five}}$.   (d) $100,322_{\text{five}}$.
7. (a) 14_{five}.   (b) 432_{five}.   (c) 21_{five}.   (d) $3,422_{\text{five}}$.
9.

+	E	F	G	H	J
E	E	F	G	H	J
F	F	G	H	J	FE
G	G	H	J	FE	FF
H	H	J	FE	FF	FG
J	J	FE	FF	FG	FH

×	E	F	G	H	J
E	E	E	E	E	E
F	E	F	G	H	J
G	E	G	J	FF	FH
H	E	H	FF	FJ	GG
J	E	J	FH	GG	HF

9-4 Change of Base

1. (a) 38.   (b) 125.   (c) 14,876.   (d) 15,625.

9-5 Base Nine Numeration

1. (a)

1 set of nine and 3 ones, written 13_{nine}.

(b)

0 sets of nine and 8 ones, written 8_{nine}.

(c)

3 sets of nine and 1 one, written 31_{nine}.

(d)

4 sets of nine and 4 ones, written 44_{nine}.

3.

Six Thousand Five Hundred Sixty-ones	Seven Hundred Twenty-nines	Eighty-ones	Nines	Ones
$9 \times (9 \times 9 \times 9)$	$9 \times (9 \times 9)$	9×9	9×1	1
9^4	9^3	9^2	9^1	9^0

5.

+	0	1	2	3	4	5	6	7	8
0	0	1	2	3	4	5	6	7	8
1	1	2	3	4	5	6	7	8	10
2	2	3	4	5	6	7	8	10	11
3	3	4	5	6	7	8	10	11	12
4	4	5	6	7	8	10	11	12	13
5	5	6	7	8	10	11	12	13	14
6	6	7	8	10	11	12	13	14	15
7	7	8	10	11	12	13	14	15	16
8	8	10	11	12	13	14	15	16	17

×	0	1	2	3	4	5	6	7	8
0	0	0	0	0	0	0	0	0	0
1	0	1	2	3	4	5	6	7	8
2	0	2	4	6	8	11	13	15	17
3	0	3	6	10	13	16	20	23	26
4	0	4	8	13	17	22	26	31	35
5	0	5	11	16	22	27	33	38	44
6	0	6	13	20	26	33	40	46	53
7	0	7	15	23	31	38	46	54	62
8	0	8	17	26	35	44	53	62	71

7. (a) 22_{nine}. (b) 136_{nine}. (c) 180_{nine}. (d) 1_{nine}.

9. (a) 48_{nine}. (b) 503_{nine}. (c) 121_{nine}. (d) $1,583_{nine}$.

9-6 Base Two Numeration

1. (a) 21. (b) 31. (c) 38. (d) 2,064.

3. (a) $1,001_{two}$. (b) $1,101,001_{two}$. (c) $1,001_{two}$.
   (d) 101_{two}. (e) $1,110,100_{two}$. (f) $1,101_{two}$.

9-7 Base Twelve Numeration

1. (a) 233. (b) 23. (c) 15,372. (d) 18,995.

3. (a) $1E_{twelve}$. (b) 65_{twelve}. (c) $1,849_{twelve}$. (d) $1,TT8_{twelve}$.

5. (a) $E3_{twelve}$. (b) $20,T56_{twelve}$. (c) $3,213,ET3_{twelve}$. (d) $TT0,E22_{twelve}$.

7. (a) $1E_{twelve}$. (b) 91_{twelve}. (c) 207_{twelve}. (d) $2,00E_{twelve}$.

9. (a) True. (b) False. (c) False. (d) False.

CHAPTER 10—INFORMAL GEOMETRY

10-1 Points

1. No. A point is an exact location in space, and an exact location cannot be moved.

3. The dot representing point A is the larger.

5. (a) False (a dot is a picture of a point). (b) False.
   (c) True. (d) True.

10-2 Line Segments, Lines, and Rays

1. (a)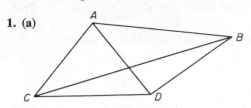
                                    (b) 6.

                                    (c) $\overline{AB}$, $\overline{AD}$, $\overline{AC}$, $\overline{BC}$, $\overline{BD}$, $\overline{CD}$.

3. (a) True.   **(b)** True.   **(c)** False.   **(d)** True.

5. (a)   **(b)** One.   **(c)** Yes.

$$\overset{\bullet}{\underset{J}{}}\!\!\!\!\!\!\!\longrightarrow\underset{K}{\bullet}$$

10-3 Planes

1. An infinite number.   **3. (a)** Three.   **(b)** Yes.

10-4 Relationships of Lines and Planes

1. (a) False (the two lines may not be in the same plane).
    (b) True. **(c)** True. **(d)** False.

3. Among the many correct answers are
    (a) $\overleftrightarrow{RT}$ and $\overleftrightarrow{SY}$. **(b)** $\overleftrightarrow{RX}$ and $\overleftrightarrow{TZ}$. **(c)** $\overleftrightarrow{RT}$ and $\overleftrightarrow{ST}$.
    (d) Plane RST and plane XYZ (only one correct answer in this case).
    (e) Plane RST and plane TSY.   **(f)** $\overleftrightarrow{TS}$ and plane RSY.
    (g) $\overleftrightarrow{RS}$ and plane RSY.   **(h)** $\overleftrightarrow{TZ}$ and plane RSY.
    (i) $\overleftrightarrow{RS}$, $\overleftrightarrow{TS}$, and $\overleftrightarrow{YS}$.   **(j)** Plane RST, plane RXT, and plane SYT.

10-5 Plane Curves

1. The drawings in **(b)**, **(d)**, **(e)**, **(f)**, **(g)**, and **(h)** represent closed curves.
3. All of the drawings in Exercise 1 represent plane curves.
5. The sides of $\triangle ABC$ are $\overline{AB}$, $\overline{BC}$, and $\overline{AC}$.

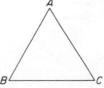

10-6 Circles

1. Among the many correct answers are
    (a) $\overline{RS}$, $\overline{MS}$, and $\overline{SN}$.   **(b)** $\overparen{RM}$, $\overparen{RV}$, $\overparen{RMW}$, and $\overparen{RNT}$.
    (c) $\overline{RT}$ and $\overline{MN}$ (only one correct   **(d)** R, V, N, T, and W.
        answer in this case).

3. (a) True. **(b)** False. **(c)** False (may not be diameters of the same circle or of circles with congruent radii). **(d)** False. **(e)** True. **(f)** True. **(g)** True. **(h)** False.

5. (a) Yes. **(b)** Yes. **(c)** Yes (since the radius has not been given).

10-7 Regions

1. (a) Yes. **(b)** B and A. **(c)** C, E, and F.
3. (a) True. **(b)** False. **(c)** False. **(d)** True.

10-8 Plane Angles

1. (a) B. **(b)** $\emptyset$. **(c)** D. **(d)** A. **(e)** $\emptyset$. **(f)** $\angle ABC$. **(g)** $\overline{AC}$. **(h)** $\overleftrightarrow{AC}$ (also named $\overleftrightarrow{EC}$ or $\overleftrightarrow{EA}$).

10-9 Congruence of Line Segments

1. (a) True. **(b)** False. **(c)** True. **(d)** True.
3. (a) True. **(b)** True. **(c)** False.
(d) False (two line segments that are not equal may be of the same length).

10-10 Congruence of Plane Angles

1. $\angle ABC \cong \angle MON$.
3. $\angle RQT$, $\angle NAP$, and $\angle DEG$ are right angles.

10-11 Classification of Triangles and Quadrilaterals

1. (a) Scalene. **(b)** Equilateral and isosceles. **(c)** Isosceles.
(d) Isosceles. **(e)** Isosceles. **(f)** Scalene.
(g) Equilateral and isosceles. **(h)** Scalene.

3. (a)   **(b)**   **(c)**

(d)  **(e)**   **(f)**

Index